HOW DOES IT WORK?

# How Does It Work?

by Richard M. Koff

Illustrations by
the Author and Richard E. Rooman

DOUBLEDAY & COMPANY, INC., Garden City, New York

Library of Congress Catalog Card Number 61-7761
Copyright © 1961 by Richard M. Koff
All Rights Reserved
Printed in the United States of America
Designed by Chet Gilbert

# CONTENTS

*Contents*

# INTRODUCTION

How does it work?

What makes it tick?

How do they make . . .?

It used to be that the answers to these questions were self-evident. Loosen a few screws and the gas lamp would come apart in your hands—its separate parts and their principles of operation as obvious as a hammer. It used to be that a man could make, replace, or repair every machine, tool, or household item he owned. Often he had made it in the first place.

But today things aren't so simple. The watch you take apart is ruined for good. Inside a radio you find a mass of confused wires, tubes, and knobs as meaningless as a foreign language. And that is the problem exactly; science *is* a foreign language. The strange words (or worse, the familiar words used in strange ways) make science seem so different, so complicated, so impossible to understand that we are tempted to give up without even trying.

It is a pity that his should be so. The miraculous in modern science and technology is not nearly as complicated as the recipe for Irish stew. It is just that men had to create new words and new meanings so that they could exchange inventions and discoveries in exactly the way cooks exchange recipes. The words aren't as important as the ideas, and having some of these ideas you might feel like cooking up an electric stew yourself one day.

Maybe you don't want to be a cook, or a scientist. But we all eat, and we all live in a technical world surrounded by machines, served by them, dependent on them for our lives. No, it is not necessary to know what goes on inside an automobile to drive it down the highway, or how a furnace heats your home, but then which is the master—the automobile or its owner?

There are men who can get that extra bit of economy out of their cars, who can coax a little more push out of an offshore breeze, and who can get a lock unfrozen and a zipper unstuck neatly and quietly in an emergency—just because they know what makes the world around them run. When they were kids they took clocks apart. They spent their adolescence under fenderless jalopies. They didn't all grow up to be engineers or scientists; they sell insurance or clerk in a supermarket or direct a large corporation. But they run this mechanical world, it doesn't run them.

Remember the little boy who let the air out of the truck's tires so it could get out from under the underpass? Well, that kind of thinking is only possible to people who know there *is* air in the tires, and why.

If a little boy could know, anyone can. Do you know how a steam iron works, or an air conditioner? Have you ever wondered what sound is, or why pressure cookers cook so fast?

That is what we'll be talking about in this book—what, and how, and a little bit of why.

# A

## AEROSOLS

The word *aerosol* refers to the spray of tiny liquid droplets, not to the container. The pressurized can, so familiar today, was first made during World War II. This prototype of our modern cans was filled with insecticide or insect repellent and issued to soldiers to debug their tents and barracks. Only a few of those cans ever reached civilians, but soon after the war the design principles were made available by the government to all manufacturers on a royalty-free license.

Like all good ideas, the principle of the areosol is deceptively simple. Fill a strong can or steel bottle with the fluid you wish to spray, add a gas (air, for example) under pressure and seal the can. As the valve in the top of the can is opened, the fluid will be forced out of the can as a spray.

There were some problems in the original design—mostly because of deficiencies in the gas used. When the compressed gas is air, a relatively high pressure is needed in the can if all of the contents are to be forced out without waste. When the can is full the spray works fine, but as the can empties the compressed air expands and loses much of its pressure just by filling the space left by the sprayed fluid. Furthermore, high pressure requires extra strong walls for the can—hence the term "bomb" for the early models.

One ingenious change, however, made all the difference. Instead of using air as the compressing fluid, engineers tried a chemical compound which would be a gas under normal atmospheric conditions but would turn to liquid when compressed to approximately 100 pounds per square inch (six times atmospheric pressure). The major chemical companies were well prepared to make such fluids—Freon is such a chemical (see AIR CONDITIONERS for another use of this fluid).

At normal room temperatures and normal atmospheric pressure (70° F and 14.7 pounds per square inch), Freon is a gas. However, if you raise the pressure on the Freon to 90 pounds per square inch, the gas will condense into a liquid taking up much less space.

This fluid is mixed with paint, for example, and put into a can not much different from an ordinary beer can. When the valve at the top is depressed, a passage is opened to the outside. The pressure inside the can forces out the paint and some Freon. The Freon bursts into a gas instantly, turns the paint into a fine spray, and helps to speed drying as well.

Some of the characteristics of aerosol cans now seem more understandable. The cup-shaped bottom of the can is designed to withstand the internal pressure without bellying—which would happen if a flat-bottomed can were used.

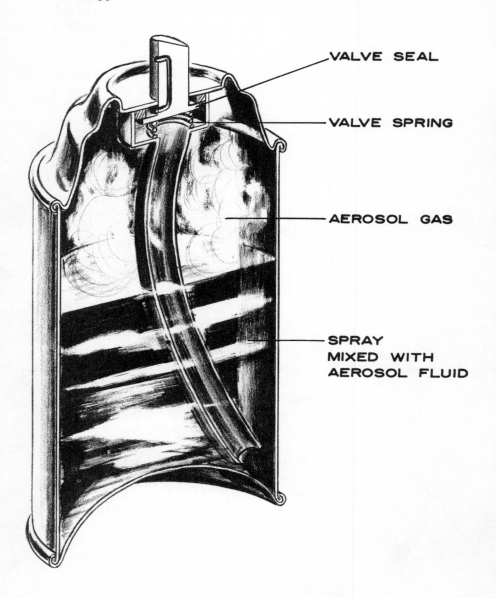

VALVE SEAL

VALVE SPRING

AEROSOL GAS

SPRAY
MIXED WITH
AEROSOL FLUID

You are often told to shake the can well before using. This mixes the aerosol fluid well with the paint or other contents so that a good spray is produced.

The instructions always tell you to keep the can away from fire or hot places. An increase in temperature of only a few degrees will be enough to make the Freon turn into gas, causing the pressure to mount, and thereby increasing the danger of explosion.

Sometimes you are told not to spray near fire or flame. This is because the spray itself sometimes includes alcohol or other flammable liquids. The mixture of flammable vapor and air could be ignited with a spark and an explosion or bad fire could result.

Aerosols should always be used in well-ventilated rooms. The fluids are released in such volume and in such tiny droplets that you are bound to breathe them into your lungs. Even nontoxic sprays can be dangerous merely because of their ability to keep oxygen from entering your lungs.

The aerosol industry has experienced rapid growth since World War II. While insect repellents are still among the most popular aerosols, you can buy deodorants, hair sets, paints, glue, shaving soaps, toothpastes, detergents, whipped cream, and even mouth washes in aerosol cans. Now dusting powders, like talcum and flea powder, are put in aerosol cans.

# AIR CONDITIONERS

The principles involved in air conditioning are the same as those used by the human body to cool itself. Most liquids require considerable heat to evaporate. Boiling water, for example, is a form of rapid evaporation resulting from the addition of heat. In a slower way, we are cooled as sweat is evaporated by body heat.

This system works particularly well in dry atmospheres. In Texas, large fans draw hot, dry, outside air through a water-soaked mat of fibers, and discharge it, cooled and humidified, into restaurants and homes. The air there is so dry (10 to 20% humidity) that it can take the additional load of evaporated water without becoming uncomfortably damp. Note that the air is cooled because it must give up some of its heat in order to evaporate the water.

In more humid areas where the air already holds nearly all the moisture that it can, this system doesn't work. So a slightly different system has been devised.

Imagine a liquid, much like water, that boils at a very low temperature, around 40° F. As soon as the temperature goes above 40° F it starts to boil, absorbing heat from its surroundings. If the evaporated gas is compressed by a gadget similar to a bicycle pump (see PUMPS), the gas gets hotter. The temperature goes up to perhaps 110° F.

Take this hot gas and cool it in tubes surrounded by moving air—even 100° F outside air will do the job—and it turns back into a liquid. It's still a hot liquid. We haven't reduced its temperature significantly by removing all that heat. We've merely turned the vapor into a liquid. Now provide a small opening through which it can expand (and vaporize). The effect is much like air coming out of a bicycle tire valve.

As it expands, the liquid uses its own heat to turn itself back into a gas, causing the gas temperature to drop—to 40° F probably. Later the compressor picks up the gas and starts the cycle over again.

Do you see the principle?

As the liquid expands in closed tubes (you don't want to lose any of the precious liquid, called Freon 12 or Genetron 12), it becomes cold enough to cool the room air. After the liquid has performed this function, the compressor squeezes it into a really hot gas. The gas is piped to a series of tubes *outside* the room, and outside air, cooler than the gas, cools it to a liquid at a still relatively hot 110° F. But as a liquid, it is now able to do a lot of good cooling once expanded (and vaporized) since the temperature then drops to 40° F.

So your air conditioner—and your electric refrigerator, incidentally—have a closed system of two sets of coils (a hot set for outside, a cold set for inside) usually finned, to give them more area for conduction of heat into or away from the fluid inside. The coils are interconnected by a constriction—a plug with a small hole—at one joining point, and by the compressor—a small pump—at the other (see illustration).

Electric motors drive the compressor and two fans. One fan circulates room air around the cold coils, the other circulates outside air around the hot coils.

In more modern home units a thermostat is added (see THERMOMETERS AND THERMOSTATS). This disconnects the compressor drive motor when the room air temperature (measured at the room air inlet) drops to a desired level. The fan continues to circulate air, but the refrigerant (the vaporizing liquid) no longer circulates. In this way the current drain is reduced. As room temperature rises, the thermostat "senses" the change and turns on the compressor to start the cooling cycle again. Most of these air conditioners have control knobs for adjusting the thermostat to activate the compressor at a set room temperature.

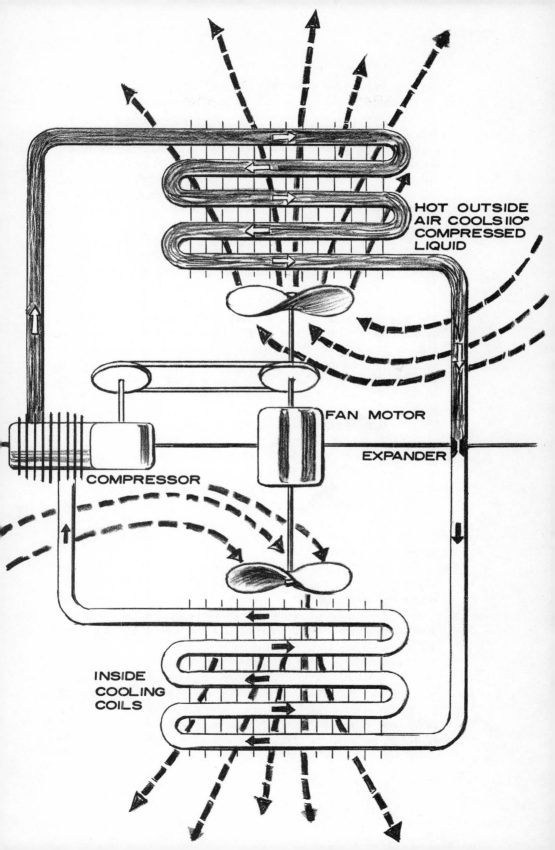

HOT OUTSIDE
AIR COOLS 110°
COMPRESSED
LIQUID

FAN MOTOR

EXPANDER

COMPRESSOR

INSIDE
COOLING
COILS

Note that the hot coils can be cooled by tap water, river water, or spring water, as well as outside air. Sometimes it is more economical to do so, and it is mandatory in large installations when whole buildings have to be cooled.

Air conditioner ratings have been standardized by the American Standards Association so that machines from different manufacturers may be directly compared in cooling ability. The standard is based on the Btu (British thermal unit)—an engineering measure of heat. One Btu is the heat required to raise one pound of water one degree Fahrenheit.

The standard of comparison used to be, and you will still hear salesmen glibly talk of, tons or horsepower. The ton is an old cooling measure based on the amount of heat removed from a ton of water in order to freeze it in a 24-hour period. This turns out to be equivalent to 12,000 Btu per hour, so if a salesman tries to sell you a "one-ton" air conditioner which the manufacturer rates as 8000 Btu per hour under standard test conditions, the salesman is a liar by 4000 Btu. "Horsepower," on the other hand, is a rating of the electric motor in the air conditioner. Its relationship to cooling ability is relatively complex. Actually the power needed by a one-ton (12,000 Btu per hour) air conditioner *is* roughly one horsepower. But with the new, more direct standards now available, it is better to check the Btu ratings directly.

# AIRPLANES

The major contribution made by the Wright brothers was to give up trying to imitate the flapping of a bird's wings and to copy, instead, the soaring flight of eagles. Fixed-wing aircraft, plus the air screw or propeller, started man on his flight to the stars. Aircraft have developed so rapidly in the 40 years between Kitty Hawk and World War II jets that millions of men alive today can remember when flight was a crazy idea, when 60-mph bobsled races made men wonder whether they could live at such high speeds. We know now they can—that there is no limit to the speed a man can withstand though there is a limit in acceleration. But more about that later. For now let's try to answer the question: What holds an airplane up? The answer is air—more specifically air pressure.

The ordinary airplane is held up by air pressure on its wings and this is explained by a very strange theorem first propounded by the Swiss mathematician Bernoulli. Bernoulli's theorem states that when a fluid flows past a fixed object the pressure exerted sidewise on the object by the fluid decreases as the velocity of flow increases.

For example, start a water hose spurting a jet of water straight up in the air, then place a Ping-pong ball on top of the jet. The ball bounces and twists but manages to stay on top of the stream of water—defying all apparent logic. What actually happens as the water flows around the ball? First it tends to slip to one side, say to the left. The water divides around the ball, much of it shooting straight up on the right side of the ball; some of it forced to take the long way around to the left. The detour makes the water slow down and as it slows its sidewise pressure builds up. Simultaneously the pressure of the high-speed water shooting up the right side of the ball has lowered, and so the ball moves toward the low-pressure side, away from the high-pressure side and back into the center of the jet.

The shape of an *airfoil* (wing section) is so designed as to increase the pressure of passing air on the underside and decrease it on the upper surface of the wing. This is accomplished in two

**THE AIRFOIL**

ways—by tilting the wing slightly up at the front so that the incoming air hits the underside of the wing and slows down (increasing the pressure), and by forcing the air to travel a longer path over the upper surface than it travels along the lower surface of the wing.

This characteristic wing shape—deeply arched over the top and almost flat beneath—is lifted by the passing air and as the wing lifts so does the body (*fuselage*) of the aircraft.

To get the wing moving through the air fast enough, a *propeller* cuts through the air and throws it backward. The reaction to the backward fling forces the aircraft forward just as the boy sitting in a cart can push himself forward by throwing stones over the tailgate. This is the same law, "every action has an equal and opposite reaction," which accounts for the thrust of Fourth of July rockets, jet engines, and satellite rockets.

By getting the aircraft moving forward fast enough along the runway, it finally develops enough air pressure on the wings (called *lift*) to get the plane into the air.

There are some very definite advantages to this system of flight. The engine power need only be sufficient to overcome forces of the air sliding past the "skin" of the aircraft. Thus relatively little power is needed to lift enormous weights. To give you some idea of how efficient wings are, just take a model airplane, "rev" up the engine, and set the model on its tail pointing straight up. It will just sit there and twitch. But put it on its wheels in normal take-off position and see how fast it climbs into the sky. The wings are doing the real lifting, the propeller just gets it going forward. Incidentally, few people realize that if the propeller does all the pulling, the propeller shaft is what really feels the tug. The entire aircraft is pulled forward, as if by the nose, by the 1, 2, or 4 propellar shafts.

Airplanes are controlled by small, movable sections of wing called *ailerons* cut into the trailing edges of the airfoils. By tilting the aileron up, the wing is forced down; by tilting the aileron down, the wing is forced up. The horizontal and vertical tail surfaces (*elevator* and *rudder*) are similarly fitted with moving sections.

**AILERON**

The pilot's controls consist of a *stick* and two rudder pedals. In its simplest form the stick is pivoted at its lower end and otherwise is free to move in all directions. In more modern aircraft the stick can only pivot forward and back. It has a modified automobile steering wheel at its top for turns. Pushing the stick sideways to the left or turning the wheel to the left simultaneously raises the left wing aileron and lowers the right wing aileron. This forces the left wing down and the right wing up, which starts the plane in a "bank" to the left. By "kicking" the left rudder pedal at the same time, a smooth turn is made to the left.

Pushing the stick forward lowers the ailerons on the elevator surface at the rear of the plane. This lifts the tail and forces the plane into a dive. Pulling the stick back lowers the tail and lifts the nose into a climb.

Obviously a great deal of co-ordination is required to control a plane in so complex a maneuver as landing, particularly under adverse conditions.

Some further details may make your next airplane trip less worrisome. First of all, airplane engine exhaust consists of burning hot gases. These fiery jets pulse out of the exhaust pipes and look as if the whole wing is about to start burning. It won't.

Sometimes little flaps surrounding the engine are opened during take-off to permit cool air to flow over the engine. The red-hot exhaust manifold is revealed. This is normal and doesn't mean the engine is about to melt away.

Just before landing the pilot lowers the wheels with an audible bump. The bump is natural—it means the wheels are locked down as they should be—and so is the sudden slowing you feel as the wind hits the landing gear struts and wheels.

The slowing down is essential for easing the plane to a safe landing. Airplane manufacturers even go so far as to add *flaps* to the wings for this purpose. Flaps act as extensions to the wing

FLAP

width. They increase the lift of the wings permitting the plane to slow down without loss in lifting power. So when you see these big wing extensions slowly creep out of the wings, relax and get set for your landing.

Helicopters are rotating-wing aircraft, the principles being similar to regular aircraft but with thin wings moving around in circles rather than forward. Thus the underside of the moving blade is lifted by the passing air and the lift is transmitted to the central shaft holding the helicopter up in the air.

Models of helicopters have been experimented with for centuries. The problem has always been to keep the body from rotating opposite to the blades. After all, if you attach the blades to the shaft of an engine and set the whole affair hanging in space, what is to keep the engine from spinning around the blade shaft rather than the reverse?

The answer is a little fan, hung out on a boom at the back of the helicopter fuselage, which opposes the tendency of the boom to swing around.

Helicopters are less efficient than regular aircraft for the simple reason that the energy used to lift the helicopter is not also applied to moving it horizontally. The mileage covered by a fixed-wing aircraft serves two purposes: lift and travel.

So in a helicopter, you pay in noise, complexity, and inefficiency for the quite considerable advantage of being able to hover and land on a skyscraper roof. The military have been the major buyers of such craft, but short-hop ferrying services have been using them as well.

It will be some time before helicopters will replace automobiles in every garage. One-man aircraft of this and many other more bizarre shapes are under development, but price and economics argue against them for now.

## ARCHES AND BRIDGES

In early days people didn't have steel and so buildings were made of stone or wood. This explains the invention of the key-stone arch and its use by almost every early civilization. Probably the first arch was made by leaning two stone slabs against each other to make a triangular door. Later, as stones were shaped by chipping, the rounded arch appeared, and soon dozens of complex shapes were created on the same principles.

The principles are these: a series of stones is cut so that the two opposite sides taper toward each other slightly. The upper and lower surfaces are usually curved so that when several such stones are placed side by side, the upper and lower surfaces meet in smooth, continuous curves. The *keystone* is the top center stone. It is the last stone to be placed in position, and it is the one that finishes the arch.

Have you ever wondered how the arch is made? What keeps the stones up as they are assembled, one on top of the other, in readiness for the keystone? The answer is a form of scaffolding. A wall of stone or wood is built under the arch and shaped to accept the curved undersides of the stones. Then the stones are piled one by one up to the keystone, the keystone dropped into position, and the scaffolding removed. The arch is now self-supporting.

Note that the arch puts considerable pressure on its base, not only straight down because of the weight of the stones, but also

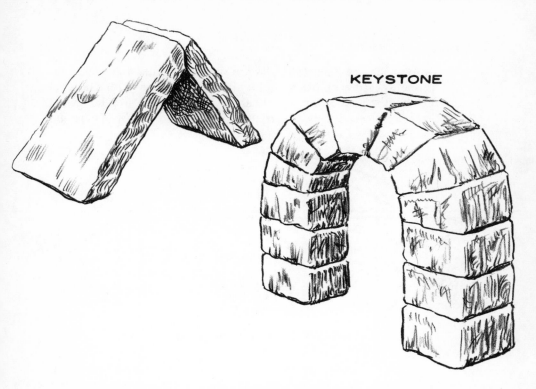

**KEYSTONE**

sideways because of the side thrust between arch stones. This is why the side supports must be very sturdy and well braced. Buttresses, particularly the dramatic flying buttresses built out from so many old European churches, compensate for the thrust. The main church vault is really just an arch requiring considerable support on the sides to hold the many keystones in place.

Arches quite logically suggested a lovely form of bridge. The stone arch bridge rises gracefully to the keystone over the water and then sweeps down again to the shore on the other side. Many steel bridges are built along similar lines. With steel, however, the individual stones are replaced by beams riveted or welded

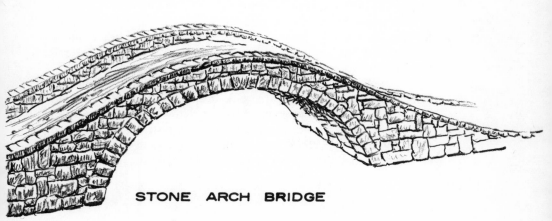

**STONE   ARCH   BRIDGE**

into rectangles. The rectangles are shaped so that two of the sides slope toward each other slightly just as the stones did. The steel rectangles make a very sturdy arch, and from this arch hangs the steel reinforced concrete roadway (see illustration). There are

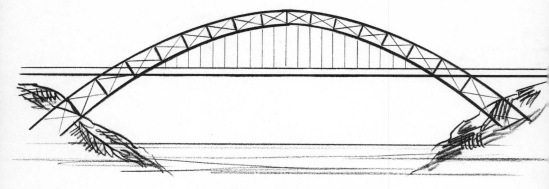

## STEEL ARCH BRIDGE

many variations. The roadway can be placed at the very top of the arch, running straight from high shore to high shore; the roadway can be halfway up the arch, as shown in the sketch; or it can be quite low, with the arch rising high above the roadway at the center of the span.

Of course steel *beams* can be placed across a pair of supports just the way a log makes a bridge across a small steam. The beams are built into the same sort of trusswork we saw in the steel arch bridge and this extends the span possibly to many hundreds of feet. But eventually steel beams reach maximum length at which they can support their own weight and then the arch, or one of the other designs, is used.

The *cantilever* bridge is made in two sections, each designed so that it balances on a single point at its center and sturdy enough to extend out a good distance to either side. Toward the center of the stream the two reaching arms approach each other and a small beam bridge spans the gap. The cantilevers also extend arms toward the river banks to complete the roadway.

The *suspension* bridge carries bridge design one step further. Here the bridge supports are sunk deep into the river bed and built high up over the water in two tall towers. Steel wires are woven into thick, strong cables and the cables strung over the two towers to form graceful curves swinging down between the towers and out to the heavy supports embedded in the river banks.

Smaller cables are tied at regular intervals along the main cables, and the roadway hangs from them. Suspension bridges use the least steel for a given span and, like the stone arch bridge, result in a beautiful as well a practical design.

## BEAM TYPE BRIDGE

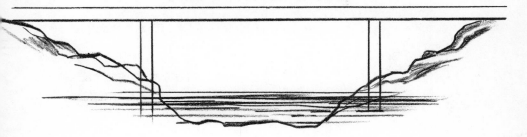

## CANTILEVER BRIDGE

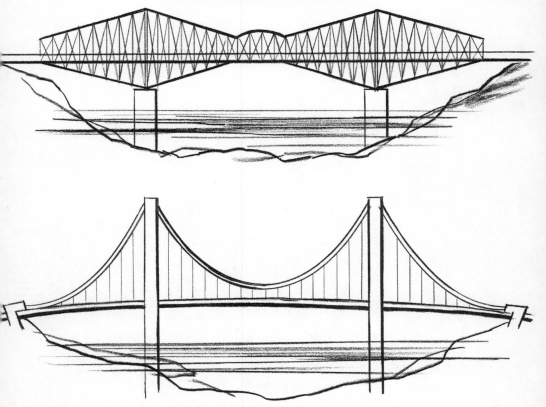

## SUSPENSION BRIDGE

# AUTOMOBILE ENGINES

These are the things that make your car go. Until recently engines were always located under the front hood of the American car. Now, however, they are almost as likely to be found in back as in front. No good engineering reason makes the front better than the back. Both positions have advantages, and disadvantages.

The engine gets it power from the chemical energy in a gasoline and air mixture. The gasoline is vaporized in a *carburetor*. Here air is sucked in through an air filter (to clean it) and then around

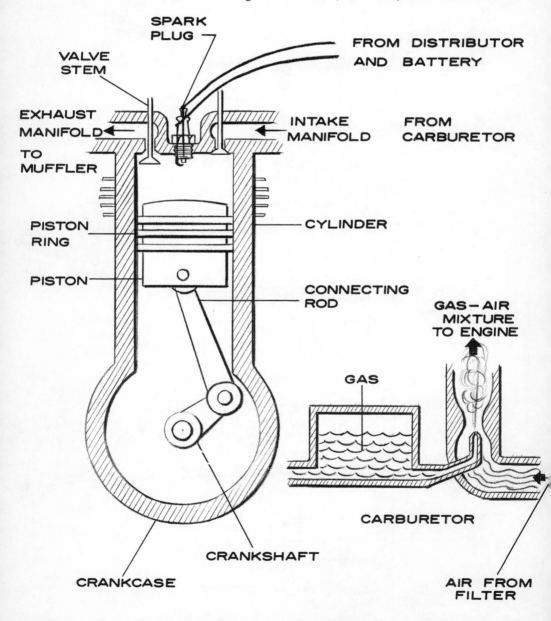

a tube filled with gas pumped from the gas tank. As the air rushes past the tube end, it carries along some gas vapor and the mixture goes to one of the *cylinders*. The cylinder is a large tube sealed at one end and blocked at the other by a movable plug called a *piston*. As the piston moves down, it sucks in the gas-air mixture from the carburetor through a pipe called the *intake manifold*. When the piston reaches the bottom of its stroke, the *inlet valve* closes and the piston moves back up the cylinder, compressing the gas-air mixture to less than one sixth of its original volume. This is called the *compression ratio*.

With a tightly compressed pocket of gas vapor and air tucked neatly into the top section of the cylinder, the *spark plug* receives a jolt of electricity from the *distributor*. The spark plug is screwed tightly into the top of the cylinder and carries two insulated electrical conductors into the cylinder. The exposed conductor ends are within a few thousandths of an inch of each other. The distributor, an automatic switch, sends the necessary current to the plug at exactly the right instant.

The current produces a very hot spark between the conductor ends and this ignites the mixture of gas and air trapped in the cylinder. The gas-air mixture burns. It does not explode. The burning, of course, is very rapid and it takes only an instant for

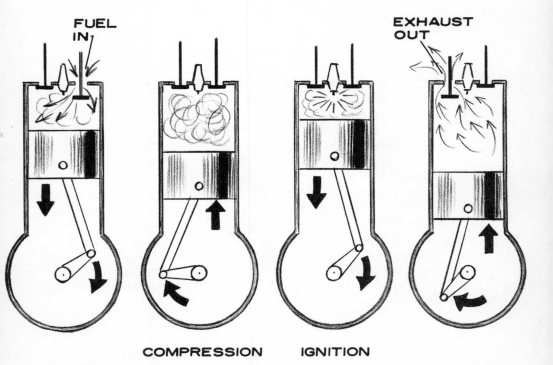

FUEL IN

EXHAUST OUT

COMPRESSION　　IGNITION

the gas in the cylinder to burn out. Actually, the gas sometimes starts burning even before the spark plug gets its jolt of electric current. This causes the *knocking* or *pinging* sometimes heard when the car ascends steep hills.

The burned gas-air mixture is very hot, and its pressure jumps from six or more times normal atmospheric pressure (6 times 15 equals 90 pounds per square inch after compression) to as much as 1000 pounds per square inch. This very high presure acts on the top of the piston and forces the piston down with a powerful shove.

When the piston approaches the bottom of its stroke a second valve, the *exhaust valve,* in the head of the cylinder opens. The motion of the piston has reduced the pressure in the cylinder considerably but it still has a pressure of 100 or more pounds per square inch. Thus, when the exhaust valve opens, the burned gases (exhaust) rush out through the *exhaust manifold* with a loud noise. To reduce objectional noise, the exhaust is piped to a *muffler* which simply conducts the gases around a series of obstacles (baffles) to reduce its speed and absorb the noise.

The piston has received enough of a push to keep the *crankshaft* turning and so it continues on up once again to force the last few wisps of exhaust out of the cylinder. When it reaches the top of its stroke the exhaust valve closes, the inlet valves opens, and a new charge of gas and air is drawn into the cylinder on the next piston downstroke.

This whole cycle is repeated several hundred times each minute. Even so, you would feel a definite pulsating drive to the wheels of the car if the manufacturer didn't add several more cylinders to your engine. He sets four, or six, or eight cylinders side by side with all the pistons connected to a single crankshaft. Each piston *connecting rod* hooks up to the crank shaft at a slightly different angle so that it receives its gas and delivers its push to the shaft at a slightly different time from the others. In this way you get a series of pulsating shoves on the crank shaft which results in a smooth flow of power to the wheels.

You change the speed and power delivered by the engine by varying the amount of gas-air mixture that goes to the cylinders. This is done in a very simple way. In the pipe going from air filter to carburetor there is an obstruction, a thin disk pivoted so as to close off the pipe when you lift your foot from the *throttle* pedal or to open it when you press down. Thus varying amounts of air are permitted to go to the carburetor and the less air that gets to the carburetor the less gas-air mixture arrives in the cylinder.

Perhaps it would be valuable to remove the mystery from some of the other words that designate various parts of the engine. The *battery* is a larger and slightly different version of the same battery that powers your flashlight (see BATTERIES). It must be kept filled with *distilled water*—water that has been boiled and the vapors cooled and collected to make an extremely pure water free of all minerals. This is what the serviceman does when he "checks your battery." The battery supplies electricity to spark plugs, headlights, radio, cigarette lighter, and other accessories.

The *radiator* is used to cool the water piped around the cylinders. It is made of a series of tubes and connecting passageways cast into a single unit and usually mounted at the very front of your car where incoming air can be directed around the tubes. A fan (rotated by a *fan belt* connected to the engine crankshaft) helps draw air through the radiator as well. The cooled water flows to passageways in the cylinders where it cools the hot metal and then to the radiator where it is cooled again. An overheated engine means trouble, so you should be sure to keep the radiator filled and not let it get so hot that the water boils and steams.

The piston is made to fit tightly against the cylinder walls by *piston rings.* These are rings of a durable metal alloy embedded in slots cut in the sides of the pistons. Several rings are used on each piston.

All of the moving parts of the engine must be lubricated to run with as little friction as possible and so there is a reservoir of oil in the *crankcase* (the enclosure at the bottom of the cylinders surrounding the crankshaft). An *oil pump* pushes the oil through tubes to all the bearings and moving parts in the engine. The *oil stick* is a metal rod that extends down into the crankcase with a mark on it showing a safe level of oil. The serviceman pulls the stick out, wipes it clean, and pushes it back into the crankcase. He then lifts the stick out to see how high the oil level has reached on the stick. When the oil level drops below a safe level he recommends the addition of oil to the crankcase.

Before leaving the subject of automobile engines, we should say something about the gas turbine which has not yet been put on the market in a standard car. The gas turbine has many advantages over the engine described above because of its mechanical simplicity, efficiency, and ability to run on practically any fuel from kerosene to aviation gasoline. But the turbine has some definite disadvantages. Some parts must run at very high temperature which means special, expensive alloys for these parts.

The gas turbine is a sophisticated water wheel—that's all there is to it. The fuel is injected into a combustion chamber in a steady stream and air is pumped in continuously to keep the flame burning. The resultant hot gases rush to a series of jet openings surrounding a wheel with vanes shaped like buckets on its circumference. The impact of the hot rushing gases on the wheel vanes starts the wheel spinning at high speed. The spent gases escape through an exhaust manifold.

You can see the simplicity of the principle which, incidentally, is older than that of the standard engine now used in automobiles. The problem is that the combustion chamber, the jets, and the turbine vanes (called *blades* or *buckets*) are all in constant contact with the very hot gases and must be able to hold their shape in this heat for many hundreds of hours. We have many alloys that can take this punishment, but they are too costly to make the gas turbine competitive with spark-ignition engines at this time. Automobile manufacturers are working hard at lowering the price and the first turbine-driven automobile will undoubtedly be on the market within the next few years.

# B

## BATTERIES

It is interesting to note that the term "battery" really refers to the *grouping* of cells—not to the cells themselves. But the term has come to mean just about any chemical generator of direct-current electricity (see ELECTRICITY). So let's be accurate and call them cells, not batteries. This will emphasize the family resemblance between them and the many new inventions going under the same name (fuel cells, solar cells) and serving much the same function.

A cell produces electricity by chemical means. That's the basic definition. The many available types have been divided into two general kinds—*primary* and *secondary*. Those cells that are not rechargeable (flashlight D cells, for example) are *primary* cells, and those that may be recharged (automobile batteries) are *secondary* cells.

A second pair of terms used to describe cells is the *dry* or *wet* cell. This distinction tells you whether or not you can tip the battery without losing any fluid. Since most cells today are made so that they can be tipped, the difference is less important than it used to be.

The familiar 6-inch dry cell (see sketch) is completely sealed, so it can be tipped without losing any fluids. The cell is made of a zinc can or shell which forms the negative terminal, and a carbon rod down the center which acts as the positive terminal.

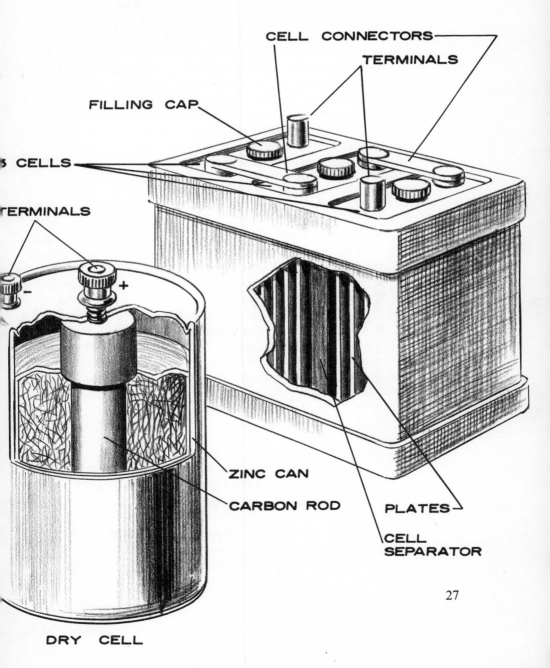

CELL CONNECTORS

TERMINALS

FILLING CAP

CELLS

TERMINALS

+

−

ZINC CAN

CARBON ROD

PLATES

CELL SEPARATOR

DRY CELL

27

The space between the two electrodes is filled with a spongy mass of porous material, soaked with an electrically conductive fluid, which permits the flow of electric current between zinc can and carbon rod.

What happens is a complicated chemical reaction, but in effect the electrons move from the carbon post to the zinc shell. This puts a negative charge on the shell which wants to push the excess electrons off the shell. The flow of current is thus really opposite to the way we usually think of it. The electrons flow out of the negative terminal, through a lamp bulb (for example) and to the positive terminal, rather than the reverse. However this flow direction is really of little importance. The circuit must be complete for current to flow, and so it makes no real difference which way it goes.

The primary cell is disposable. It is so inexpensive that you can afford to throw it away and buy a new one when the old one has been drained. The secondary cell is rechargeable. When drained of current, it can be recharged by applying an external voltage supply to the terminals and reversing the chemical action that took place during discharge.

The size of a secondary cell is usually measured in ampere-hours. This is the time a current of given strength (amperes) can be drawn from the cell before it goes dead. Automobile batteries, for example, are usually 100 ampere-hour units. You can drain 1 amp for 100 hours from them (or 10 amp for 10 hours). In the U. S. they are usually 6-volt batteries and the total power contained in the battery is 6 x 100 or 600 watt-hours. More recently, with the additional current drains for electrically raised windows, automobile air conditioners and the like, the 6-volt batteries have been replaced with 12- and even 24-volt units for passenger cars.

The automobile battery is made up of three cells, supplying about 2 volts per cell, hooked up in series (see sketch). The cells are watertight compartments hollowed out of a hard-rubber container. Each cell contains a series of positively and negatively charged plates separated by porous rubber insulators soaked with a weak solution of sulphuric acid. The acid is the electrolyte, acting as the electrical connection between adjacent plates. The acid is kept at the proper level in the battery by periodic addition of distilled water. Distilled water is specified by all battery manufactureres because impurities in the sulphuric solution reduce electrical output and hasten corrosion and destruction of the plates. Incidentally, many battery additives are sold, at relatively high prices, with all kinds of claims as to how they will improve the life or power of your battery. No reputable battery manufacturer recommends any of them and the Bureau of Standards has made tests that show no improvement with the additives at all.

Secondary cells of this kind are recharged by applying a reverse direct current to the cells. This forces the current to flow backward into the battery and to re-establish the original chemical balance. Your automobile generator is perfectly adequate for this purpose and any reasonably long trip will permit the generator to recharge the battery completely. Of course, very cold weather or a slow-starting engine may drain the battery unduly and then a visit to the service station may be necessary. But this is rarely required with new batteries, indicating that they hold their charge better and recharge more quickly than older, corroded, and inefficient batteries.

Two other kinds of cells should be mentioned here. They are of importance not because they are now used in many products, but because they will be used as engineering development reduces the manufacturing cost and increases in efficiency. The first is the *solar cell*—a cell that transforms light energy into electricity. The solar cell does not store energy; it simply transforms it from light to electricity.

Perhaps you didn't realize how much energy there is in sunlight. It has been estimated that the sunlight that falls on the roof of an average home could supply more than three times the electricity needed to heat, cool, cook, light, and operate all the other electric appliances. The problem is that an efficient transformer is needed to change that light energy into electricity (we only approach this with the solar cell, which transforms about 10 per cent of the incident light into electric current) and more important, an efficient storage battery that would accept the electric current produced by the solar cells and store it for use at night and on cloudy days.

Right now solar cells are used in artificial satellites—up where the sun is much brighter than it is on earth and where the weight of primary cells couldn't be tolerated. They are also used in remote locations as the source of power for portable radios and radar equipment. Here the high price of the cells and their relative inefficiency is unimportant compared to their portability.

The second new cell coming along is called the *fuel cell*. This is a true cell in that it produces electricity from chemical reaction, but the fuel cell uses gases (oxygen or air plus bottled hydrogen) as its power source rather than zinc or copper or carbon. The cell is not recharged by forcing electricity back into the cell; it is recharged by replacing the emptied tank of hydrogen gas with a new one.

Again the chemical changes are complex, but eventually the gases combine without heat or flame and produce electricity in a very efficient reaction. Several companies are seriously experimenting with fuel cells as the source of power for tractors, industrial trucks (like lift trucks), and small automobiles for suburban runabouts.

Again the problem is efficiency and price, but the advantages of electric-powered transportation are very tempting. Think of it —no auto exhaust, no auto noise, smooth, readily available power easily replenished, and possibly the fuel could be made in your garage continuously by a hydrogen generator powered from your electric outlet.

# BEARINGS

You're always hearing about burned-out bearings in your car or vacuum cleaner. What are these things? In its simplest form a bearing is a shaft surrounded by a close-fitting cylindrical *sleeve*. Oil lubricates the touching surfaces of sleeve and shaft to reduce sliding friction. That's all there is to it (see FRICTION).

Engineers spend a great deal of time determining what materials the shaft and sleeve should be (bronze, steel, aluminum, etc.) and how to inject the oil or grease where it is needed to keep things running smoothly. Once the oil dries out in a bearing of this kind, the shaft rubs against the sleeve; the shaft heats, swells, and eventually seizes—and you've got a burned-out bearing.

To prevent this you keep your bearings well oiled. But people forget, and so engineers have come up with some ingenious lubricating schemes. Many "lubricated-for-life" bearings have sleeves made of a porous bronze. Under a microscope this bronze looks like a very fine sponge, but it is rigid, of course, unlike natural sponges whose base material is flexible. The porous bronze sleeve is soaked in oil until all the little pockets are filled. Then the bearing is assembled and shielded to keep dust out. As the lubricant dries or drips slowly away, new oil is drawn out of the bronze and into the space between sleeve and shaft. These bearings can be renewed after long periods of service by resoaking in oil.

*Ball bearings,* sometimes called frictionless bearings, are intended for service where even the little friction of the sleeve bearing cannot be tolerated. Ball bearings are not completely frictionless, of course, but they're much more so than sleeve bearings. The rea-

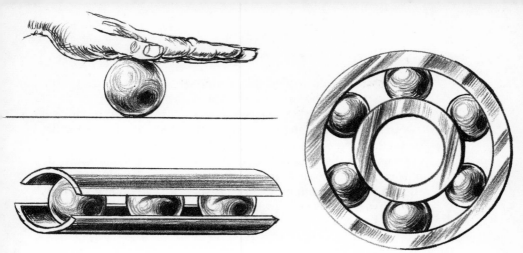

son is simple to demonstrate. Take a tennis ball and put it on a flat surface. Put the flat of your hand on top of the ball and roll the ball back and forth on the table. Note that the ball rolls on both your hand and the table. Now hold the ball in your fingers and try to slide it along the table top without rolling. It's a lot harder, the difference being the difference between rolling and sliding friction.

Imagine a tube cut in half the long way. Put the bottom half on your table and line up two or three balls inside the trough of the tube. Take the top half and place it on top of the balls. You can run the top half back and forth very freely and the balls will roll along with it.

If you bend the tube halves into a circle and fill the space between them with balls, the outer half (called a *race*) can spin around the inner trough and the balls just keep rolling around and around indefinitely. Slip your shaft into the center hole and put a tire on the outer race and you've got an automobile wheel or a roller skate. Fit a ball bearing into a motor housing and let the shaft extend through the inner race and you have a neat ball-bearing motor.

Ball bearings are made so tiny you can barely see them and so large you can drive a truck through the inner race. They're made to run on straight rods instead of balls, tapered rods, and needle-like rods, too. Why not? The oldest method of moving anything too heavy to lift or slide is to get two or three logs under it. Roll the object forward until it frees a log at the back, then pick up the log and put it in front.

How are the balls inserted in the first place? Sometimes grooves are cut in the edges of the races and lined up in order to slip the balls in. When the races are full, retainers are used to keep the balls evenly spaced around the bearing and to keep the balls from falling out when the two grooves line up.

Sometimes the outer race is split—actually broken in one spot —and spread to fill the races with balls. Later it's held together by the housing or by a thin, tight-fitting sleeve.

Sometimes the balls are large relative to the race diameters. By pushing the inner race over to one side, five or six balls can be slipped into the remaining crescent-shaped space. Then the balls are redistributed evenly around the bearing with a retainer.

# BOOKBINDING

Bookbinding was an invention of the Middle Ages that replaced the rolled-up scroll. Possibly the scribes got bored with writing on endless strips of paper. At first the individual pages were cut and just piled up. Wooden boards were put on top and bottom to protect the stack. It was only a step to attaching the boards permanently to the stacks of paper, and that's how books, as we know them, were born.

Today bookbinding refers to all the techniques used to hold books, pamphlets, and magazines together. Most of this is done by machine—certainly all of today's bestsellers and periodicals are machine bound. However, old-fashioned hand bookbinding is still a thriving trade. In Europe, for example, where paperbound books are commonplace, many people have their purchases hand bound for their private collections. First editions and special library bindings are hand made even in the United States.

The bookbinder receives from the printer a series of folded *signatures* (see PRINTING). The signatures are 16, 32, or 64 consecutive book or magazine pages and a collection of such signatures in proper order makes up the body of the book. The signatures are uncut at their outer edges but they will be trimmed later. In Europe they are bound untrimmed.

Covers are made separately for machine-bound books. A fabric cover is glued to board stiffeners and wrapped over the edges with a lap of ½ inch or so. The cover is then printed or embossed with title, author, etc.

The body of the book, meanwhile, is assembled by sewing threads through the center fold of each signature as it is stacked in proper order on previous signatures. The finished stack is pressed tightly together to eliminate air trapped between pages and the top, bottom, and outside edges are trimmed straight by a powerful paper-cutting machine. A cheesecloth backing is glued

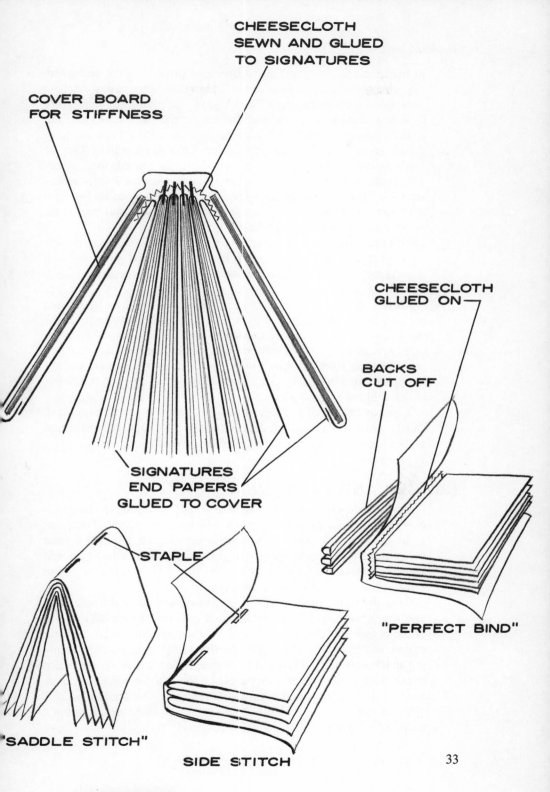

CHEESECLOTH
SEWN AND GLUED
TO SIGNATURES

COVER BOARD
FOR STIFFNESS

CHEESECLOTH
GLUED ON

BACKS
CUT OFF

SIGNATURES
END PAPERS
GLUED TO COVER

STAPLE

"PERFECT BIND"

"SADDLE STITCH"

SIDE STITCH

33

MAGAZINES

to the uncut backs of the signatures and this forms the stiff *spine*. The cheesecloth extends beyond the first and last pages where it overlaps the cover boards to which it is glued. The *end papers* are then cemented to the inside of the cover (front and back) and lap slightly onto the first and last book pages to conceal the inside of the cover and the cheesecloth backing. That finishes the book.

Magazines and pamphlets are usually stapled rather than glued. The thinner magazines are *saddle stitched* with each new signature straddling all of the earlier ones. The cover goes on last and then the whole stack is held together by staples that run from cover through to the center fold.

Thicker magazines are stapled from front to back at the left edge of the pages. The signatures are collected just as book signatures are, and the cover is wrapped around the stapled body and glued to the spine.

More recently a method called *perfect binding* has been used for paperback books as well as for certain periodicals. In this case the backs of the signatures are trimmed just as the other three sides are, leaving a stack of separate pages. The back is scored to give the glue a better "bite" into the pages and then cheesecloth is applied and held on with a special penetrating glue. Last, the cover is glued to the spine.

The advantage of perfect binding is that a book or magazine can be opened flat. However, it is relatively expensive and must be done well, otherwise the pages fall out easily.

# BRAKES AND CLUTCHES

Brakes and clutches serve very different functions in the automobile, but their principles of operation are the same. The principle of clutch or brake is this: two rotating shafts facing each other turn at different speeds. A mechanism is needed that will slowly connect the two shafts so that they rotate together at the same speed and in the same direction.

Actually both shafts need not be rotating, one could be at rest and the other spinning. The difference between the clutch and the brake is that the clutch usually connects a rotating shaft (say the engine shaft) to a standing one (say the wheel axle) and the standing shaft eventually rotates at high speed. The brake, on the other hand, always takes a rotating part (like the automobile wheel) and slows it down or stops its rotation completely. The second "shaft" of the brake can be considered the car chassis itself which doesn't rotate at all—hence it "runs" at zero speed.

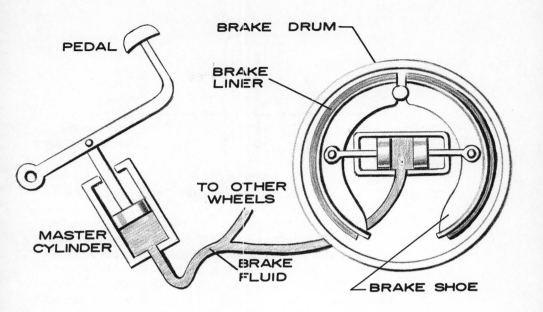

PEDAL

BRAKE DRUM

BRAKE LINER

TO OTHER WHEELS

MASTER CYLINDER

BRAKE FLUID

BRAKE SHOE

In each case a pair of rubbing surfaces—usually an asbestos pad and a metal disk or cylinder—are brought together. Friction between the two surfaces provides the clutching or braking action.

In an automobile brake, when you push down on the pedal you force oil (brake fluid) out of a master cylinder concealed under the floorboards through tubes to smaller piston-and-cylinder arrangements in each of the four wheels. The fluid pushes the pistons out of the small cylinders. This forces a pair of curved asbestos bands (asbestos because it is heat resistant and strong) against the spinning brake drum surface attached to the wheel. The effect is exactly the same as if you stuck your foot out the door and dragged it along the pavement, except that the dragging forces of brakes are much greater.

The clutch is used to control the flow of power from automobile engine to wheel axle. Just behind the engine, and connected to the crankshaft (see AUTOMOBILE ENGINES), is the clutch. When you take your foot off the clutch pedal you permit a spring to compress a series of movable disks in the clutch. Half the disks are connected to the engine crankshaft, the other half (alternating with the first group) are connected to the wheel axle. By releasing the clutch pedal you actually connect the two shafts and the engine then drives the wheels. Depressing the clutch pedal frees the clutch plates and disconnects the engine from the wheels—so you can pause at a stop light (the wheels at standstill) and still race your engine.

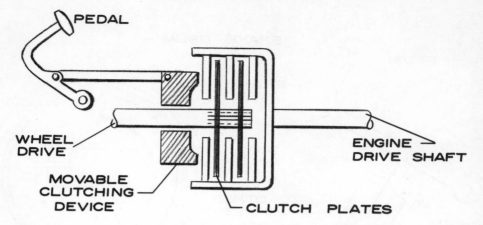

By letting the clutch pedal up slowly you compress the clutch disks—lightly at first so the two sets of disks barely rub against each other. This rubbing action starts the automobile wheels turning. As the wheels pick up speed the clutch disks can be more tightly engaged because the wheel axle is turning almost as fast as the engine crankshaft. Soon you can let the clutch up completely and engine and wheels run as one. As you approach a stop sign and brake the car, the slowing wheels also slow the engine. You'll stall the engine if you forget to depress the clutch pedal before braking to a stop.

All of this discussion assumes that the transmission (seeTRANS-MISSION AND REAR END) is a manual gearshift type. Automatic transmissions have what amounts to an automatic clutch and the engine won't stall even when fully braked and in gear.

# C

## CAMERAS

The camera doesn't care where you point it. It takes the light rays that bounce off Junior, your maiden aunt, or the George Washington Bridge and focuses them on a sheet of film for an instant. This light makes chemical changes in the coating on the film which, when developed, produces an image in blacks and whites or color (see FILM).

A *still* camera has three important adjustments. The lens must be positioned between film and subject so that the image will be in *focus*—meaning crisp and clear rather than blurry. The *dia-*

*phragm* or *f-stop* must be set to let enough light in without over-exposing the film. The *shutter* speed must be set to stop the motion of the subject. Just what are these things and what is their influence on the final picture?

The lens consists of one or more shaped pieces of clear glass. It is the eye of the camera, and like your own eye, cannot simultaneously keep far away objects and nearby objects in focus. You make your choice when you set the distance scale on the camera, thereby estimating how far the object is from the lens. Some cameras have rangefinders built in to eliminate the guesswork. You look through a peephole and see the picture cut in two with the top half offset from the bottom half. By turning a knob the two halves are lined up and the lens set to the correct distance in front of the film.

Actually the closer the subject to be put in focus the farther away the lens is set from the film. Some cameras include *extension rings* or *bellows* which are placed between the lens and the camera so that you can take a picture of very small objects very close up—like pinheads, thimbles, or an eyelash.

So much for the distance setting and focus. The *diaphragm* is built into the lens. It consists of a series of thin, overlapping leaves

**DIAPHRAGM**

of metal which can block off almost all the light hitting the lens or open so wide as to let all the light through. Diaphragms are set to various *f-stops*—numbers which determine how much light will be permitted to enter the lens.

*F*-stops, or diaphragm settings, may seem an arbitrary and absurd series of numbers. Usually they run through all or part of this series: $f/2$, 2.8, 4, 5.6, 8, 11, 16, 22, 32. The lowest number on your camera is determined by the diameter of your lens since the diaphragm is then wide open. Each succeeding higher number means you are closing down the opening a little more—just enough, as a matter of fact, to cut the open area exactly in half. This means an $f/8$ opening lets in half the light of the $f/5.6$ and one quarter the light of $f/4$. Incidentally some cameras have $f/3.5$, 4.5, 6.3. These may be considered half stops or between points on the above scale.

The *shutter* also keeps all light away from the film, except when tripped. When tripped the shutter opens and, for a split second, exposes the film to the light coming from the subject through the lens and past the diaphragm. Shutters are of two kinds. The between-the-lens type is similar to the diaphragm in that it is made of a set of thin, overlapping leaves of metal set near the lens. It flips open and shut by spring action and can be adjusted to stay open for as long as several seconds or as short as ½₀₀₀ of a second.

The focal-plane shutter is so named because it operates right near, and just in front of, the film (the plane in which the image is in focus). It consists of a sort of curtain of flexible material with an adjustable gap—rather like a partly open theater curtain. The gap moves swiftly across the film. You can open the slit wide to get long exposures or narrow it way down to get exposures on the order of ¹⁄₁₀₀₀ of a second. Focal-plane shutters are used primarily on small cameras in which the film size is not too large (the larger the film the larger the curtain would have to be). They tend to be noisier than the between-the-lens types and you've got to be careful of objects moving quickly across the scene. The slit exposes one side of the film at a slightly different time than the other so image distortion may result. But this is a technical detail. For all practical purposes you will not care what kind of a shutter you have.

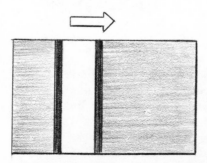

**FOCAL PLANE SHUTTER**

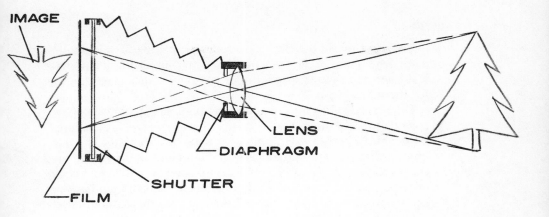

IMAGE

LENS

DIAPHRAGM

SHUTTER

FILM

Shutter speeds tend to go in multiples of two: $\frac{1}{25}$, $\frac{1}{50}$, $\frac{1}{100}$, $\frac{1}{200}$, for example. And so for any given picture situation you may find yourself with a choice of many combinations of *f*-stop and shutter speed. This is because $f/8$ at $\frac{1}{50}$ is equivalent to $f/5.6$ at $\frac{1}{100}$ and $f/4$ at $\frac{1}{200}$. In each stop you have doubled the open lens area (doubling the entering light) but halved the shutter speed or time of exposure.

Usually you choose a speed $\frac{1}{50}$ of a second or faster because slower speeds may permit hand motion to blur the picture. Some photographers choose $\frac{1}{50}$ as their standard speed and do all adjustment for varying light conditions by changing the diaphragm setting.

Film is so designed that a certain amount of light will expose it perfectly. The blacks will be rich and velvety, the whites clear and brilliant (see FILM). Different films need different amounts of light to achieve this tonal variation and you must adjust your camera for each individually lighted situation so as to get the desired amount of light on the film.

To do this you make two adjustments. You determine how much to open the diaphragm and how fast to set the shutter speed. The combination of diaphragm and shutter speed determines the amount of light to reach the film.

Many guides are available to estimate just how much light there is in a given scene. Most rolls of film include little tables showing what settings to use. As an alternative you may buy a lightmeter— an instrument that measures the amount of light striking its photocell. On a dial of the lightmeter, set a number which depends on the kind of film used. It is a measure of the *film speed*. This procedure will give you the various combinations of lens openings and shutter speeds which will put just the right amount of light on the film.

The most recent development in cameras is the so-called automatic type. This is a camera with a built-in lightmeter that automatically sets the shutter speed and diaphragm to the correct setting for the subject light.

Other accessories for gadget-happy photography bugs include: *tripods,* to hold the camera steady for long-exposure pictures; *flashguns,* to permit taking pictures when natural light is inadequate; *filters,* to emphasize certain colors and wash out others; extra *lenses,* to bring faraway objects up close (as with a telescope) or to get the full sweep of a building when you can't get back far enough; and, of course, all the darkroom paraphernalia of developing, printing, enlarging, and projecting.

*Movie cameras* are essentially the same, except that a whole series of still pictures are put on a continuous strip of film. This complicates the design because you have the considerable problem of moving a new bit of film in front of the lens 16 or more times a second. The shutter on these is automatically set to 1/30 of a second for normal speeds so all light adjustments must be made at the diaphragm. Otherwise most of the same picture-taking principles apply. Be sure to move slowly and hold the camera as steady as possible.

# CANDLES

Most people think candles burn slowly because the wax takes a long time to melt. Actually the melted wax itself burns—not the wick.

It works this way. The wax near the wick is melted by the heat of the flame. It soaks into the wick and rises up to where the flame heats it to a vapor and then slowly burns it away. As the wick burns away the flame automatically lowers to melt the next layer. Seems simple, but good candles have to be very carefully proportioned—wick size and chemical treatment as well as candle size and wax type must be matched so that the flame will not smoke or sputter and the wax not drip.

Most candles are made of paraffin wax mixed with higher-melting-point compounds to keep them stiff and straight in warmer climates or during the summer months. Try storing your candles in the refrigerator—they'll burn more slowly when cold. Beeswax is also used and it is prescribed for the candles used in the Mass of the Roman Catholic Church.

Candles are nearly all molded in shaped forms nowadays. At one time, they were dipped—the wick lowered slowly into a vat of melted wax and lifted with a layer as much as ⅛ inch thick for each dip.

Years ago candles were used for checking the freshness of eggs (*candling*). You held the egg in front of a candle and the shadowy shape of the yolk revealed its age. Candles were also used in the wine decanting ceremony that preceded every important English dinner. The port is carried in a wicker basket to the decanting shelf, the cork drawn, and the wine slowly poured into the decanter through a glass or silver filter. The candle burns under the neck of the bottle so you can see when to stop before the sediment flows into the bottle.

# CAN OPENERS

Man's wonderful discovery of how to preserve food in airtight cans is matched only by his ingenuity in making it difficult to get into the things. The problem is that although the can must remain airtight for long periods of time, years if necessary, it must be possible to open the container easily and quickly. The problem has received considerable attention from a host of basement geniuses with the result that there are probably more patents issued for novel ways of opening cans than there are for better mousetraps.

The tin can isn't really tin all the way through. The can is made of steel with a coat of tin on its surface to protect it against rust and food acids. The can is held together by folding the mating edges and squeezing them flat in special machines. These machines can make as many as 300 cans per minute. They're obviously worked overtime since each year Americans buy more than 20 billion cans.

Cans come in two basic designs. The first is supplied with a key used to tear off a strip of metal near the top. Coffee is packed in this kind of can. The key is a rod of metal with a slot at one end and winged fingergrips at the other. The can has two rings scratched in the surface of the metal near the top and a tongue extends from the strip so marked out.

You slip the key slot over the tongue and wind the key around the can, tearing away the strip as you go. You've got to be adept with this key since the strip will wind into a thick stack on the key before the can is opened. If you permit the coiled strip to slide off the key or let the key slip out of your hand, you're in trouble; it's not easy to get the stack neatly lined up again. You're better off pulling the rest of the strip away with a pair of pliers.

The second style of can has no built-in method of opening. For these you use one of the hundreds of patented openers, a few of which are described below.

The most familiar opener is a short, sharp, curved knife blade that is mounted on a handle and has its sharpened edge up. Above and back of the tip of the blade is a flat crosspiece used as a fulcrum when the can is being cut open. You start by punching the knife point into the can top just inside the raised rim. By resting the fulcrum on the can edge, a series of tilts on the handle will cut the can top out.

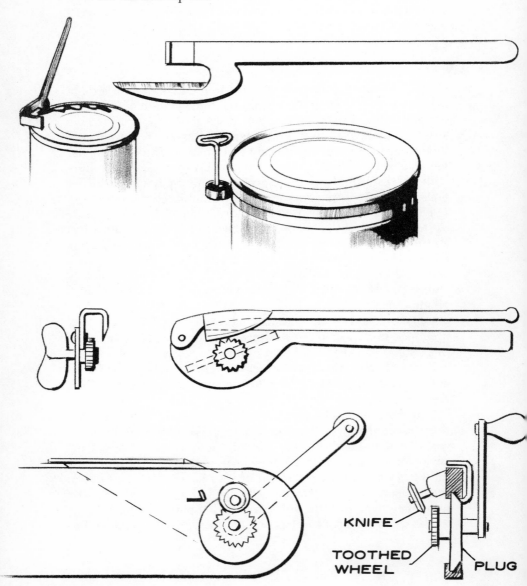

KNIFE

TOOTHED
WHEEL

PLUG

Another common opener is made with two rods pivoted to each other at their ends. The upper section has a short, sharpened knife blade curving downward (see sketch), the lower section a toothed wheel. You squeeze the two sections together, bringing the knife edge into the can top while the wheel grips the lower edge of the can rim. Now by turning the wheel with the fingergrips provided, you drive the can around under the knife and remove the top of the can.

The wall-mounted opener is similar. Here the can is brought to the opener. The knife blade is the sharpened rim of a wheel. Just beneath the knife wheel is the toothed wheel turned by a hand-crank on the other side of the opener. The wheel and crank are mounted in a plug which can be turned by a second swinging crank usually nested on top of the sharpener. This second crank pulls the wheel away from the knife so that the can can be inserted between them. When returned to its normal position, it pushes the toothed wheel up and forces the can rim behind the knife. The knife cuts into the top of the can. Turn the handcrank and the toothed wheel carries the can around under the knife. In this way the top is neatly cut out.

Very recently two new innovations in can openers have been getting a lot of advertising attention. The first is a magnetic top holder. This is a small magnet mounted so as to touch the top of the can. When the disk has been cut free, it clings to the magnet instead of dropping annoyingly into the can.

The second innovation is the electrically powered can opener. The motor drives the can around under the cutter so all you have to do is carry the can to the opener, push down a handle, and the motor does the rest.

## CASTERS

These gadgets make furniture roll easily. Most people take them for granted, but if they had to make a caster themselves they might find the problem a lot more complicated than it looks.

The basic principles are obvious. You want a means to roll a table freely. A wheel suits this purpose very well except when you want the table to go around corners. Then you also need some means of turning the wheel. The simplest way to accomplish this is to put the wheel in a bearing mounted in the furniture leg. This permits the wheel to swivel around on a vertical axis like the front wheels of an automobile. But suppose you make a sharp turn. Then the wheel jams up because it can't move sideways and won't swivel.

So to give a wheel this ability to turn sharp corners, casters were invented. This only required setting the wheel axis slightly back from the swivel axis. When you push the furniture sideways the wheel will always fall behind and around the turning axis and follow neatly in the wake of the motion.

The principle is fine, but designing a working caster is another matter. The vertical shaft (see sketch) must run in a bearing of some kind. Ideally this would be a ball bearing. But to take up the unbalanced thrust, two rings of balls (see BEARINGS) are needed. The center post fits into a socket in your furniture leg and holds the top and bottom races of the two bearings. The wheel housing is formed into a plate that fits between the two rings of balls and turns freely between them. This permits the wheel to spin around the vertical axis, and around its own axis, to make a good, free-moving, caster.

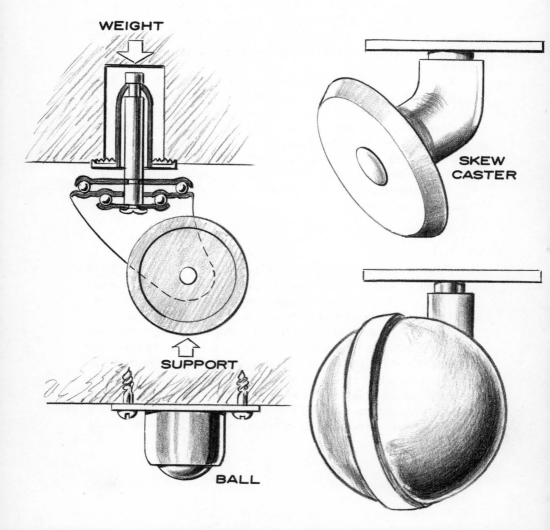

WEIGHT

SUPPORT

BALL

SKEW CASTER

Casters can be designed either in this way or with a flat plate substituted for the vertical shaft so that they can be secured to flat surfaces. Such a flat plate is shown with a *ball caster* in the second sketch. In this design a ball rides in an oiled bearing and can turn freely in any direction. It is not a true caster, but it serves the same furniture carrying function.

The *skew caster* looks very strange, but works as well, or better, than the regular kind. Two shafts are set in bearings in a bent rod that points directly up at the furniture at one end and slants down toward the floor at the other. The large diameter of the wheel and the small diameter of the bearings, makes this an extremely free-moving design. The skew caster is also made with a ball-shaped wheel. It is based on exactly the same principle, but it looks neater with its spherical housing and seems to be taking modern office furniture designs by storm.

When selecting a caster for a particular application you will want to keep several basic characteristics in mind. First, the mounting (pin or flat plate) will depend on your furniture. They work equally well, but furniture legs require the pin, flat surfaces can usually take either mount.

The degree of mobility required depends on the purpose to which the rolling furniture will be put. You may want to move a piano only on rare occasions. In that case a small, strong wheel is adequate. Or you may have a heavy marble teacart to be wheeled out into the garden on summer afternoons. In this case you need larger wheels with greater offsets to make the caster very responsive.

The floor surface will determine the type of wheel material. You can buy hard or soft rubber, metal, or plastic wheels. The hard rubber is for very heavy equipment—industrial machines and pianos. The soft rubber serves well for most home furniture. The plastic is best for linoleum and plastic tiles (which soft rubber will mark) and for heavy, napped rugs (to which soft rubber will stick). Metal wheels will work well on most rugs, and on cork tile, though their strength is usually reserved for industrial equipment. Metal is noisy on wood floors (it rumbles on the smoothest-looking surfaces) and will mar wood or tile or even cement.

Incidentally, for that teacart, consider two fixed wheels and two swiveling casters for best maneuverability. With an all-swiveled set the cart will drift off in any direction when you try to walk it over a long distance. With all-fixed wheels the cart has no maneuverability at all. The two-fixed, two-movable combination can be pushed with the movable pair at the front for best control, at the rear for ease in holding to straight-line motion.

Casters come with brakes—usually on two of the four in a set. The brake is a twin-winged metal plate attached to the wheel shaft. You press down on one side of the plate to lock the wheel and on the other to unlock it. The plate turns on the wheel axis and jams the wheel tight. Note that the brake does not keep the caster from swiveling about the vertical axis.

 **FRONT WHEEL
TILT ON AUTOS**

The problem with casters is that they have a tendency to wobble if pushed at high speed. They will swivel back and forth uncontrollably. For this reason the front wheels on an automobile are not made like true casters. Note that auto wheels always return to center when the steering wheel is freed. This is done by tilting the main bearings slightly out, in a Vee (see sketch, which is exaggerated somewhat). When you turn the steering wheel to swing the front wheels to the right or left, you also lift the entire weight of the car a fraction of an inch. This weight acts on the wheels as long as they are held in a turn. When you release the steering wheel it spins back to the center, forced back by the weight of the car.

## CIGARETTE LIGHTERS

The appeal of cigarette lighters is not their convenience—and certainly not their reliability. The appeal is the delight most people take in a gadget that is small, useful, and a challenge to your mechanical ability to keep in working order. You can buy lighters in pencil tops, in key rings, built into cigarette cases, watches, and stag horns. They're covered in gold, platinum, silver, tin, diamonds, rhinestones, and petit point. They're engraved with "*his*" and "*hers*," "*Kilroy was here*," and "*fire burns within*." They've got them to suit every occasion: weddings, funerals, bar mitzvahs, and sales campaigns. Ask anyone you know—smoker or nonsmoker—not whether he's got one but how many.

Most lighters are started by the spark thrown when a serrated wheel scrapes against a piece of flint. The hot spark strikes a wick soaked in a highly flammable liquid and starts the fluid burning. The wick is a two- or three-inch string woven of glass fiber. Its lower end is packed in a wad of cotton soaked in the lighter fluid. As the fluid at the top of the wick burns off, more soaks into the top to replace the depleted fluid. In this way the lighter continues to burn (at least theoretically) until all the fluid has been used up.

Actually, the fluid can't soak into the wick as fast as it burns off unless the cotton wad is really saturated. So you often have to wait a minute or two before the wick will take fire again after a long session with a cigarette. Other problems include lack of spark when the flint is worn down, or when the abrasive wheel teeth are filled to a nearly smooth surface by the bits of flint.

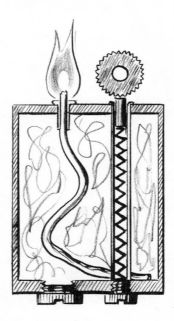

The same fluid-spark problems are associated with newer lighters using compressed butane gas instead of a fluid-soaked wick. The gas jets out of a tiny hole when the lighter is operated. The flint spark ignites the stream of gas which will burn until exhausted or closed off. The lighter is refueled from a can of compressed butane gas through a valve much like those used on automobile tires.

In an attempt to bypass the problems of flint and wheel, manufacturers have experimented with electrically heated wires. A small coil of wire is heated to incandescence by a tiny battery in the lighter. The hot wire ignites the wick and is then retracted and disconnected from the battery to save current (see ELECTRICITY). Here the troubles are dead batteries, burned-out coils, and dirty electrical contacts.

Automobile lighters similarly have an electrically heated coil of wire, but the coil lights the cigarette end itself. Electricity is readily available from the car battery. For the few seconds when you push the lighter button in, current is conducted through the coil in the lighter making it red hot. When the coil is hot enough a little release mechanism snaps the lighter out, indicating readiness. These are probably the most reliable lighters now available. It is surprising that manufacturers have only recently started making plug-in models of this kind for the home.

Two other wartime lighter designs should be mentioned here. Neither is in widespread use today since they were primarily intended for outdoor operation in wind and weather. The first is a small tube of plastic filled with chemicals that give off heat when brought in contact with the air. You push a button, stick the end of your cigarette into the shallow hole provided, and puff to ignite the cigarette end. They don't work well for very long.

The second type replaces the fluid-soaked wick with a closely woven cord about ⅜ inch in diameter. The flint spark hits the feathery edges of the cord end and starts a small spark burning. By blowing on the spark you spread it over the entire end of the cord to make a glowing coal. The stronger the wind the better this lighter works. Of course, it smells somewhat of burning cord.

With all this technical accomplishment you'd think matches would have been made obsolete. Quite the contrary. Book matches still light more cigarettes than any other means, and probably they will continue to do so until the really practical invention comes along.

Some day, so the science fiction writers would have us believe, each cigarette will have a specially treated end which bursts into flame at the first puff. No lighters, no matches, and no long, thoughtful pauses while you light up.

# CLOCKS AND WATCHES

What is time? Even Einstein couldn't have answered that question. The thing we measure is motion, not time—the motion of the earth spinning on its own axis, the motion of the earth swinging around the sun. These we divide into years, days, minutes, seconds. And this is what we think of as time.

Equal divisions of time are registered by clocks and watches and in practically all cases the basis is the *pendulum.* The pendulum is a light, thin rod or wire pivoted at one end and weighted at the other. Once the pendulum starts swinging back and forth on its pivot, it takes almost exactly the same amount of time for each swing no matter how small or how large the swings. If you increase the length of the rod, or lighten the weight, the swings go more slowly, and so the pendulum can be adjusted to swing exactly 86,400 times each day—one for each second.

This is how the old-fashioned pendulum clock measures time. The swinging pendulum paces the hands around the clock face. It would seem simplest to attach a ratchet to the pendulum and have the clock hands driven by the slowly stepping ratchet (the hour hand would turn 60 times slower than the minute hand, the minute hand 60 times slower than the second hand). But this isn't quite enough, because friction in the bearings and even the wind created by the pendulum's swing absorbs energy. The pendulum would slowly come to rest, and the clock hands with it. So some form of stored energy must be made available to the gear train. It must be doled out bit by bit as needed to turn the hands and keep the pendulum swinging.

The first energy storage men used was a hanging weight whose cord coiled around a rotatable drum. As the weight slowly falls and unwinds the cord, it gives up its energy to the clock. At the end of a day or week you come along with a big square-nosed key and wind the weight up again.

More modern clocks and watches use a coiled spring for energy supply, which is considerably more compact than the hanging weight. The spring is a flat ribbon of steel enclosed in a cylindrical housing. One end of the spring is attached to a shaft at the center of the housing, the other end is attached to the housing.

When you wind up your watch you coil the spring tightly about the central shaft which is then held by a clicking ratchet. As the watch ticks away the seconds and hours, and the housing turns around the fixed shaft, the spring slowly unwinds. A gear attached to the housing drives all the gears used to move the hands of the clock.

Let's see how the pendulum and *escapement* work. The pendulum may be the weighted rod described above, or it may be a small wheel of metal held by a hair-thin spring. Either pendulum simply swings back and forth on its pivot and pushes the escapement legs first one way and then the other. At each stroke the escapement releases one tooth of the escapement wheel and so the wheel slowly steps around, driving all the gears attached to the escape-

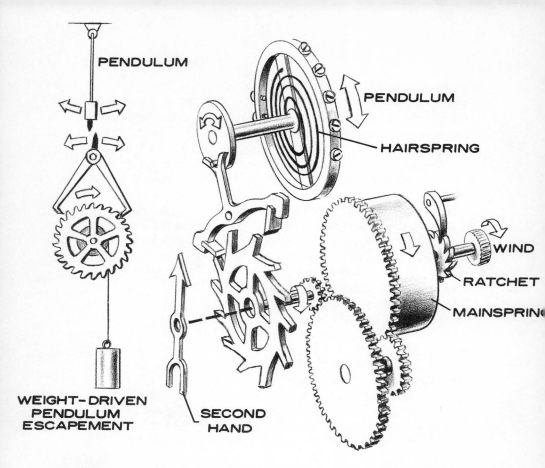

PENDULUM

PENDULUM

HAIRSPRING

WIND

RATCHET

MAINSPRING

WEIGHT-DRIVEN
PENDULUM
ESCAPEMENT

SECOND
HAND

ment shaft. As each tooth is freed it gives a small push to the escapement which in turn give the pendulum a "kick," to keep it swinging.

Thus the pendulum acts strictly as a timer for the clock works. The escapement provides a means for keeping the pendulum swinging, and it receives the timing impulses from the pendulum which drive the rest of the clock works.

Once again, here are the component parts, and the functions of the components, of a watch or clock. You start with a source of energy—a weighted chain or wire, a spring. This keeps a steady twist on the toothed wheel of an escapement mechanism which turns one tooth at a time regulated by the swings of a pendulum. The turning escapement wheel provides the driving force that keeps the entire clockwork mechanism—a series of geared shafts ending, ultimately, in the hour, minute, and second hands that show the time on the clock face—in motion.

So much for clocks and watches driven by springs. Electric clocks are probably more familiar and they have a distinct advantage in that they require no winding. Electric clocks are really much simpler than spring- or weight-driven ones. You replace the pendulum, the spring, and the escapement with a tiny *synchronous motor*. This motor is powered by the electricity available at your socket outlet. The electricity there is, in most of the U.S., 60-cycle alternating current. The 60 alternating voltage swings that occur each second are carefully regulated at your power station and so they can be relied on to swing *exactly* 60 times each second, or 5,184,000 times during each 24-hour period.

Since the speed of the synchronous motor is strictly dependent on the frequency of the electric power, the more accurate the number of current cycles the more constant will be the speed of the motor. So we rely on the power company to keep sending us 5,184,000 cycles of current every 24 hours. This keeps our synchronous motors running at the right speed. The motor drives the clockwork gear train which sets the hands, and that's all there is to it.

The one problem with electric clocks is that they are "tied" to the wall socket. If you blow a fuse or move the clock from one side of the room to the other, the time during which current didn't reach the clock will never be registered. Some clocks have little red flags in their faces that show when the clock has been stopped. You make the flag disappear by resetting the hands or by touching a little button to show that you have corrected the time.

# COFFEEMAKERS

Take hot water, mix it with roasted, ground coffee beans, strain out the grounds, and serve—that's coffee. All percolators, Dripolators, French *filtres*, and Italian *espresso* machines are based on this principle. They differ in the method of mixing and straining, and in the type of coffee bean used, but that is about all.

Simplest is the slim, hourglass-shaped coffeemaker. The upper section is open at the top. You fold a round piece of filter paper in half and in half again and drop it into the top section. By spreading the folds, the filter neatly seals the upper section off from the lower one except for a venting channel along one side. You put the ground coffee in the top section, pour a measured amount of hot water over the coffee, stir and let the coffee seep through the filter to the lower section. When the water is all down you remove filter and coffee grounds in one easy motion.

The French or Italian *filtre* also works on the drip system. The top section of the pot has a perforated bottom, and a cover. Ground coffee is put in the upper section and boiling water poured over it. The waiter puts the covered pot so prepared next to your empty coffee cup and you watch it for a quarter of an hour.

" CHEMEX"    "FILTRE"    " SILEX"    PERCOLATOR

The familiar double-globed gadget, sometimes called a Silex, is very similar. When assembled you have a lower bowl and an upper bowl whose bottom is a tapered tube that extends down into and almost touches the bottom of the lower bowl. A cloth or glass filter seals the opening at the top of the tube. The lower bowl is filled with water and the upper holds the ground coffee. Note that the only opening for the water to leave the lower bowl is up through the tube and filter. As the water boils it produces steam that is trapped above the water surface in the lower bowl. The steam builds up pressure on the water surface and pretty soon the pressure is high enough to force the water up through the center tube and into the upper bowl. Steam is still boiling off in the lower bowl when most of the water has been forced into the upper bowl. This makes the water churn and bubble, mixing the coffee and water well. After a few minutes you turn the heat off and slowly the water and trapped steam cool. Once the steam condenses the coffee is free to filter through to the lower bowl, leaving the grounds behind. Incidentally this can be speeded by wrapping a cold, wet cloth around the lower bowl—but take care you don't crack the glass.

Percolators are the most ingenious of all. The pot is filled with water. A hollow stem (called a pump) is surrounded at the top by a perforated cup which holds the coffee grounds. The foot of the stem is in the shape of a shallow inverted cup. When the water boils, steam is produced at the hottest spot, the bottom surface of the pot. The steam is trapped under the foot of the stem. It rises up through the stem, forcing ahead of it any water trapped in the tube. The water shoots out of the top and strikes an inverted glass cup in the pot cover. This cup spreads the water and drips it down over the coffee grounds to seep back into the pot.

Professional type coffee machines are larger, of course, but that is really the only difference. The big stainless steel cylinders are usually in sets of three: coffeepot, boiler, coffeepot. Water is heated in the boiler and then piped to the top of the adjacent pot where it pours over a cloth bag full of coffee. When the pot is full, beakers of the weak coffee are repeatedly drawn out of the spigot and poured by hand into the bag at the top until the coffee has the desired strength.

*Espresso* machines are just complicated hot water boilers and every cup of coffee is freshly made. Coffee grounds are put into a little cup that attaches to one of many spigots that surround the bottom of the boiler. Steam and hot water are forced into the coffee and then drip slowly into the coffee cup held below. The big advantage is that many different kinds of coffee can be made quickly in this machine.

# COMPASSES

Originally man could only tell direction by the stars. This is still the most widely used method of determining true north. You locate Polaris, the North or Pole Star, and measure all directions away from that.

Have you ever wondered why it is that the North Star always points north while all the other stars turn with the rotation of the earth? After all, what is so special about that one star?

Well, the answer is that the line between North and South Poles points at the North Star no matter what time of day or night, or what time of the year it is.

Perhaps a model will make it clearer. Take an orange and push two toothpicks into opposite ends so that they appear to make a continuous line through the center of the orange. Hold the orange so that the top toothpick points at the roof of a distant building. Now slowly slide the orange around on a table top in a large circle, always keeping the top toothpick pointed at the building. This is the earth swinging around the sun and the distant building is the North Star. Each time around the circle is one year. At the same time the earth turns on its own axis and you can spin the orange

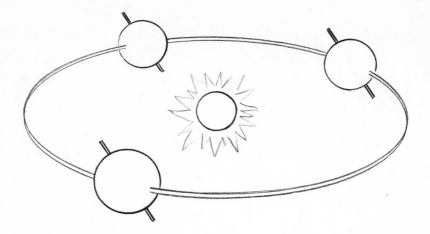

around the toothpicks to simulate this motion. This creates day and night.

Now pretend that you stand on the surface of the orange. You are very small and "down" appears to you always toward the center of the orange, "up" is straight up and away from the orange—no matter if the spot you stand on is actually facing down, or sideways, or up.

Note that as you ride along with the earth you can see the "sun" (at the center of the circle) only when that side of the orange on which you stand faces it. You can see the North Star (the distant building) only when you stand on the top half of the orange (otherwise the curvature of the orange blocks the star from view) and it must be nighttime or the "sun" will blot out all the stars by its brightness.

With all of these restrictions, it is still possible to see the North Star from the surface of the orange and the distant building will always be in a direction "north" of the person standing on the orange no matter what the time or season.

The limitations of location, nighttime, and the need for a clear sky, have encouraged men to look for other methods of establishing direction. The next improvement was the magnet or *loadstone* (which tended to point to the *loadstar,* Polaris). This is a naturally magnetic ore first discovered by the Chinese many hundreds of years ago. A straight bar magnet can be hung from a string or lightly pivoted on a needle point so that it is free to turn in the horizontal plane. The magnet will always swing around so that it points approximately north and south.

The reason this happens is that the earth itself is a huge magnet. Just as iron filings align themselves with the magnetic field surrounding a tiny magnet, so do magnets themselves try to align themselves with the earth's magnetic field. The *magnetic compass*

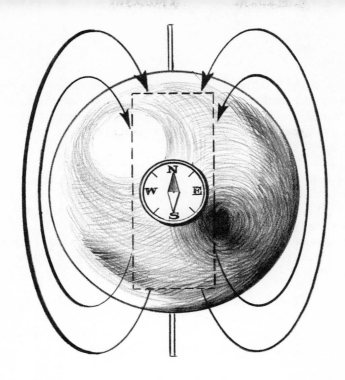

consists of a small magnetized needle, freely pivoted in the horizontal plane (or floating on a bowl of liquid). Usually it is designed so you can align a compass card with the north-pointing needle so that all compass directions can then be readily determined.

MAGNETS

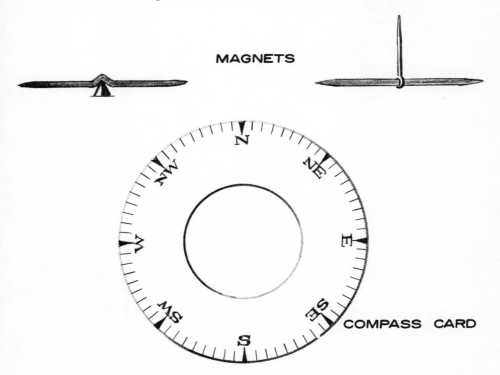

COMPASS CARD

Actually the magnetic lines of force surrounding the earth do not run exactly north and south; they vary in direction somewhat depending on the location. Thus the magnetic compass doesn't point to "true" north, it points to "magnetic" north, which is nearly the same thing.

To overcome this limitation, navigators (particularly airplane navigators) use a *gyroscopic compass*. The gyroscope is a fascinating device that has several peculiar characteristics. It is a weighted flywheel spinning at high speed and mounted in special bearings (called *gimbals*) which permit the axis of the gyroscope to take any position it likes. Note in the sketch that each pair of bearings gives the gyroscope another direction in which it is free to turn.

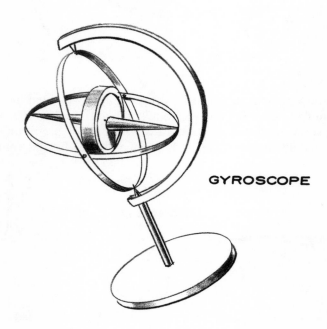

**GYROSCOPE**

When mounted in this way the gyroscope will maintain exactly the same position no matter how you twist and turn the outer mounting rings. As a matter of fact if you try to push the gyroscope it resists stubbornly by moving off to the left or right as if with a will of its own. This is what gives the toy gyroscope such a strange feeling when you try to swing it in your hands. Since the earth is a heavy mass turning on its axis, it also acts as a gigantic gyroscope and that's why its axis always points in the same direction.

The characteristic is put to good use in a compass because no matter where you are on the earth, or how you got there, the gyroscope axis will always stay in its original position. Precision is essential in these devices since the slightest friction in the bearings will appear as a force on the gyroscope and tend to turn it away from the set direction. In addition, the gyroscope flywheel cannot be allowed to slow down because once it stops all the special gyroscopic characteristics will disappear. To keep it spinning, air jets are sometimes aimed at small cups cut in the rim of the wheel or the flywheel is surrounded by coils of wire carrying electric current so as to make it into a simple electric motor.

Gyroscopes are now used to guide all our rockets and satellites, our ships, and planes.

# CORKSCREWS

There are probably as many different kinds of corkscrews as there are can openers. Actually there should be more. After all corks are older than cans by a long shot.

First of all, what is cork? Cork is a layer of bark that surrounds the cork oak, a tree that grows in southern Europe and North Africa. About half of the cork volume is made up of tiny air cells (200 million in a cubic inch of cork). Since the woody bark itself is relatively flexible, we have in cork a combination of characteristics—good insulating ability, compressible yet resilient, watertight but porous to small quantities of air—that makes it so perfect a stopper for wine and liquor bottles.

The corkscrew has as its essential part the helically twisted steel shaft that is driven into the cork as a gripper. A series of tests have established that the corkscrew should be long enough to drive down through the entire length of the cork and slightly beyond. The French say not all the way through because the screw may break off a few pieces of cork and drop them onto the surface of the wine.

Since it is sometimes necessary to exert a 300-pound pull to draw a stubborn cork, some form of leverage is essential. This is why the straight corkscrews with a cross-bar handle and nothing else are the hardest to use.

One form of lever is simply a ring built out from the hub of the screw which rests on the mouth of the bottle and keeps the screw from moving farther into the bottle neck. Since the screw keeps

57

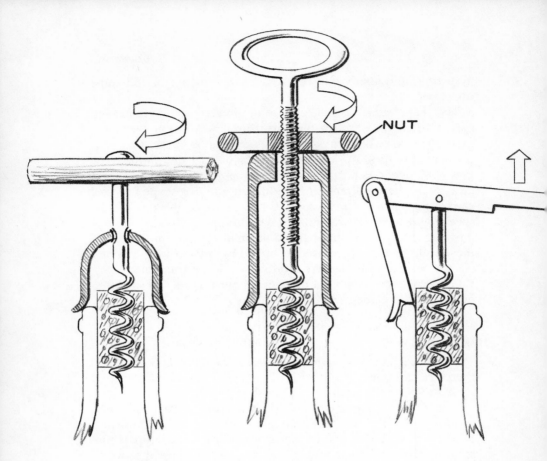

NUT

driving into the cork, the cork must climb out on the screw. The disadvantage here is that corks break too easily under such treatment.

Another method has a double screw arrangement. The back end of the corkscrew shaft is threaded to take a nut. At the start the nut is run up as high as possible on the corkscrew shaft and the corkscrew twisted well down into the cork. When the screw has gone as far as it can the nut rests on top of a cup fitting snugly on the neck of the bottle. Twisting the nut slowly pulls the cork out of the bottle.

Probably the most familiar one is the waiter's corkscrew. In this the cork is pulled by a lever pivoting on a hinged boot that leans against the neck of the bottle.

Very recently a totally new design has reached the market. It is not really a corkscrew, but a cork drawer. It consists of a hypodermic-type needle whose back end is supplied with high-pressure carbon dioxide from one of the cartridges used to make sparkling beverages in the home. You plunge the needle straight down into the cork until its tip is exposed in the bottle just above the wine surface. Then you press a button which sends a charge of carbon dioxide into the bottle and this internal pressure pops the cork out. The device doesn't change the taste of the wine.

# D

## DOORBELLS

All electrically operated doorbells are based on the *electromagnet.* An electromagnet is a coil of wire wrapped around an iron core (see ELECTRICITY). A magnetic field is generated within the core when electricity flows through the wire—just as if it were a strong permanent magnet like the U-shaped gadgets you find in any hardware store. But electromagnets have an advantage over permanent magnets; they can be turned on or off at will just by starting or stopping the electric current to the electromagnet coil.

The usual home doorbell has an electromagnet of this kind connected so that when the button is pushed current flows to the magnet coil. The iron core (now a magnet) attracts an iron *clapper* normally held away by a light spring. As the clapper moves toward the magnet it opens a pair of contacts in the circuit to the coil (see sketch). The current stops flowing to the electromagnet

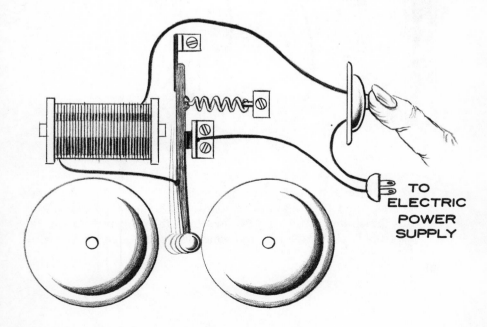

TO
ELECTRIC
POWER
SUPPLY

when these contacts are separated and the magnetic attraction disappears. The clapper is then pulled back by the light spring. If your finger is still on the button (as it probably is since this entire action takes only a fraction of a second), the return of the clapper re-establishes current flow when the contacts touch and once again the clapper is attracted to the electromagnet. The clapper, therefore, is kept in a constant state of nervous indecision—swinging back and forth between the electromagnet and the contacts.

On the far end of the clapper there is a metal ball which bounces between bell cups. Each impact rings the bell and you hear a regular series of clangs. Note that the loudness or tone can be varied by limiting the swing of the clapper, or by varying the size and thickness of bell cups, or by holding a felt pad against the cup to damp its ring.

*Chimes* are similarly struck by a moving hammer, but they usually are powered by true solenoids—that is, the hammer is attached

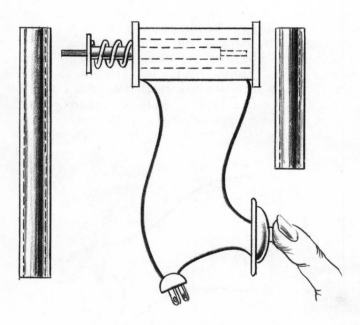

to an iron rod that moves freely inside the coil. No make-and-break contacts are used since you do not want a repeated striking of the chime, just a single blow. Press the door button and the solenoid attracts the iron rod which moves through the coil compressing a light spring. It strikes the chime and bounces back slightly to be held in the coil's magnetic field until you release the button and stop current flow. Then, with the magnetic attraction released, the spring pulls the hammer back to strike the second chime on the other side of the coil.

Try it the next time you visit your friends. At the instant you press the button the first chime sounds, when you release the button you hear the second chime.

## DRAPERY TRAVERSE RODS

The purpose of these rods is to facilitate drawing the drapes away from the center of the window so that the window may be opened or the blinds adjusted. The method of operation is very much like that of the Venetian blind (see VENETIAN BLINDS) in that a strong cord looping down to the sides of the drapes is used to position them.

The drapery traverse rod has a single continuous string running from the right-hand slider (where it is tied) along the rod to the right corner, down to the floor, around a pulley at the floor and back up to the rod. It runs through the rod from right to left, around a wheel at the left end of the rod and then back across the drapery rod to the right-hand slider where the second end is tied.

Note that as you pull down on the cord the two lengths running across the top of the window move in opposite directions past each other. This permits the main sliders to move in opposite directions. The sliders are attached to the cords, one slider to each cord, so that they separate when the control cord is pulled one way. They come together when the control cord is pulled the other way.

The right-hand slider is built so that it overlaps the left-hand slider with an extension. Thus the drapes close with a slight overlap.

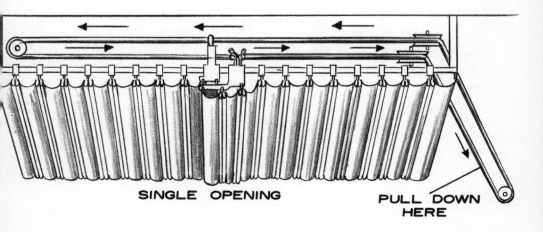

**SINGLE OPENING**          **PULL DOWN HERE**

The moving ends of the drapes are hooked to the sliders, the other hooks in the drapes are hung from plastic eyes that slide freely along the rod. The sliders draw the ends of the drapes together. These ends move away from the collected drapes at the right and left ends and slowly pull the rest of the drapes after them. The sewed pleats are carried along with the drape giving it soft, full folds as the fabric moves across and covers the window. Eventually the two sliders meet. The drape ends overlap slightly, the rest of the width of the drape is spread evenly across the window.

This represents the typical application, but there is no reason for the drapes to open only at the center. With slider stops placed at convenient points along the rod the drapes can be made to open and close from widely separated points. The center could

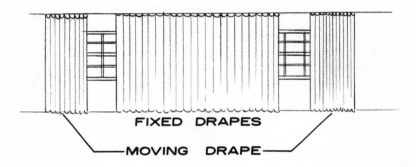

FIXED DRAPES

MOVING DRAPE

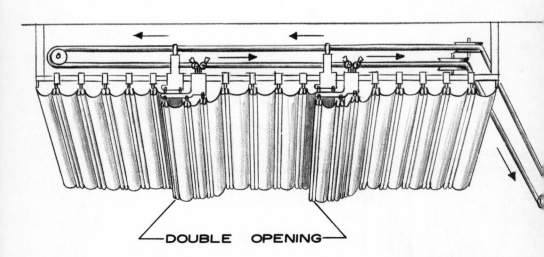

DOUBLE OPENING

be covered with a fixed set of drapes hanging from plastic eyes on the rod.

Two or more sets of sliders can be added to the single rod. The first and every other slider, say from the left end, is attached to one of the cords moving through the rod. The second and every even slider from the left end is attached to the second cord. Thus all the even sliders move right when all the odd sliders move left. If you've got two separated windows and wish to draw the drapes simultaneously over the pair you hook the left-hand drapes to the odd sliders and the right-hand drapes to the even sliders. The single control cord will open or close both sets at once. In each case you must be certain to allow enough plastic hooks between the various pairs of sliders to take all the drape hooks.

The single-cord principle is the same for all traverse rods including round rods operating with rings instead of sliders. The cord runs through the hollow rod, and is attached to the rings by an ear that moves in a slit in the rod. Even theater curtains are essentially the same, though wire replaces the woven cord and motors replace muscle power.

## DRYERS

In many respects the clothes dryer is the twin of the washing machine. Both can use a rotating drum to tumble the clothes. The only difference is that the clothes tumble in soapy water in the washing machine while they tumble in warm air in the dryer.

Actually the dryer is simpler, because the control cycle is strictly *on* or *off.* When *on,* the drum is rotated by a motor, a fan blows hot air into the clothes as they tumble, an exhaust flue carries the moisture-laden air outside directly or through a special filtering arrangement. This continues for 40 or 50 minutes at which time the dryer automatically shuts itself off.

Individual dryers vary only in detail. For example, you can choose dryers operating on gas heat or electricity. There are advantages and disadvantages to both. Price, availability, and your local gas and electric rates will determine which is best for you.

The gas dryer warms the passing air in the flame of a burner. The electric dryer uses heating elements much like those in an electric oven or range—a heating wire, surrounded by electric insulation, is protected by a metal tube. When current flows through the central heating element, it warms the entire assembly. Range elements of this kind glow red hot. The dryer fan blows air past the heating elements and into the drum carrying the clothes.

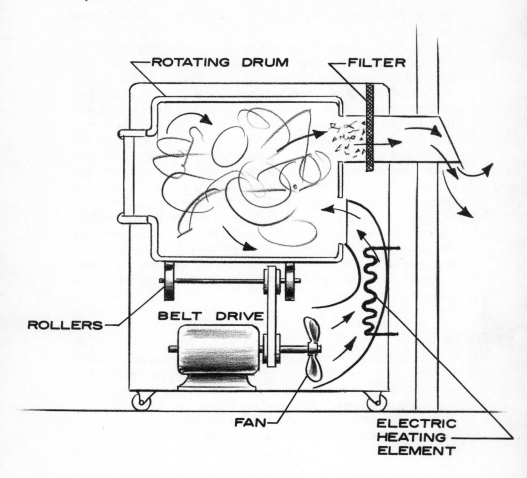

ROTATING DRUM    FILTER

ROLLERS

BELT DRIVE

FAN

ELECTRIC
HEATING
ELEMENT

Getting rid of the air is more complex. Wet, lint-filled air is to be carried through a flue to the outside. All dryers have filters, fine meshed screens, through which the air must pass before it reaches the flue. The filter stops the lint carried by the air. It packs thicker and thicker on the screen until the air has a hard time passing through the lint. At this point the dryer has lost a lot of its efficiency. The clothes just don't get as dry as they did when the dryer was new and the filter clean.

The answer to this problem is simple—remove and clean the filter. Your directions will tell you how to go about removing the filter and how often. It makes good sense to follow these directions carefully.

Several dryers now on the market have been designed to eliminate this filter cleaning chore. Air from the dryer passes around a series of tubes carrying cold tap water. The hot, wet air coming from the clothes is cooled and the moisture condenses on the cooling tubes. The lint is carried along with the water to the house drain line. The cool, relatively dry air that remains can be vented to the room rather than through a flue.

Only two control devices are needed in dryers. The first is a clock timer (see WASHING MACHINES). The clock timer counts off a preset number of minutes from the time you start the drying cycle and automatically shuts the dryer off at the end of the desired time. You can rerun the cycle if the clothes aren't dry enough or, in some dryers, you can vary the time to suit the washload.

A thermostat is used as a safety device and sometimes also as a temperature controller. The bimetallic strip will turn the dryer off completely if the temperature exceeds a safe limit (usually around 200° F). Sometimes thermostats are also used to control the temperature of the heated air. When the air gets too hot the thermostat reduces the amount of electric current or gas going to the heating element. This is exactly the same type of control as used in temperature-controlled ovens.

# E

## ELECTRIC BLANKETS

Here is an invention that promised to revolutionize the sleeping habits of the world. Certainly a light woolen blanket that can keep you at a comfortable sleeping temperature no matter how cold the weather, is a very desirable thing. The heavy weight and bulk of winter bedding could be dispensed with and a saving in furnace fuel might even be possible.

In practice things aren't quite so rosy. The problem is that the delicate wiring woven into the blanket is easily torn. If the blanket is to be light weight the heating wires must be so thin and flexible that they simply cannot stand up to the robust twists and turns of an active sleeper. So an electric blanket will last only two or three years, and repair is usually not economical. It will cost as much, if not more, than the original blanket price. Some companies have begun to offer high trade-in allowances on old electric blankets, and this is a temptation well worth considering.

The second disadvantage is a psychological one. Many people just don't like the idea of sleeping under electric current. While most blankets are Underwriter approved and exceedingly unlikely to give you a shock, electric blankets *have* been known to start fires.

Most of these disadvantages do not apply to small heating pads. The pads can be much thicker than the blankets and so the danger of shorts or broken wires is practically eliminated. The pad is made of heavy rubberized material with molded-in wires. The wires themselves are thicker and so the entire device is sturdier, more reliable and longer lasting.

In either case the heating element is a pattern of thin heating wires (see TOASTERS) woven in a spiderweb network. The wires never get cherry red, as they do in your toaster, but they do get warm when current flows. This warmth is spread through the wool or other fabric and over a large area. If the pad or blanket hangs freely in air the heat is quickly carried off by air currents. If the blanket is placed on a mattress and then covered with another wollen blanket the heat can't escape and the bed will be quite warm in a few minutes.

You should avoid folding a blanket too tightly in storage or when put on the foot of the bed. Also you should avoid sitting on the electric blanket if possible. The delicate wires are likely to be broken. This does not apply to the heavier electric pad which is made to withstand rough treatment.

The pattern of wires is intended to spread the heat over the entire surface of the blanket. To permit some form of heat control the manufacturer divides his wires into two or more groups. The switch is set so that it supplies electric power to one or the other or to all of the wires in the blanket. This permits three levels of heating (see sketch): *low* is circuit A alone, *medium* is circuit B alone, and *high* is circuits A and B together.

This is the simplest kind of heat control. A more elaborate system uses a thermostat (see THERMOMETERS AND THERMOSTATS) to control the heat. When you turn a knob on the control box near your bed you actually set the thermostat to a desired temperature. The full heating network is used to raise the temperature of the

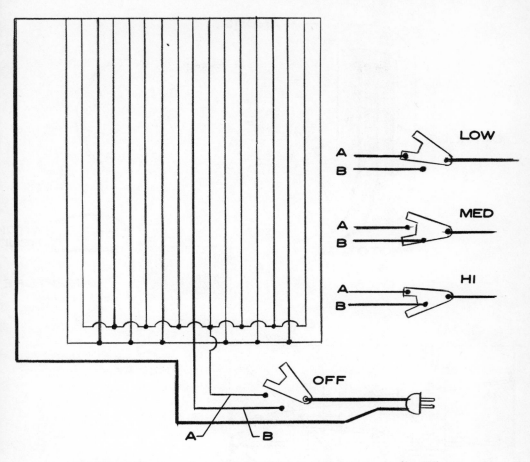

blanket to the set value and then it turns off automatically. When the temperature drops a few degrees the current turns on again automatically.

## ELECTRIC EYES

They are usually used to open a door, ring a buzzer, or set off a burglar alarm when a beam of light is broken. Later we will learn how such alarms are made, but first what makes electric eyes sensitive to light?

The heart of the gadget is the *phototube*. This is a vacuum tube (see VACUUM TUBES) that conducts electricity when light strikes it. In the normal vacuum tube the filament heats the *cathode*, boiling off electrons (negative electricity) which are then attracted to the *anode* (a positively charged sleeve) surrounding the cathode.

The phototube also produces a flow of current between cathode and anode, but here the situation is reversed; the cathode partly

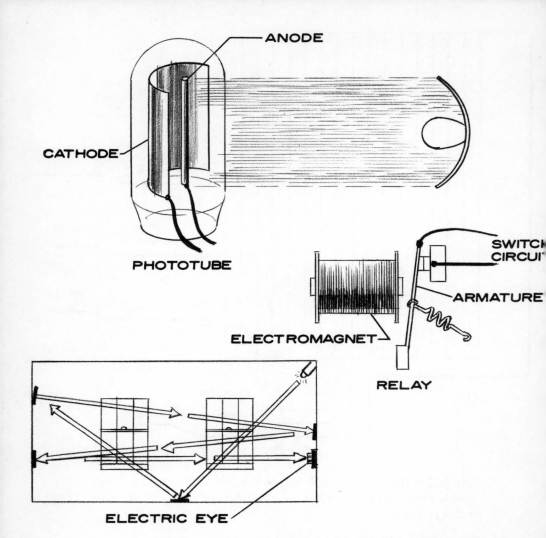

ANODE

CATHODE

PHOTOTUBE

SWITCH
CIRCUIT

ARMATURE

ELECTROMAGNET

RELAY

ELECTRIC EYE

surrounds the anode. When light strikes the treated surface of the cathode, electrons are kicked off its surface and are attracted to the anode. Thus there is a flow of current between the two tube elements.

Of course the flow is extremely small, and before switches can be thrown or alarms rung, the flow must be amplified. But amplification is easy with standard vacuum tubes once the original flow has been produced.

The amplified current operates a relay (see RELAYS)—a gadget used in many of the more complex electric appliances. The relay consists of an electromagnet that attracts a movable strip of magnetic iron called an *armature*. The armature has a contact button, like a switch, which is pulled toward or away from a second contact when current flows in the electromagnet. This automatic switch will turn *on* or *off* depending on whether current flows in the electromagnet, and the current depends on whether light does or does not strike the phototube.

Obviously it doesn't matter to the relay which direction of armature travel makes the contacts touch. Sometimes it is connected (as the sketch shows) so that the signal goes *on* when light stops hitting the tube. The switch reacts when a beam of light has been broken. A door is approached, for example, and you block the beam.

In this way, electric eyes are used to operate doors in railroad stations, restaurants and some garages. Generally a light source is placed on one side of the entrance and perhaps five feet in front of the door. It sends a beam of light across the approach to the door into the receiving eye on the other side. When you break the beam a relay is flipped and an electric motor opens the door. It closes automatically after a few seconds, unless the beam is broken again.

Phototubes can be made sensitive to ultraviolet (or "black") light and these are used in burglar alarms. Here the light source may be anywhere in the room. It shines into a mirror across the room and is then reflected to another mirror and so on, making several sweeps back and forth across the room in front of all windows and doors. Finally the light reaches the phototube. A burglar has to be skillful indeed to avoid breaking such a network of invisible light.

Electric eyes are used to turn house lights on when the sun goes down. They're used to guide rockets to enemy planes whose engines give off infrared light. They're used in "light amplifiers" where an electric eye more sensitive to light than the human eye can view a dark scene and produce a bright duplicate of the scene on a screen.

Phototubes are the eyes of the television camera. Modified to sense *changes* in brightness, they scan the field of view and translate the light and dark areas into high and low voltages for your set (see TELEVISION).

# ELECTRICITY

It is well established that electricity is the flow of loose electrons. Electrons are tiny, negatively charged particles, which normally swing around the positively charged nucleus of atoms, much as the moon swings around the earth. In certain molecules there are electrons which are less powerfully held by the nucleus and they are easily dislodged. Consequently, such molecules are electrically conductive—the degree of conductivity depending largely on how free the circling electrons are.

When a molecule loses an electron it has an excess of positively charged particles (protons) in its nucleus. For example, in a dry-cell battery the chemical action within the cell pushes the free electrons to the outer shell of the battery leaving the center post positive. This chemical push overcomes the electron's natural attraction to the positively charged nuclei (the old opposites-attract rule). Given an external path like a wire touching both outer shell and center button, the electrons race through the wire to equalize the charges (see BATTERIES).

Electron flow is relatively slow but the numbers of electrons in a bit of metal are truly unimaginable. It has been estimated that the number of electrons that flow through a normal 50-watt light bulb in one minute is the same as the number of drops of water that flow over Niagara Falls in 100 years!

Electricity, however, can't flow through all materials. Wood, air, most plastics and fabrics, rubber, pure water (not salty or mineral-filled tap water) are relatively poor conductors. They are called *insulators* and act as a barrier to flow.

The idea that electricity flows as water does is a good analogy. Picture the wires as pipes carrying water (electrons). Your wall

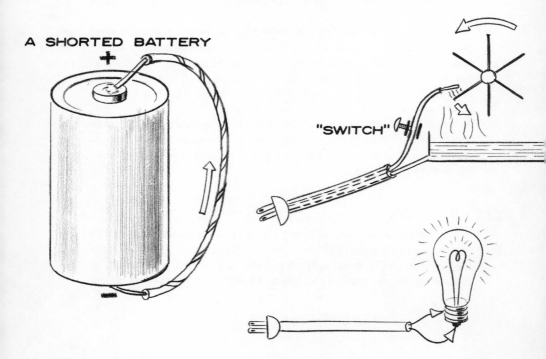

A SHORTED BATTERY

"SWITCH"

plug is a high-pressure source which you can tap simply by inserting a plug. The plug has two prongs—one to take the flow to the lamp, radio, or air conditioner, the second to conduct the flow back to the wall. A valve (switch) is used to start or stop flow.

The *voltage* rating is a measure of pressure, the amount of push behind the electric current. The *ampere* (or amp, for short) is a measure of current flow—increasing with increasing pressure and with decreasing resistance to flow, that is, some materials conduct less easily than others, as if the flow channel narrows down in places.

So you have to have a complete circuit, of more or less conductive materials, and a voltage pressure to push the electrons through. Motion of electrons through wires can be both useful and dangerous. The first characteristic is that electricity heats the wire as it passes through—heats it faster and hotter the greater the current. This means that electrical energy is being transformed into heat as current flows. This is a very important idea since electric light bulbs (tungsten wire heated to incandescence by the flow of electricity) and toasters (with a wire that turns cherry red when electricity flows) are dependent on the heating effect of electricity.

Of course, heat can be a disadvantage as well. When too much current flows in house wiring you have fires and shorts in the walls started by the heat of electric current. That is why fuses are installed to break the circuit before trouble starts (see FUSES).

The measure of energy used in an electric circuit is the *watt*. Usually you measure watts by multiplying the volts times the amperes in your circuit. A watt is a small quantity in most power circuits, so engineers speak of a *kilowatt* (1000-watts) of electricity. When your circuit draws one kilowatt for an hour you have used one kilowatt-hour (abbreviated kw-hr) of energy and your electric power company charges you accordingly.

Let's get the ac-dc problem out of the way before going any further. Electrons are so light and small that they can stop and reverse in no time. It is sometimes convenient to generate electricity (that is, supply the pressure to push electrons out of your wall plug) if it is made alternately to push and to pull the electrons through the wire. For $\frac{1}{120}$ of a second the electricity goes one way around the circuit, for the next $\frac{1}{120}$ of a second it reverses and goes the other way. A full cycle is repeated 60 times each second and so it is called 60-cycle alternating (ac) current to differentiate it from the unidirectional, direct (dc) current.

While ac and dc current are very different to electrical engineers and designers of radios and such, they need not concern us too much here except that you should remember never to plug an ac appliance into a dc outlet or vice versa. You will certainly ruin the appliance and possibly blow some fuses as well. Most United States homes and offices are ac but if you're traveling in Europe, be careful. Their voltages and cycles-per-second are very often different from what your appliance was designed for.

One additional effect and you can quit this subject which, incidentally, is the basis of two distinct courses of study in engineering school. Electricity is intimately concerned with magnetism—and the problem is that no one really knows quite why. We do, however, know a lot about how to use this interesting effect and much of our scientific and industrial progress of the last 100 years can be directly attributed to the science of electromagnetism.

When electricity runs through a wire it creates a magnetic *field* around the wire. You can prove this by taking a sensitive magnetic compass and moving it around in the plane perpendicular to the wire carrying direct current. You will find that the compass always points in circles around the wire—never toward or away from the

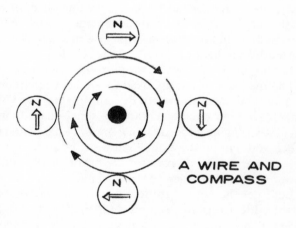

**A WIRE AND COMPASS**

wire. The magnetic lines of force—that is, lines along which the magnetic forces act—are circles centered on the wire. Conversely, if you take a short length of wire and move it across a magnetic field (across a permanent magnet's face for example) you will generate an electric current in the wire.

These interesting phenomena make electric generators and motors possible. You generate electricity by moving lengths of wire across magnet faces at relatively high speed, collect all the current developed in this way, and pipe it to your house outlets. Having this current available at the house you can plug in a motor which conducts the electricity to wires whose magnetic field opposes that of the surrounding magnets. The interaction of the two magnetic fields (one created by the electricity in the wire, the other by permanent magnets) forces the wires around, spinning the shaft of the motor.

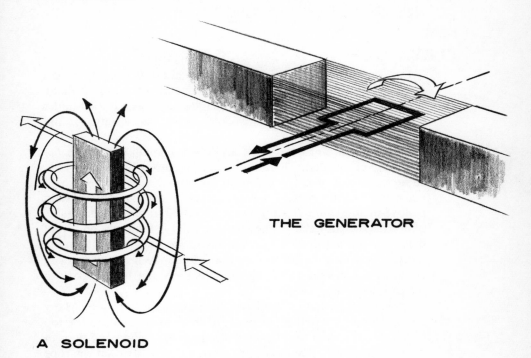

**THE GENERATOR**

**A SOLENOID**

In these motors and generators, the permanent magnets may be replaced by coils of wire wrapped around chunks of iron. The field around each coil of wire reinforces the other separate magnetic fields to make a single strong field. Or sometimes a coil of wire is wrapped around a piece of iron to make a simple electromagnet which attracts other magnetic metals when the current flows, and is dead when the current stops. In this way cranes lift scrap iron to load trucks and barges.

A *solenoid* is such a coil of wire with a loosely sliding rod of magnetic metal inside the coil. When current flows, the rod tries to move in the direction of the lines of force. It will jump in and out of the coil if it isn't restrained. Thus it can be used to open a valve (see WASHING MACHINES) or throw a switch when current flows.

To summarize: electricity is electron flow. To flow, the electrons must have a complete circuit—a wire path to the appliance and a return. Any break in the circuit interrupts the flow and the appliance won't work. Once given a completed circuit, electricity hates to stop. When you open a switch sparks fly—the current actually jumps through the air causing the blue flash and crackle.

## ELEVATORS

Like many other things, elevators have not only become bigger, faster, and more powerful, but they have also picked up so many complex controls that the basic principles have been buried under banks of electron tubes, transistors, lights, push buttons, and switches.

The basic idea of how to lift and lower a small room (the elevator) is very simple. There are several methods but we are concerned with just two. The older one is the *hydraulic elevator* which consists of a long piston—a round rod of steel—which moves in a close-fitting cylinder sunk deep into the building foundations under the elevator shaft. The elevator itself is mounted on top of the piston like a flagpole sitter. When you want to go up you simply pump water into the bottom of the cylinder. When you want to go down you open a valve that permits the water to flow back to the storage tank.

Some older buildings still have these hydraulic elevators. Many are operated by a pull rope that runs from the bottom to the top of the elevator shaft and through a hole in the ceiling and floor of the elevator itself. The operator can pull down or up on the rope at any time in his travels and he thus opens or closes the valves that control water flow to the cylinder.

There are several disadvantages to this system. Obviously the piston and cylinder have to be as long as the height of the top floor. An Empire State Building elevator could be pretty troublesome if the cylinder had to go as deep into Manhattan bed rock as the building is tall. A second serious disadvantage is that the speed of the hydraulic elevator is limited by the maximum speed of the water flowing through valves, pipes, and such. This amounts to a speed of about one floor per second—much too slow for modern hasty times and tall buildings.

The alternative is the *electric elevator*. Here the car is hung from a set of wire ropes. The ropes go up to the penthouse where they

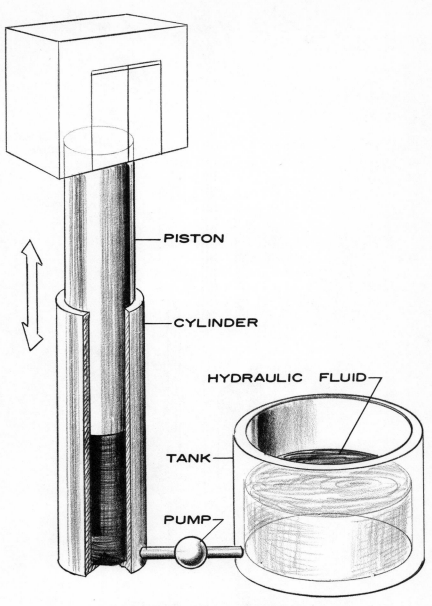

PISTON

CYLINDER

HYDRAULIC FLUID

TANK

PUMP

HYDRAULIC ELEVATOR

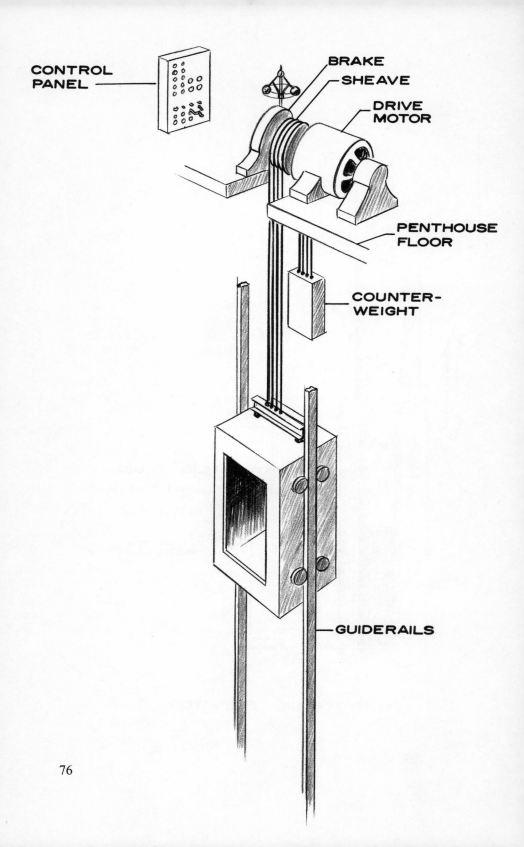

CONTROL
PANEL

BRAKE

SHEAVE

DRIVE
MOTOR

PENTHOUSE
FLOOR

COUNTER-
WEIGHT

GUIDERAILS

76

wrap over a grooved wheel (called a *sheave*) and down to a stack of weights that just balance out the weight of the car when it is a little less than half full (40 per cent full is considered the average load of an elevator).

The sheave is mounted on the shaft of a heavy, slow-turning electric motor powered by its own electric generator. (Alternating current is not as good for speed control as direct so an ac motor drives a dc generator which powers the dc lifting motor.) This system interposes an electric power supply between line current and the lifting motor, and control of the power supply provides a convenient way to vary elevator speed and position.

A heavy-duty brake is mounted on the shaft of the main lifting motor so that in the event of an accident or malfunction of the control system, the brake grabs the shaft and holds the elevator car fixed. If you ever got caught in a "stalled" elevator, that is what happened. A malfunction somewhere along the line signaled the brake to grab, and it did. It will not release until the trouble has been corrected and the safety system reassured that all is well.

The elevator slides on guide rails placed on either side of the shaft to keep it from swaying. Various roller type switches are attached to the car so that they are snapped when the car approaches a chosen floor level. Usually, at first, the quickly moving car touches a switch that reduces the speed for the approach. Then, as the car gets very near the desired stopping point, a second switch signals for a full stop to the motor in the penthouse.

Controls have become progressively more complex. This simple floor-landing device made possible complete push-button operation. In many apartment-house automatics, the passengers push their various floor buttons. The elevator stops at each floor in turn to pick up or discharge passengers. Any button pushed—either in the elevator or on a floor—will signal the elevator to stop when going up (if the *up* button is pushed) or going down (when the *down* button is pushed). This system was soon expanded to work with more than one car. If any car stops at a signaling floor the other cars ignore the signal.

Today the most advanced automatic elevators are true thinking machines as well as car lifters. Neither operators nor starters have anything to do with the controller, which sends a whole series of cars up or down according to need, time of day, and traffic flow pattern. For example, cars can be set to start down as soon as they have reached the highest signaling floor (for heavy down traffic at closing time), or they can automatically switch to high-zone and low-zone operation when one-way traffic gets heavy. In this system half the elevators serve the top half of a building, becoming expresses to the ground floor after some middle floor level has been reached. The other half of the elevators only go as high as that middle floor.

Under the control of these automatic elevator systems the elevators wait until loaded up to capacity before leaving the ground floor in the morning rush; they head back up as soon as they are unloaded in the evening rush hours.

## ESCALATORS

Each stair tread on an escalator is actually a small four-wheel truck. Two of the wheels extend down and forward, two are up close under the back edge of the tread. The wheels are offset in this way so that the top of the tread can be kept level as the truck moves up on sloped tracks. The upper tracks take the upper pair of wheels; the lower tracks carry the pair extending downward.

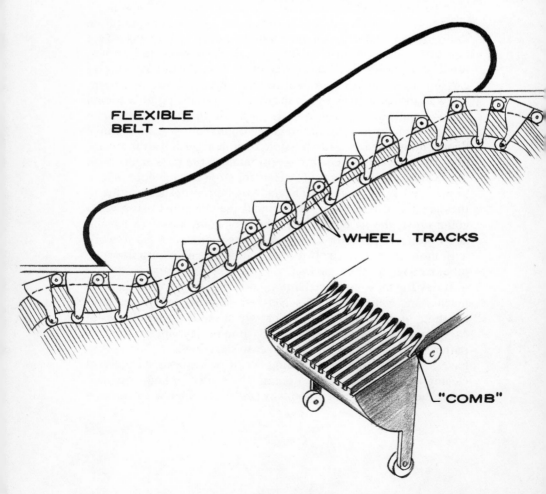

FLEXIBLE BELT

WHEEL TRACKS

"COMB"

The tracks are shaped so that they slowly approach and then run parallel to each other up the slope and then separate again as they come to the top of the stairway. This forces the individual treads to change their relative position from a flat horizontally moving platform, to the familiar stepped pattern, as they travel up the tracks (see sketch).

At the top and bottom, the level portions slide into a *comb*. This is a plate with teeth that extend down into grooves in the tops of the treads. The comb is a protective device intended to make sure that anything on the tread will slide gently onto the platform. The forgetful person or seated child could be badly hurt otherwise.

The treads make a continuous loop running up the stair, around a large wheel and then back down and around ready to carry a new passenger up the stair. Each tread is linked to the others with a heavy chain that loops around a sprocket wheel at the top of the stair. The sprocket wheel is geared to a heavy electric motor that supplies the power and controls the speed of the stairway. The motor can be reversed to carry passengers down as well as up.

On either side of the stairway smooth-faced balustrades rise from the sides of the moving treads. They are topped by a flexible rubber or coiled metal belt that serves as a handrail. Most people naturally take the handrail as they step on the stairway—it helps you adjust to the new faster speed. The moving handrail also indicates when it is time to step off the stairway at the top by curving forward and down into the base of the balustrade. The belt returns to the lower level in an endless loop just as the treads do.

Escalators play an important role in lifting people to higher floors in department stores and similar public places. They can handle large numbers of people—thousands per hour—but they only work well over a relatively small number of floor levels. Once they get above the fifth or sixth floor, people don't have the patience to stay with the up-around-up-around-up pattern; they prefer elevators even though waiting may be necessary.

It is interesting to note that there is no equivalent horizontal transportation bearing the same relationship to trains or buses that escalators do to elevators. It wouldn't be hard to imagine one, however. The moving belt has been used very successfully in industry; why couldn't it be adapted to roadways and streets? Several may soon be tried. The first application is to be in airports where the passenger must walk some distance from the check-in counter to the plane. The belt might be a woven fabric, impregnated with a rubberized substance. It would slide on a flat load-carrying surface and wrap around large driving wheels at each end.

You would step onto the platform much as you do on an escalator, hold a moving handrail, and travel in comfort at walking speed.

# F

## FANS

All the fan does is move air. In some cases the movement of air serves a specific purpose—to drive it around cooling tubes in an air conditioner, to bring fresh oxygen into a furnace, etc. In others, the movement of air is an end in itself, as a house fan circulates fresh air into hot, smoke-filled rooms. Air movement increases evaporation and so people find fans a definite aid in making hot days more comfortable particularly in dry climates. When high humidity accompanies high temperatures (see HUMIDITY), the fans are less effective as coolers.

There are two distinct types of fans or blowers. The more familiar *propeller-type* fan creates a breeze by cutting into the air at an angle (see sketch) and forcing a spiral wedge of air out one side of the blade. These are the fans that oscillate back and forth slowly in our offices and homes, and cool us on hot dry days.

These are the same fans, modified for higher speeds and power, used on propeller-driven aircraft. Here the purpose is to use the reaction force of the air on the blade to move the plane (the every-action-has-a-reaction law). When the air is pushed to the front of a fan and moves out into the room to cool your sweating brow, a similar force acts on the fan blade pushing it into its bearings or, if the fan vibrates slightly, walking the fan back along the table top.

The oscillating motion of house fans comes from a crank that turns slowly at the bottom rear of the fan motor. This crank turns approximately one revolution in ten or more seconds. The crank is linked to a fixed pivot on the base of the fan and when it turns, the entire assembly—motor, fan, and fan shield—is swung back and forth. You start the fan swinging by tightening a nut which clamps the crank to its slowly rotating shaft.

The second type of fan is called a *centrifugal fan* since it uses centrifugal force to drive the air. The *impeller* of a centrifugal fan looks like a squirrel cage with many short ladder steps set in a ring. The casing is a carefully shaped spiral with a delivery passage off

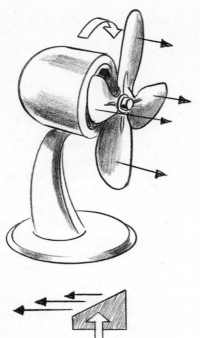

**WEDGING ACTION
OF
PROPELLER FANS**

**THROWING ACTION
OF
CENTRIFUGAL FANS**

one side. As the impeller turns, the air trapped between blades spins around in a circle. The spinning action forces the air outward just as a weight on the end of a string pulls outward when you swing it around your head. In this case the air is stopped by the casing where it is compressed. The air moves around and eventually reaches the outlet where it rushes out in a concentrated mass.

There are several interesting facets to the centrifugal fan. First the delivered air isn't twisted into a vortex, as the propeller-driven fan twists the air. Second, the inlet air is sucked in along the axis of the shaft to the center of the impeller, but the air is delivered at right angles to the inlet at the exhaust pipe.

Both these fans are used in air conditioners. A propeller-driven fan sweeps outside air over the hot coils on the outside but a centrifugal fan is often used to suck room air in and blow it around and back through the cooling coils and into the room.

81

# FAUCETS AND VALVES

Say *faucet* and most people think *drip*. Now faucets don't *have* to drip. As a matter of fact, considering the vast number of them in the world, the percentage of "drippers" is extremely small. Yet it only takes one drip to spoil a good night's sleep—and that's how faucets got a bad name.

But how does the water get to your faucet in the first place? Let's follow the water as it travels into and around your house. The utility company brings it to your cellar wall in a large pipe branching off the main street line. This is cold water of course, and usually has been pumped from a reservoir nearby. The water pressure is 30 to 50 pounds per square inch, which means it can lift a vertical column of water only 70 to 100 feet high—enough for a six-story building. If you live or work in a ten-story building, you've probably got auxiliary pumps pushing the water up to a tank on the roof. The water at your faucet is piped down from that tank.

Somewhere near the main water inlet you'll find a big shut-off valve. This valve has a good-sized spoked wheel sticking out of the top or side, and by turning the wheel clockwise until it's tight you can cut off all the water coming to the house. When water pipes freeze and break, or the boiler needs repair, the plumber usually starts by shutting off this valve.

From the main shut-off valve the water branches off in several directions. It is piped to your water heater, to the furnace if your home is heated by steam or hot water, to the water closets and to the cold faucets of sinks, showers, and baths. Water from the water heater goes to the hot water faucets around the house.

The whole purpose of valve or faucet is to offer a means of controlling the flow. Pipe valves rarely drip (or leak, which is the same thing) simply because they stop the flow of water with a metal-to-metal seal jammed tight. The problem with valves is that they take considerable effort to close tight and the same effort to open. We would soon get tired of all that work just turning water on or off, and so a faucet is designed to flip on or off at the touch of a finger.

The sketches show how these work. Note the metal plug in the valve and how tightly it can be forced into the tapered hole. In the faucet a rubber, fiber, or plastic washer is the seal. It butts up against the round nipple, and after hundreds of uses a groove is pressed in the washer. Finally the washer is cut or torn until it can no longer seal the opening. Then the faucet drips until someone replaces the old with a new washer.

At the end of the faucet you often find an *aerator*. These handy

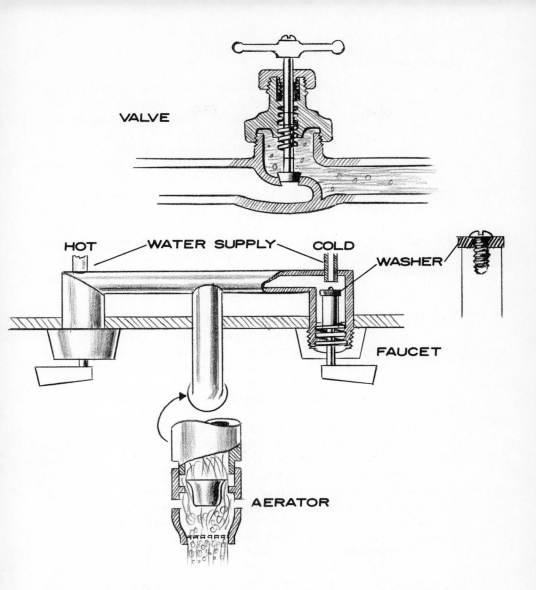

VALVE

HOT          WATER SUPPLY          COLD          WASHER

FAUCET

AERATOR

little gadgets appeared only recently but quickly gained in popularity since water flowing out of them doesn't splash and splatter but tends to hug the dish or cup and flow around and over the sides. The trick is to fill the water with air bubbles as it comes out of the faucet. To do this you force the water to flow around a plug in the pipe. The water spreads into a cylinder of flow and is directed past holes or slots in the periphery of the faucet. The water moves so fast it can't turn and run out of the holes (unless you close off the bottom exit). Instead, air is sucked in and mixes with the water, which then leaves the aerator in a foamy jet.

83

Note how the hot and cold water are mixed before they pour out of the spout. You control the water temperature and volume by controlling the flow at the two faucets. A newer control faucet is now on the market that does this with a single lever control. The lever is pushed up and down to adjust the volume, left and right to change the temperature. Thus you can keep the same amount of water flowing but raise its temperature by pushing the lever straight to the left. You can keep the temperature constant but increase the flow by pushing the lever straight up.

The newer shower valves are a little different. They have no real need of flow control, so the shower is either *on* at full force or *off*. You dial the temperature by turning the pointer to the desired mixture of hot and cold water.

# FILM

To this day chemists and physicists are not exactly certain of what happens when light strikes film. They are beginning to get some inklings, but it wasn't until the invention of transistors and the growth of the whole field of solid state physics that they began to understand what photographers have been doing for almost 100 years.

The essential process is this: sensitized film is exposed to light for a brief instant of time. This forms a *latent* or potential image on the film. The image is made real by later development in special chemical baths. The result is a *negative* of the original scene—blacks are transparent, whites are black on the film. A *print* is made by exposing a similarly sensitized white paper to light directed through the negative. When the print is developed you have a *positive,* or natural-looking, image.

The sensitized layer, or *emulsion,* is made up of crystals of silver bromide mixed in and held by a layer of gelatin. When light strikes the silver bromide crystals a few atoms of silver separate out from the compound. At this point the latent image has been formed. Areas hit heavily by light have relatively large numbers of freed silver atoms. Areas touched only slightly by the light have few or no silver atoms separated from the silver bromide.

So few silver atoms have been separated that the change is invisible to the eye and even to the most sensitive instruments. However, when the film is placed in the developing solution the isolated atoms of silver are centers about which much more silver collects and the clumps become plainly visible. When the unexposed silver bromide crystals have been washed away by the *hypo* solution, you can take the film out into daylight without fear of ruining it by further exposure.

The resultant negative has clumps of black where the bright areas in the original scene were, and clear areas where the original scene was dark. By placing the film on a sheet of sensitized white paper and exposing this sandwich to light you transfer the image to the paper and simultaneously reverse it. Blacks on the negative develop as white areas on the paper since no light has penetrated to the paper in these areas. Clear areas on the negative transmit light and develop into dark areas on the paper.

The print is a reasonably good facsimile of the original scene, but it is monochromatic—it reduces all of the many colors of nature to black, white, and shades of gray.

Color transparencies and, more recently, color prints, have overcome the original limitations of black-and-white photography. In color film the sensitized layer is actually made up of three separate sensitized layers with filtering dyes in each layer to control the transmission of red, green, and blue light. A silver image is formed in each layer corresponding to the red, green, and blue light of the original scene. This image is made apparent in the development process which creates red-, green-, and blue-colored layers in the film instead of black ones.

Transparencies are color-for-color duplicates of the original scene. They must be viewed by transmitted light—the light must pass through and be filtered by the transparent colors in the film. You can project transparencies directly onto the wall or screen and re-create a scene that closely approximates what the camera originally saw.

Negative color films are also available. They produce color negatives of the original scene—all colors are replaced by their complements (reds appear as green on the film, etc.). The color negative is used to make a print on sensitized white paper also having three layers of emulsion, just as the film does. The paper, when developed, is a positive color print of the original scene and need not be projected to be viewed.

# FIREPLACES

As air is heated it expands and becomes lighter. Lighter air rises just as air bubbles rise in water. We will see this convection effect working above radiators (see HEATERS), how much more so does it work above the fire in fireplaces. As warm air fills the chimney flue, it is pushed upward by more air coming in at the bottom.

Thus the smoke and dust can be carried up the chimney rather than flowing out into the room. That is, it will as long as the fireplace and chimney are properly designed. Most of this magic of proper chimney construction dissolves once you think concentratedly about what a rising column of warm air needs to "draw" well.

First, it must be tall enough to be unaffected by strong wind turbulences near the roof. Experts recommend a minimum of 35 feet from grate to chimney top and the top should extend two to three feet above the roof to free it from disturbances caused by the roof itself. The flue should be more square than rectangular to ease the flow of air, the shorter dimension no less than sixty per cent of the larger one. Round flues are excellent in this respect. The flue area should be at least 8 by 8 inches and preferably more. One rule of thumb for flue cross section is 15 square inches of flue area for each square foot of open fireplace.

You will find that the back of your fireplace slopes forward to a long narrow opening leading to the flue. This opening is called the *throat*. The throat may be closed off by the *damper*—a hinged metal door used to control the flow of air up the chimney. Behind the damper is a smoke box. Here downflow of cool air collects, warms, and reverses itself flowing up the flue and assisting in lifting the smoke up the chimney. The smoke box also provides a

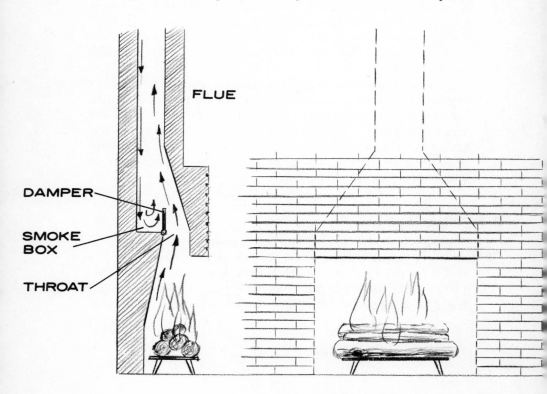

FLUE

DAMPER

SMOKE
BOX

THROAT

place for smoke to collect when momentary downdrafts stop the normal flue action.

Fireplace proportions should follow pretty closely those you find in the sketch: width roughly equal to height, depth about half the width; sides vertical until well past the throat; throat 8 inches or more above the top of the fireplace opening.

Today we are much more concerned about a well-drawing fireplace than we are about its heat-producing ability. Tightly sealed homes with weather stripping around all the doors and windows create something of a problem since the air to supply the fire must come from the rooms themselves. If everything is sealed tight a slight vacuum is created in the house and the fireplace has a hard time pulling more air out of the rooms to send up the flue. The answer is to open a window somewhere in the house, preferably upstairs, so the incoming air will be warmed a bit before it flows around your guests in front of the fire.

## FISHING REELS

Until very recently there was only one kind of fishing reel. It looks like a small metal squirrel cage with a spool of fishing line at its center. By turning the handwheel you spin the spool and draw the line in. A small traveling eye moves back and forth across the spool and lays the line down in even layers.

Several little knobs and attachments extend the usefulness of the reel. For example, you can disengage the handwheel and permit the spool to spin freely for casting; you can apply a brake to the spool so as to control its rotation and the release of line; you can lock the spool and thus apply the full strength of the line to hold the caught fish.

The reason for all of these gadgets is that a reel must perform several distinct actions. Its primary job is to store the fishing line neatly. However, the reel must permit the line to be thrown off easily during the cast; it must restrain the line when a fish is hooked and played, but not apply so much drag as to break the line when the fish makes a particularly strong lunge.

Perhaps you can imagine some of the troubles the familiar rotating-spool reel creates. The worst is the backlash snarl which occurs when the spool keeps on spinning even though the lure has landed and the line is not paying out any more. Here is where the expert fisherman's trusty thumb should save the day. It doesn't always. The result is an unholy mess of line that jams behind the little moving loop. For an hour or two, the fisherman usually tries

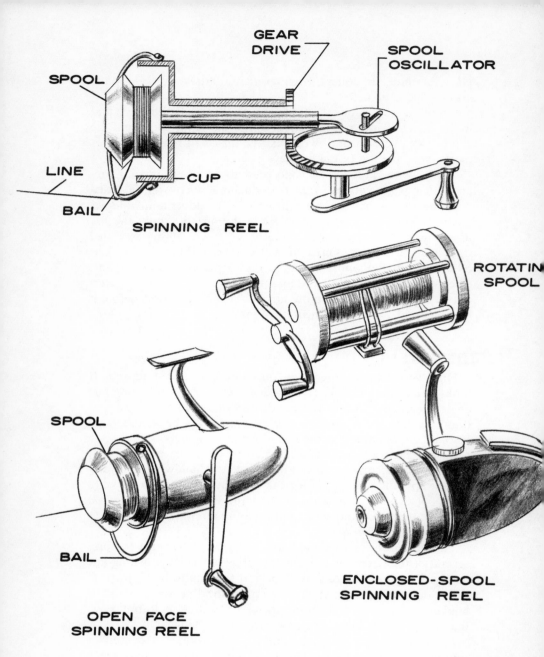

GEAR DRIVE

SPOOL OSCILLATOR

SPOOL

LINE

CUP

BAIL

SPINNING REEL

ROTATING SPOOL

SPOOL

BAIL

OPEN FACE
SPINNING REEL

ENCLOSED-SPOOL
SPINNING REEL

to clear things. He might better save his fishing time by simply cutting the line and winding on a new one.

The clicking, braking action installed on these spools reduces the problem somewhat since it slows the spool quickly when the lure lands. However, the solution brings its own disadvantage.

The brake shortens casts by retarding free spin of the reel, hence free release of the line. Another improvement has been to make the hollow, perforated rotating spool of a light aluminum alloy. This reduces the inertia (see FLYWHEELS) and so eases the spin stopping problem. Note that inertia creates a starting problem too. You can't get a good long cast without starting the entire spool and line rotating freely and this takes a lot of casting energy and a deft hand.

The answer to most of these problems is the *spinning reel.* This is really a revolutionary design in fishing reels. Here the spool is fixed—it cannot turn. Its axis is parallel to the rod and so when the line wants to pay out there is nothing to stop it, it just loops off the end of the reel. Only the line itself moves and so there is no inertia problem—neither starting nor stopping. To reel in the line, a *bail* is attached to a cup surrounding the spool. The bail is swung into position across the face of the spool and this picks up the line. When you turn the handwheel you spin the cup around the fixed spool and carry the bail around and around the spool. This feeds the line back onto the spool and performs the winding function neatly and as easily as ever the rotating spool did. As you spin the bail the spool moves forward and back so as to lay the line down in even layers.

The advantages? No backlashes; much longer casts because of the reduced inertia; the drag can be set (with the bail in place) so as to eliminate the possibility of a snapped line.

But there are disadvantages. The careless cast may throw loops of line as easily as it will throw the light lure, and this can make a bad snarl between rod tip and lure.

To reduce the loop throwing possibility the *enclosed-spool spinning reel* has been invented. The principles are exactly the same as for the open-face spinning reel. The difference is that a cone has been placed over the front end of the spool and a hole drilled into the apex of the cone so that the line is fed out of a single point rather than around the spool lips.

This closed-spool reel eliminates the need to flip the bail back and forth. To release the line you simply back up on the handwheel for a fraction of a turn, and this retracts the bail hook. To reel it in, just turn the handwheel forward.

The problems? Both spinning reels use relatively lightweight lines, and so larger fish can't be hooked and played. Great care must be taken in laying the line on the spool for the first time and deciding the permissible amount of line since the relation of line and spoon lips is critical for free paying out and spooling.

# FLYWHEELS

"A body in motion tends to remain in motion; a body at rest tends to remain at rest."

This simplification of Sir Isaac Newton's law defines what we know now as *inertia*. It led to his law of gravitation, a reasonably accurate analysis of the motion of the planets, and gave physics a good start toward atomic energy and relativity theorems.

It was not an easy idea to accept—and despite your high school physics, you probably don't really believe it to this day. This is because every real-life experience we have makes a lie of the "law." Start an ice cube sliding across the floor and it will stop— Newton or no Newton. Someone says "friction," as if that has any meaning even to the one who said it.

But the fact remains, a body in motion will continue in its path and at full speed, unless impeded in some way. The impedance may be friction between rubbing surfaces, or the need to push aside molecules of air or water. Each inch of sliding or pushing aside of air takes its toll. The ice cube slows and eventually comes to rest.

Not all things move by sliding or in air. The moon, the planets, and many artificial satellites are above the air blanket surrounding the earth. Some satellites eventually quit the high, wispy air spaces and slowly come down to earth; others, like the two that missed the moon and were trapped by the sun, will go on forever.

On earth there are few, if any, situations that can avoid losses due to friction or air turbulence. To overcome the losses you reduce friction to a minimum (with BEARINGS, for example) or increase the inertia to keep things rolling as long as possible.

Inertia is a measure of something closely associated with mass or weight. The greater the weight the greater the inertia, all other things being equal. For example, start a small ice cube sliding across the floor at a certain speed and it will stop much sooner

THIS ICE CUBE TAKES THIS LONG TO COME TO A STOP

A BLOCK OF ICE AT THE SAME STARTING SPEED TAKES MUCH LONGER TO STOP

**THIS HEAVY WHEEL
WILL CONTINUE TO SPIN MUCH LONGER THAN THIS
LIGHT ONE WILL**

**PULL YOUR ARMS IN AND YOU SPEED UP**

than a large one. A heavy cast-iron wheel will continue to spin freely much longer than a light plastic one. Of course, it takes more pushing to get the heavy ice cube or wheel going, but that's the penalty you have to pay.

One more important point: inertia in ice cubes, or other bodies that are intended to move in straight lines, is strictly dependent on mass (or weight). Inertia of rotating bodies, like wheels, is highly dependent on the distribution, as well as the amount, of mass. The farther away from the pivot point the mass is, the greater the inertia—by a very great amount. You can prove this by sitting a friend in a swivel chair and spinning him around with his arms and feet extended. As he spins tell him to pull his arms and legs in close to his body. See how much faster he turns! Note that ice skaters do this all the time. They start a spin with arms and legs extended, then pull their arms in and turn into a blur of high-speed grace.

A flywheel is a wheel specially designed to have high inertia. It is used to store energy, and this is a very interesting application of Newtonian principles. Suppose your electric power were very uncertain—available most of the time, but likely to be cut off for a minute or two now and then. However, you need a constant and reliable source of power to drive your sewing machine; otherwise, it would stop in mid-stitch. You could attach a heavy flywheel to the machine. The motor would get the flywheel spinning at top speed and keep it at that speed as long as power was on. When the electricity failed the flywheel would keep on turning for a long while—long enough, perhaps, to last until power was restored.

This may seem like a crude method, and for sewing machines perhaps it is not too important to store energy in this way. Yet Swiss trolleys work on the same principle. Instead of having the electric drive motor connected to an overhead power line all the time, as ours are, they tap into the electric outlet only at stations. At this time the electric motor in the trolley spins a heavy flywheel which stores enough energy to take the trolley to the next station.

Probably everyone has had, at one time or another, a toy flywheel-powered car or truck. The principle is the same—a relatively heavy flywheel is geared to the rubber tires of the toy. You spin

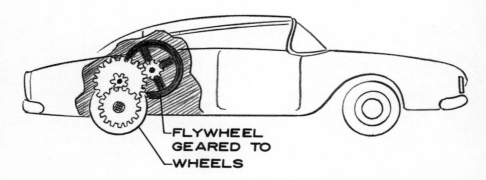

FLYWHEEL GEARED TO WHEELS

the wheels by forcefully pushing the car forward on the floor until the wheels (and flywheel) are spinning well, and then lightly set it down to run along under its own power for a surprising distance. You've done the work of storing energy in the flywheel which then drives the car until friction burns up all your labor.

## FRICTION

To engineers, friction often seems like a dead loss (see FLY-WHEELS), but without friction our lives would be very difficult indeed. You couldn't pick up a glass, or walk, or swim without it, yet few people actually understand what friction actually is.

Friction is a resistance to motion. The resistance can come about when two solid bodies try to slide on each other, or when a solid body moves in a liquid or gas, or when layers of a liquid or gas move at different speeds. In each case the mechanism of friction is a little different.

Consider first two solid bodies. They may look as smooth as glass, but under a powerful microscope the surfaces show up as many peaks and valleys. Metal, wood, plastic, glass, the surfaces may differ somewhat but the essential hilly characteristic is the same. When two such surfaces touch, their peaks and valleys interlock in some places. To move one relative to another the surface has to be lifted out of contact or else it will tear off the interferences. This tearing action (remember, it is microscopic peaks and valleys we are talking about) is what causes the resistance to motion called friction. It is also what causes the normal wear in sliding surfaces.

Now if you oil the surfaces, the oil fills the spaces. Oil is thick enough (it is made of molecules, too) to separate the peaks and valleys. Thus, the peaks don't have to be torn off and friction is considerably reduced.

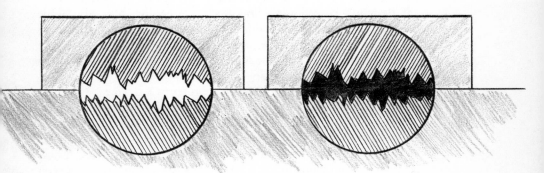

**WHAT "SMOOTH" SURFACES LOOK LIKE UNDER A MICROSCOPE .**

**WITH OIL TO SEPARATE THE SURFACES .**

But even oiled surfaces are not frictionless. The oil molecules must roll and bounce across each other as the top layer moves relative to the lower layers. Rolling and bouncing also creates a resistance to movement. The ease with which the oil molecules move across each other is a measure of the oil's lubricating ability. The thinner the oil the easier it slides. If it is too thin, however, you run the risk of squeezing the oil out from between the solid bodies and then the peaks and valleys may start interfering again.

So the engineer reduces friction losses in motors and engines by oiling the bearings or by designing them so they roll rather than slide (see BEARINGS). But he needs friction between the wheels and the road; otherwise, the wheels would just spin and skid as they do on ice. Increased friction is possible by using rubber wheels (flexible materials sink more deeply into the valleys and add to the interferences) and heavy weights. Gritty particles like sand, or rough surfaces like grinding wheels, dig deeply into wood or rubber and give good "purchase." Rubber-soled shoes are better than leather for getting a good start in a race.

Can you picture walking on slippery ice at home, on the streets, in your office? That is just a small taste of a life without friction.

# FUSES

Every home has at least one, and many modern apartments boast fuse boxes with two to six of these sawed-off light bulbs. If you're lucky, you will never need to know what they do—or how. If you are unlucky or operate too many air conditioners for safety, you've been replacing fuses at regular intervals. Some people are scared by the violent voltages so close to their fingertips when replacing a fuse; others blithely pop pennies into the sockets and screw in the burned out fuse only to be awakened a few nights later by fire engines.

First and foremost, a fuse is a protective device. It doesn't protect you, or even your home, so much as it does the main lines and the electric company at the other end of your electric plugs.

Fuses are basically low-melting-point connections between the electric mains and your house circuit. If you look inside a new household fuse, you will see a band of silvery metal wired between the center contact (at the nose tip of the fuse) and the side contact (the metal screw threads or a pair of spring contacts on the shoulder—see sketch). Some fuses, usually built into appliances, are made out of a glass tube with metal caps at either end and a strip of low-melting-point metal running between them.

In either case, all the household current running from the electric company to your house must first run through a fuse. If your electricity requirements are high, the main line (with its fuse) later splits into two or more subbranches, each of which has its own

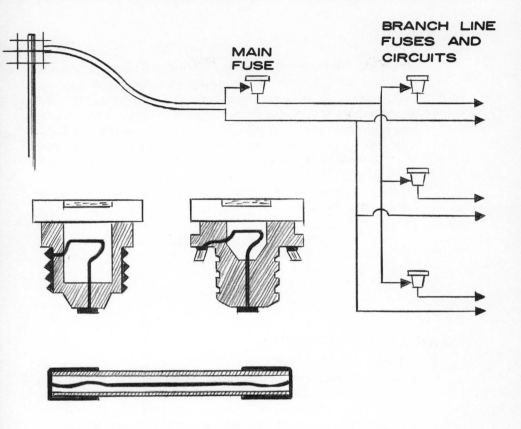

fuse. Each branch-line fuse monitors all the current going to its circuit—living-room ceiling lights, baseboard plugs, and entrance hall, for example.

Now suppose one of the lamp sockets shorts out—that is, the two wires, which should carry electricity to the bulb, touch each other. Sparks fly (see ELECTRICITY) and the current being drawn by the lamp circuit is much too high for safety—too high because the current meets no resistance, the light bulb filament has been bypassed. The wires in the wall will overheat and start a fire if the current isn't stopped.

The fuse (low-melting-point metal, remember?) carries the current too. It melts away and breaks the circuit, so current no longer flows to the offending lamp—or to anything else in the circuit served by that fuse.

If there were no fuses your shorted lamp would endanger the house, the main lines, and even the generating station supplying all its current to your short circuit.

So a fuse tells you when something is wrong with your appliances. It makes no sense just to put a new one in its place. Whatever caused the first one to blow will do the same to the second. First you must find the offending appliance and pull its plug. Then replace the fuse with one of equal ampere rating. The amperes marked upon the fuse refer to the maximum current the fuse will permit to pass. Any higher current will burn it out. Then, with light once again in the room, examine the appliance and repair it yourself if you can, or get a repairman to fix it for you if you can't.

Don't forget to reset the electric clocks. They weren't running for the time you spent in darkness.

# G

## GARBAGE DISPOSERS

There's nothing complicated about these—it's just as easy to grind the garbage in a gadget under the sink as it is to do it on a large scale at the garbage disposal plant down the river. Waste foods, bones, fruit and vegetable parings can all be ground to a soft pulp in the disposer and then flushed down the sewer drain. Paper is less easily handled in large quantities by the home units, and tin cans, bottles or bottle caps had better be disposed of in some other way.

The body of the disposer is a hollow balloon-like container which holds the unground garbage and feeds it to the *impeller*. The impeller consists of a pair of shaped metal shoes that swing from the motor shaft and spin around in the bottom of the housing. At the lower end of the housing the walls are cut through with a series of sharp-edged slots. The slots permit fluids or crushed particles to go down to the drain line that leads to the sewer pipe.

The limitation on home units is that the electric motor in the disposer has only a certain amount of power. The impeller spins food against the slots and if it won't break up and slip through the slots it will stall the motor or fracture the spinning impeller. That is why glass or metal shouldn't be put into the disposer— they are sure to cause trouble.

Generally these disposers are intended to run wet; cold water pours into the disposer while it is running. The water carries the crushed waste through the slots and to the sewer. It also cools the fats which would melt in hot water and coagulate and clog farther down the line.

Sometimes the disposer motor is wired so that it can't be turned on until the cold-water faucet has been opened to insure a minimum flow of cold water. Disposers should always be interlocked so that the motor will not run unless the plug has been placed in the sink drain. This keeps groping hands away from the spinning impeller. It's best to follow the instructions and obey the rules. You won't get into trouble that way.

The disposer is going to be noisy when grinding up pits and bones, but otherwise it should make an eager growl. Jams can occur when bones or particularly hard fibers slip between the impellers and the housing. Run plenty of water into the unit and flick the switch on and off a few times. If this doesn't free it, call a serviceman.

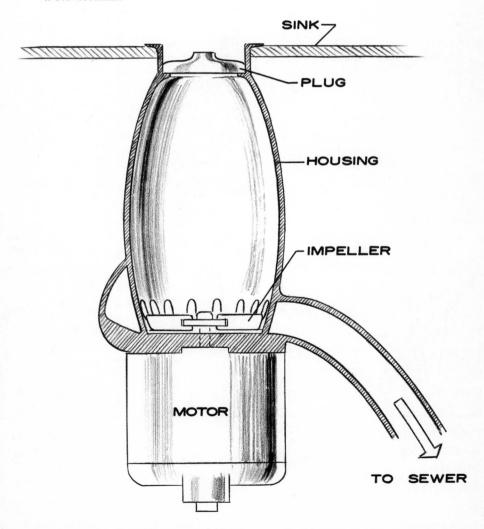

# GLASS

We always think of glass as a hard, transparent, brittle material that comes in many thousands of beautiful shapes, and is fragile in all of them. Actually, glass has another property shared by very few other materials. Glass doesn't melt suddenly at a given temperature as ice does. It starts out hard and brittle, and then as the temperature goes up, glass turns into a molasses-thick fluid which gets progressively thinner as it gets hotter.

The peculiar property of a progressively more liquid material is what makes glass-blowing possible. The glass blower dips a metal pipe into the pot of molten glass and gathers a *gob* on the end of the pipe. The glass is solid enough to be cut by shears, but it is liquid enough to expand when the glass blower puffs into the cool end of the pipe. By a combination of blowing, shaping and trimming, he can make anything from a large decanter to a small light bulb.

Obviously this method is much too slow for the large-scale manufacture of bottles, light bulbs, and electron tubes. Machines now do the job automatically. First a mold is made of cast iron. The mold has a hollow inside of exactly the shape desired for the finished bottle. This will even include the threads at the top.

A measured gob of molten glass is dropped into the mold. A plunger is then forced into the center of the gob of glass to make a pocket and then air pressure is applied creating an air bubble in the glass. The air expands and forces the soft glass to take the shape of the mold. The glass is then cooled enough to set and the mold separates so the bottle may be removed and the next one started.

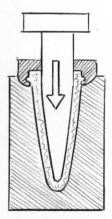

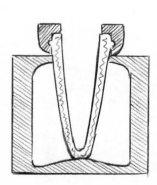

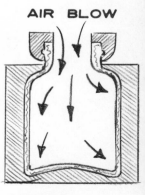

**PRESS IN
A BLANK
MOLD**

**BLANK IN
BLOW MOLD**

**AIR BLOW**

The cycle is repeated over and over again until thousands of identical bottles have been made. Modern machines can turn out a million light bulbs a day by these methods.

Sheet-glass *drawing* is another important form of glassmaking. You may have imagined that a sheet of glass is made by pouring the molten glass into a large tray and letting it cool and solidify. Actually sheet-glass manufacture is much more complicated.

You start with a rectangular pot of molten glass. The pot is kept full from a glass-melting furnace nearby. A clay *boat* floats

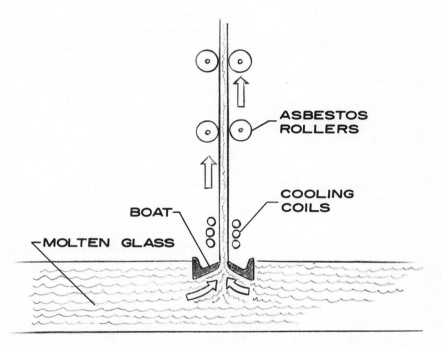

in the surface of the molten glass. The boat has a long, narrow slit in its center and the molten glass tends to rise up through the slit. The rising glass passes between water-cooled banks of tubes and then to a set of asbestos-covered rollers. The rollers draw the glass up at a regular rate.

The sheet so formed can only be as wide as the slit in the boat is long, while its length is limited only by the amount of space above the pot. The thickness of the glass depends on the width of the slit in the boat and the speed of drawing.

But what *is* glass? Glass is mostly sand (silicon dioxide) with a small amount of soda (sodium oxide) and lime (calcium oxide) added. The combination, with additives for color or other special properties, is well mixed and then heated to over 2700° F, at which temperature the mixture fuses into molten glass, and when cooled turns brittle and transparent.

# GLUE

Nobody is really sure why glue holds some things together and not others. The generally accepted theory is that two different kinds of clinging are involved. On porous materials, like wood or fabric, the glue penetrates into the surface somewhat and after it hardens the fingers of glue can't be easily pulled out again. But then how can glues stick to glossy smooth surfaces? Well, for this situation there's a theory that involves the molecular attraction between the glue and the glass. The bond is explained as the result of a chemical reaction between the two materials.

Probably glue holds for both these reasons and possibly others as well. We know that people have been sticking things together for as long as we have written records. They didn't know why cooked animal bones or skin produced a fluid that could be used as glue, but it worked thousands of years ago and it works today.

But today you can buy a lot of other kinds as well. Some are better than animal glues, others are not as strong but they are more convenient to use for specific applications. For example, *rubber cement* is familiar to anyone who has worked in an office. It replaced the paste pot for gluing paper since it is reasonably strong; it will stick to glass, plastic, and other smooth surfaces; and you can pull the glued parts apart without too much trouble, particularly if solvent is dripped over the bond. Rubber cement consists of a rubber—either natural or synthetic—dissolved in a chemical solvent. When the solvent dries the soft rubber remains permanently tacky and able to hold with a firm but not brittle grip.

Rubber cement will make an immovable bond if you let the two surfaces dry completely. They can be touched lightly with your finger or another piece of paper without any stickiness at all, but when the two dry rubber-cement-coated surfaces are brought together they stick immediately and won't budge without solvent.

*Pressure-sensitive tape* is a thin layer of a form of rubber cement on a plastic strip. You get it to stick well by pressure which makes a close contact between adhesive and the object, and by a smoothing action to eliminate the air bubbles or wrinkles.

Of course you wouldn't use rubber cement for a wood cabinet. Here *animal glues* are more frequently used—particularly by the old-fashioned cabinetmaker. Animal glue comes as a powder that must be soaked in water and heated before application. Cabinet makers mix up a fresh batch every morning for the day's gluing and toss out the remainder at night since it won't keep.

The old flour-and-water routine, while reminiscent of childhood, is not as childish as it may seem. The best *vegetable glues* are made with tapioca flour and water and a caustic. The mixture is cooked awhile and the result is on par with the best animal glues for cabinet and woodwork.

*Casein glue* can also serve as a furniture cement or for other odd jobs around the house. It is made from powdered sour milk curds which are mixed with cold water and lime. You don't need a special solvent to wash the stuff off, water will do, but once dried it won't dissolve in heat or water, unlike the animal or vegetable glues.

Industry tends to prefer the *synthetic resins* because they're more easily controlled in strength and setting characteristics than are the natural glues (see PLASTICS). *Thermosetting resins* are heated to make them set and once set they can't be softened by repeated heating. *Thermoplastic* resins are heated to make them fluid enough to spread. When cooled they harden into firm bonds, but you can reheat and resoften the resin as often as you like.

The most important thing to remember in any gluing job is that the surfaces to be glued must be clean and dry. Oil film (even the natural oil on your fingers) or dirt will defy the best glues in the world.

The second thing to remember is to leave the joint alone for as long as the instructions say. Many glues will not hold once the joint has been moved.

Sometimes the instructions tell you to coat both surfaces and let them set before making the joint. This is to permit the glue to soak well into the surfaces and to get a little tacky for faster, surer drying. But not all glues work well with this method.

All glues work better in thin coats over broad areas. This means the joining surfaces must fit each other well, with matching areas flat and level so that only a thin, even coat of glue is needed to fill the spaces. Thin coats of glue will be stronger than the parts they join, thicker layers are often brittle and much weaker.

Spread the glue evenly, clamp the joint or weight it if possible, and leave it alone. You'll be much happier only having to do the job once.

# GUNS

Not many people today consider a pistol or rifle an indispensable home appliance, yet enough of us go hunting or fired guns during the war to make a brief description of how they work worthwhile.

All such weapons are powered by an explosive powder which is ignited and sends a shaped bullet down the length of a tube called a *barrel.* Longer weapons have *rifled* barrels; a set of spiral grooves are cut into the inner surface of the barrel and the bullet is guided into a quick twisting motion which sends it spinning around its own axis in a much more accurate flight path than it would take otherwise.

In general, the longer the barrel the more accurate the path of the bullet since each additional inch of barrel length gives a little more guidance to the bullet. This is why rifles are so much more accurate than pistols. Longer barrels also have more time for the exploding gases to expand and so they give the bullet a stronger shove and the bullet has a longer flight.

Throughout history the two major problems in firearms have been to ignite the powder and to achieve high-speed reloading. The igniting problem was solved in part by the flintlock in which a bit of flint strikes a piece of steel sending a shower of sparks through a hole in the back end of the barrel (called the *breech*) and setting off the powder charge.

The percussion principle of firing is based on the fact that fulminate will ignite on impact. The trigger releases a hammer which strikes a small quantity of the fulminate sending a hot flame into the powder charge.

Up to this point in the history of firearms bullets and powder had to be loaded separately. The percussion cap suggested the *cartridge*—a combination of bullet and powder-filled shell with a bit of fulminate in a tiny percussion cap at the back end of the cartridge. A sharp blow on the percussion cap (by firing pin) will set the cap off which, in turn, sets off the main powder charge.

Cartridges made high-speed reloading an easy matter and to-day automatic rifles and pistols are standard Army weapons. The idea is to bring each new cartridge into the breech as soon as one is fired. In the early Springfield rifle the exchange was done manually: pulling back on the bolt lifted out the empty shell and tossed it aside and pushing forward fed in a new cartridge from the magazine.

Automatic weapons use the power of the exploding powder to

make this exchange. The expanding gases drive the bullet forward and out of the barrel but they also have lots of power left over. The automatic rifle uses this power to throw out the spent shell and replace it with a new cartridge. Machine guns and automatic rifles operate on essentially the same principle and they can fire hundreds of rounds per minute.

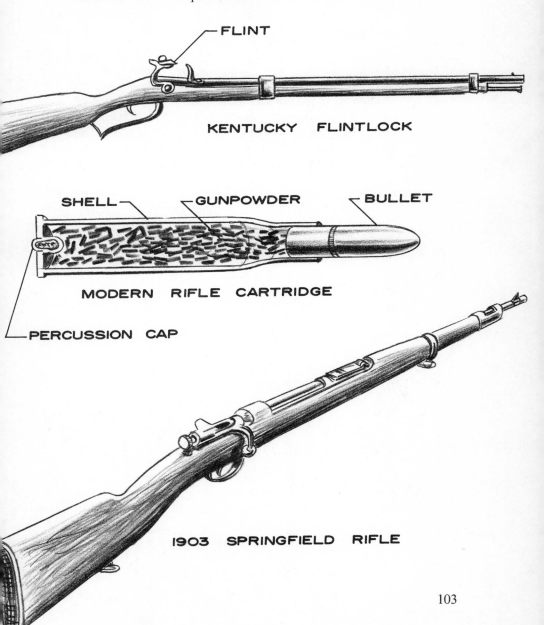

FLINT

KENTUCKY FLINTLOCK

SHELL     GUNPOWDER     BULLET

MODERN RIFLE CARTRIDGE

PERCUSSION CAP

1903 SPRINGFIELD RIFLE

# H

## HAIR DRYERS

The sun is the oldest hair dryer, but ladies in colder, more humid climates begged science for a quicker surer method. The hair dryer is the answer. It is now in every beauty parlor and a portable version is moving into homes as well.

Hair drying is invariably based on heat and moving air. Coils of heater wire (see TOASTERS) draw current directly from the wall plug and warm the air. A fan moves the air past the heater coils in a continuing stream. That is the entire working mechanism of all dryers.

The simplest home hair dryers are gunlike affairs in which a small fan blows hot air out of a screened nozzle. You lift a combful of hair and play the warm air stream over it to dry it quickly.

More popular today for home use is the hooded hair dryer. Here the heater coils and the fan are mounted in a box that sits on a

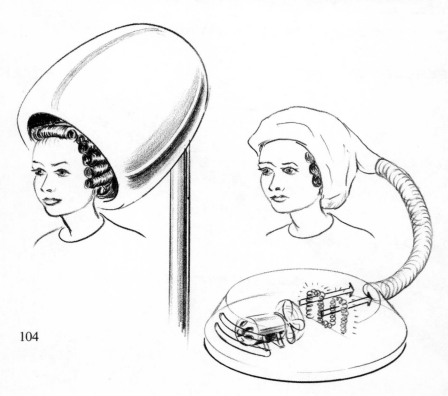

table. A flexible tube about one inch in diameter comes out of the enclosure and attaches to a flexible plastic hood that goes over the head. Warm air is forced into a compartment in the back of the hood and from there through small holes blowing directly onto the hair. Damp air leaves through a series of openings around the edge of the hood or through a single large opening in the front over the forehead.

The beauty parlor hood is, of course, a heavy-duty form of the home-heating hood. Here the hood encloses the head in a sheath of steel. The heating coils are larger and more widely spread, the fan blows a large quantity of warmed air in even distribution over the head. Usually the lady has a control button permitting her to select one of four or five different temperatures. She is faced with the difficult compromise between high temperature and fast drying or low temperature and hours under the dryer.

# HEATERS

Home heating has come a long way since open fireplaces and ember-filled bedwarmers. Engineers have now designed and tested some of the most advanced equipment known to science for warming your bedroom on a cold winter morning.

First, some basics: Only three methods are available for transferring heat from a hot object to a cold one—conduction, convection, and radiation. *Conduction* transfers heat by contact; you touch a hot iron and your fingertip feels the heat at once—too quickly, almost, to pull your hand away in time. *Convection* transfers heat through a middleman. Hold your hand above the iron and you feel the warm air rising. Air heated by the iron is lighter than the surrounding air, rises and warms your hand. *Radiation* is a direct transfer of heat by infrared waves. The winter sun can warm you even when the air is bitter cold. You feel the difference immediately when you move from shade to sun. The interesting thing about radiant heat is that all warm bodies give off some of this infrared radiation. Even your skin does. The amount of heat transferred depends on the temperature of the radiating object and the receiving object—more heat for greater temperature differences.

In general, homes are heated by the last two methods, radiation and convection, in differing proportions. For example, the familiar steam *radiator* is really a convector. The boiler sends steam to the unit. A special valve permits the trapped air inside to escape, but closes as soon as the hot steam hits it. (This accounts for the

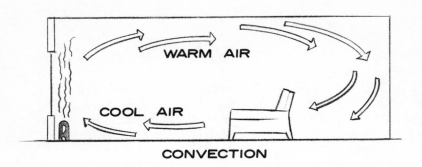

**CONVECTION**

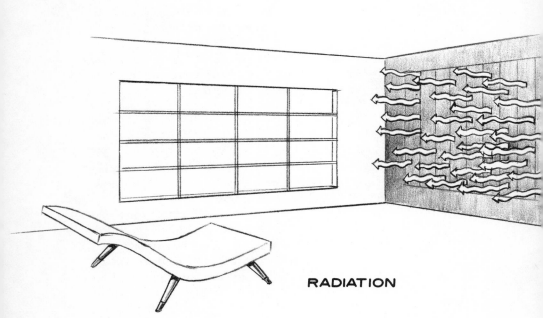

**RADIATION**

whistle you sometimes hear in the early morning.) The radiator is heated until it, in turn, starts to heat the air around it. Note that the prison-bar shape increases the area of contact between radiator and air. The warmed air rises and is replaced by cool air from nearby creating a circulating current of air in the room. The problem here is that the warmest air is up near the ceiling—well over the heads of the room occupants. The floor, where the children crawl is coldest of all.

However, this system has worked very well in millions of homes and even has several variations: Hot water sometimes replaces steam as the heating fluid. Some systems are one-pipe affairs—the condensed water runs down the same pipe carrying the steam to the radiator. Others have a supply pipe plus independent return lines.

A relative newcomer is the *radiant heating panel*. Here a good-sized panel of several square feet, mounted in wall or floor, is warmed by water, steam, or electricity, and radiates heat directly to the objects it "sees" in the room—chairs, tables, and human bodies. Theoretically the air can be at freezing temperatures and the room occupants will still be comfortable. Actually the room air is warmed by contact with the warm floor or wall and circulates nearly as much as in a radiator-heated room. But it is true that the proportion of heat transferred by radiation is much higher for these panels than from the under-the-window, silver-painted "radiators."

Radiant panels are fine when built into bare floors and walls. If madam likes the wall-to-wall carpeting or ceiling-to-floor drapes, some other method is indicated.

*Hot-air heating* is simplest of all. The furnace warms a quantity of air which is piped to *registers* (screened openings) down near the floor. The warm air spreads and rises through the room and is collected near the ceiling to return to the furnace for reheating.

Next question: Where does the heat come from originally? Most homes burn oil or coal in a *furnace*. The fire heats the air or water, boils it if the system is based on steam, and then sends the hot fluid up to radiators, panels, or registers.

Furnaces are just enclosed fireplaces—the coal is carried in to the grate by a stoker, the oil squirted in by a pump. Air enters through holes spaced around the bottom of the furnace. The hot flames and gases play around the water-filled tubes and then are conducted up to the roof through a stovepipe and escape to the outside air.

Electricity is an alternate heating method, sometimes used for radiant panels in climates where heating is needed only at rare intervals. It also serves for small auxiliary heaters—portable units designed to warm a single chair, or room corner when the central heating system is inadequate. However, electricity is an expensive alternative to oil or coal, at least at present prices.

Electricity also serves to run the motors in *heat pumps*—air conditioners used backward—which take heat from the outside and bring it in to warm the house. Instead of "pumping" this heat from icy cold outside air to inside air, heat pumps generally work with underground well water which is at an even temperature—well above freezing usually. The description of air conditioners (see AIR CONDITIONERS) will give you a good idea of how heat may be shifted from the low to the high-temperature side of a wall. The equipment doesn't care which side is outside and which inside and so it works just as well in either direction—some are specially designed to do just that.

Thermostats are described under THERMOMETERS, but it is interesting to see how well adapted they are for home temperature regulation. The thermostat is set on an inner wall of the house where the surrounding temperature is representative of the whole house. The thermostat controls the furnace oil pump or coal stoker—turning it *on* when the temperature drops below a set value and *off* when the house is comfortable. More sophisticated controllers measure outside temperature as well, since it will take more heat to warm the house on an especially cold day than on a coolish spring day, even though the indoor temperatures may be the same.

Most thermostats also have provision for idling the furnace at a relatively low temperature during the late night and early morning hours when the family is snug in bed. It automatically starts the furnace up again in time to warm the house for the earliest riser.

## HIGH FIDELITY

The 1950s may well go down in history as the era of the golden ear—the ultimate in sound sensitivity. High fidelity all started as an electrical engineer's hobby—an attempt to take Edison's invention of the talking machine one step further. It was obvious to anyone not blinded by the wonder of sound from a box that recorded music, particularly classical music, sounded very different on the old 78 rpm shellac records than it did in the concert hall. Since the theory of sound, its nature, and creation were well established, engineers wondered why concert hall sound couldn't be duplicated in their homes.

The answer was, it could within limits. New "unbreakable" record materials, better preamplifiers and amplifiers, and vastly improved speaker systems have brought recorded sound to the point where concert hall audiences can be fooled into thinking they hear an orchestra behind a curtain on a stage, when all the sound comes from three speakers tended by a recording engineer. The musicians are out in their dressing rooms having a smoke.

How does it work? First read the section on SOUND so you will know the nature of the raw material we are working with. Then glance through VACUUM TUBES for some background in the tools of the trade. Then come back here and we'll follow a sound wave from horn to record to your living room. In this section we'll cover sound recorded on disks. For RADIOS and TAPE RECORDERS, see those titles separately.

The train of sound waves (compressions and rarefactions in the air) is picked up by a microphone and transformed into electrical signals. Voltage generated by the microphone goes up and down as the compression part and later the rarefaction part pass the microphone. This transformation of sound energy into electrical energy happens very quickly (extremely high pitched sounds may go from maximum to minimum and back again 15,000 times each second) and so the microphone must be able to respond to these speeds. Further, the microphone may not distort the sound by changing the shape of the wave as it turns it into electrical energy.

Real sounds are quite complex. Mixtures of sounds from many instruments playing at the same time make of the wave a highly irregular shape. But if the sound to be reproduced in your home is to be a good replica of what happens in the concert hall, each twist and turn in the sound wave shape must be faithfully reproduced. Hence the term, high fidelity.

Microphones are made that can do this job. Their only problem is that their electrical signal output is extremely weak. It must be

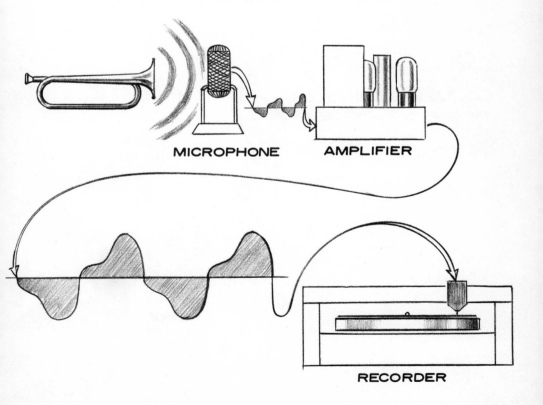

**MICROPHONE**　　　**AMPLIFIER**

**RECORDER**

amplified—made stronger—by vacuum tube circuits. So the signal from the microphone goes to an electric box where it is amplified to good-sized electrical proportions.

Up to this point the amplified signal retains exactly the same curve shape as the original sound. It will be modified for recording purposes (see *equalization,* later in this section) but let's assume for simplicity that no modifications are made. The signal goes to a special record-cutting machine used to cut a wiggly groove in soft waxlike material. A pointed needle is pressed into the record and then, as the record turns under the needle, the needle wiggles back and forth in response to the electrical signals coming from the amplifier.

This process freezes the sound waves into a shaped groove in the record. By a series of casting processes a metal *master* is made of the recording from which thousands of vinyl duplicates are made for sale. Each record has exactly the same wiggly grooves originally cut from the microphone and amplifier signals.

Now you take the record, set it on a turntable spinning at the same speed as the original recording machine, and place a *pickup* on the starting groove. As the groove moves, the pickup needle rides back and forth in the groove and an electrical signal is generated in the pickup which exactly duplicates the electric signal

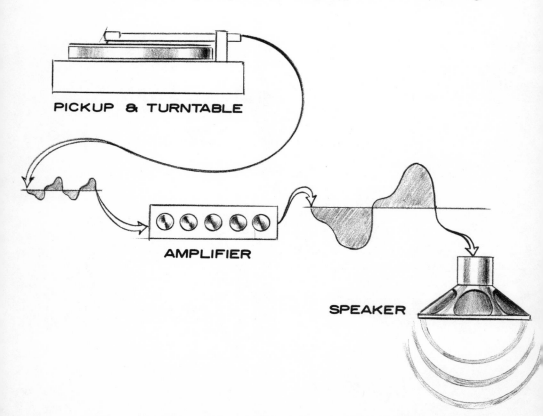

PICKUP & TURNTABLE

AMPLIFIER

SPEAKER

originally produced by the microphone. Once again it is a very weak signal and so it must be amplified (strengthened) by vacuum tube circuits to make it powerful enough to operate a *speaker*.

The speaker receives the amplified signal and sets a cone moving back and forth in response to the electrical signals. The back-and-forth motion creates compressions and rarefactions in the air of your room, and thus the sound originally heard by the microphone is re-created in your living room.

Obviously this is a very complicated process. The original sound goes through so much equipment it's a wonder that it is recognizable when it comes out of your speaker, much less a "faithful replica." Yet the genius of the engineers who devised and perfected this system is such that many people can't tell the difference—live or "canned" sounds are so much alike to their ears.

Part of this perfection arises from a good understanding of and compensation for the problems. For example, *distortion* is the name given to any alteration in the shape of a curve as it is processed. Each component in the chain falls short of perfect duplication by some small, measurable amount. If the total exceeds 15% that is, if the reproduced sound differs by as much as 15% from the original, the sound cannot be called high fidelity. Now 15% may seem like an awful lot, and it is. But here are some typical distortion figures for a system of this kind:

| | |
|---|---|
| Microphone | 2.0% |
| Amplifier | 0.3 |
| Recorder | 2.0 |
| Duplicator | 1.0 |
| Pickup | 2.5 |
| Amplifier | 0.7 |
| Speaker | 3.5 |
| Total | 12.0% |

And this is a very good system indeed. Many recording companies and equipment manufacturers do less well.

The reason that your ear can accept even these high figures is that the human ear is easily deceived. Until you have heard a really good system you are quite pleased with your own—distortion and all. But watch out, once accustomed to good sound reproduction you'll never again be satisfied with less.

A second measure of equipment excellence is *frequency response,* that is, the ability of your system to reproduce, with equal fidelity, the very high as well as the very low notes without preference.

The measure of response is called the *decibel*—a sound engineer's term for electric or sound signal strength. It turns out that one decibel difference in loudness is very close to the minimum difference in sound level discernible to the human ear. Once again, to show how poorly the ear really is, an increase of three decibels—three times the minimum discernible difference to the human ear—is actually equivalent to a doubling of the sound level! So when sound salesmen talk disparagingly of "only 3 db" differences, it is a very great difference in sound even if your ear is not too likely to be aware of it.

Engineers have been able to make amplifiers practically perfect when it comes to frequency response. Variations under one decibel (1 db) over the entire frequency spectrum are the rule rather than the exception. Even pickups and microphones approach this ideal. However, speakers tend to be quite poor. They are so bad that the speaker manufacturers rarely advertise frequency response in quantitative terms saying merely, "response from 50 to 15,000 cycles per second" rather than "response plus or minus 3 db from 50 to 15,000 cycles per second." Variations of 5 and 10 db from frequency to frequency are not unusual. The ear can be fooled luckily, but better speakers are better to listen to, so the deception is probably less effective than we think.

This is why most experts tell you to buy a good speaker no matter how inexpensive the other components.

One more aspect of high fidelity, and if you want more go buy a book on the subject. You'll find a series of knobs on your system labeled "bass," "treble," and "equalization," or "LP, RIAA, AES," etc. Bass and treble are self-explanatory. If you boost or lower the bass you increase or decrease the low notes without altering the high ones. Similarly for the high notes with the treble control. By varying these controls you tailor the sound to suit your ear and your living room.

The *equalization* control compensates for a purposeful variation in recorded sound. As hinted above, the electrical signal coming from the microphone is modified before being sent to the recorder. The high notes are made stronger and the low notes are made weaker than normal. This is done for two reasons. High notes might be lost in the imperfections of the recording and reproducing process because they are so short (as little as one thousandth of an inch between successive peaks on the record) and usually so weak. So they are artificially boosted in the recording process— and they must be cut back down during reproduction in your home or else they'll scratch your eardrums off.

The very low notes are like deep ocean swells—they swing back and forth in such great sweeps that the recording needle would have to make deep curves on the record and it might even break into the adjacent groove. For this reason the low notes are cut down for recording and must be emphasized when playing back or you'll lose them completely.

These equalizations are made automatically in your preamplifier when you plug your pickup connection into the "magnetic" input. Ceramic or crystal ("Xtal") inputs do not need amplifier correction of this kind since the proper emphasis of low frequencies and de-emphasis of high frequencies is accomplished automatically in the pickup.

Stereophonic sound (see STEREO) is still another step toward more realism in sound reproduction, but you've had enough on this subject for one day.

# HINGES

The amateur carpenter or doorhanger always seems to get into violent trouble when he approaches the hinges. The doors never fit properly; they scrape against the sills or jamb or they won't open or close once the hinge screws are tightened.

The problem is not choosing the wrong hinge; it is in forgetting that the important part of the hinge is the hinge pin. The location of the pin determines the success or failure of a hinge since it is this center about which the door will rotate. Seem obvious? Well, let's look at a couple of door possibilities and see which are right and which are wrong.

Before you put a hinge in, or when you are planning to redo the credenza hardware, make a sketch of the door as seen from above. Imagine how the door will swing out. Then experiment (in your mind, or on paper) with different methods of mounting the hinges until you find the one that satisfies your needs.

Once the location of the hinge pin has been decided on, the proper hinge can be found and mounted without any difficulty. The *leaves* (the flat or bent pieces of metal that swing on the hinge pin) may be placed in one of many positions to suit the surfaces to which they will be mounted. It doesn't matter, only the location of the pin matters.

For example, the *surface hinge* mounts flat on the outside surface of door or jamb or both. The *mortise hinge* mounts on the butting surfaces of door or jamb or both. There are hinges that have double bends in the leaves to present their surfaces to the

113

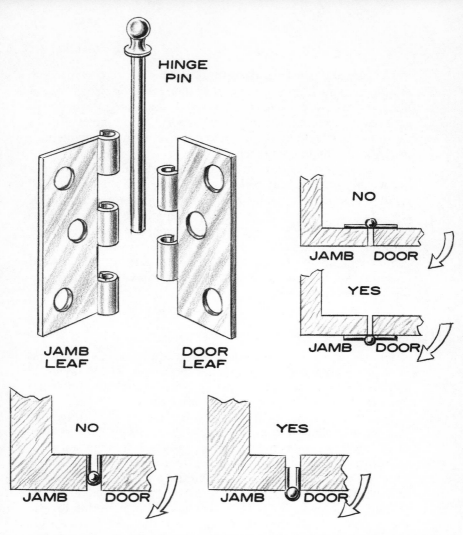

HINGE PIN

NO

JAMB DOOR

YES

JAMB DOOR

JAMB LEAF

DOOR LEAF

NO

JAMB DOOR

YES

JAMB DOOR

flat side of a thin door so that decorative bolts can be used instead of wood screws. But these are really just modifications of the basic surface or mortise hinge.

Several rules or recommendations of hinge installation might be worth noting. Most hinges are made of flat strips of metal cut and bent into loops along one edge. The loops are called *knuckles,* and there are usually more knuckles on one leaf than on the other, mating leaf. The hinge pin drops down through the knuckles when they are aligned and holds the two hinge leaves—and their associated woodwork—in the pivoting relationship. The leaf with the two end knuckles should be placed on the door jamb—not on the door. This gives greater top and bottom support to the hinge which, after all, carries the weight of the door.

All hinges come with removable pins otherwise you could probably never install one. Once installed the pin ends may be capped over so as to hold them in place indefinitely, or they may be simply dropped in and kept from falling out by a head on the upper end. Usually two hinges will be used for each door. Be absolutely sure that the hinge pins line up or else the first time you swing the door the hinges will be wrenched right off their screws.

All mortise hinges should have the screw holes recessed (countersunk) so as to take a flat head screw. The round head screw will not permit the hinge leaves to fold flat.

Some hinges are made to be taken apart at regular intervals. For example, typewriter cases have removable covers. The hinge has only two knuckles: one on the cover, the other on the base. The

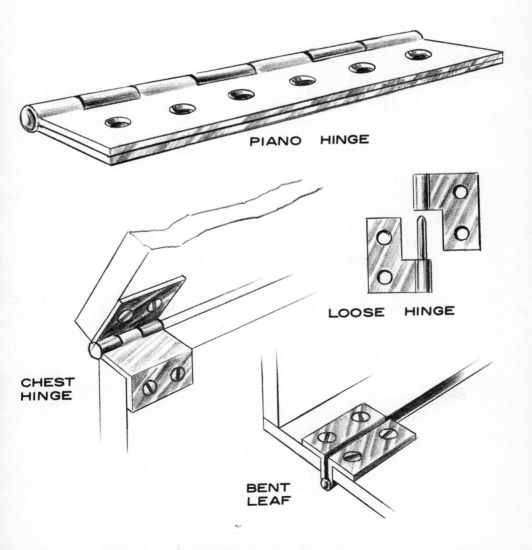

PIANO HINGE

LOOSE HINGE

CHEST HINGE

BENT LEAF

base knuckle holds the hinge pin. The cover knuckle is just a pivot hole for the hinge pin to move in. You assemble the case by slipping it over the hinge pins.

Before we leave this subject we should mention the piano hinge. This is simply a long pair of metal strips with alternating knuckles. The hinge pin is a single rod running down the length of the hinge. You cut off as much hinge as you need for a particular job and mount it in place—this eliminates problems of hinge pin alignment.

## HUMIDITY

Our atmosphere has pressure (see PRESSURE COOKERS), it has temperature (see THERMOMETERS AND THERMOSTATS), and it has humidity. Humidity refers to the amount of *water vapor* in the air and perhaps we should digress for a moment to find out exactly what the weatherman means when he says *water vapor*.

Water can take three distinct forms. It freezes into ice below 32° F, it turns in to a flowing liquid above 32° F, and it boils off into steam at 212° F. Normally we picture the steam as a white cloud that rises and disappears into air. Actually steam is invisible. You can't see it right above the teapot spout; it turns into a white cloud a fraction of an inch away when it condenses into minute droplets of water which *are* visible.

At normal atmospheric temperatures (say from 50° to 90° F) water would seem to be limited to its liquid phase. But we know that a glass of water will evaporate—and it must go somewhere. What happens is that some of the molecules of water jump into the air and are carried away by the moving air currents. These separated molecules of water are what the weatherman calls *vapor*.

Note that if you cap the container of water it doesn't evaporate. The air above the water can take up a certain amount of water vapor until it becomes saturated with the water molecules. At this point a balance is reached. The same number of molecules leave the liquid state and turn to vapor as leave the vapor state and return to water.

The interesting thing about air and its relationship with water vapor is that while air can carry only a severely limited amount of vapor before it starts throwing it back as fast as it picks it up, this limiting amount is different for each temperature. As the temperature goes up the maximum amount of water vapor air can hold increases tremendously. This maximum amount is called the *saturated* amount and the meteorologist has tables which tell him exactly how many pounds of water vapor will saturate a pound of air at each temperature.

Of course the amount of water vapor in the air may be much less than the saturated value—down to practically zero. It can also go above the saturated amount, but then the excess no longer remains as a vapor—it appears as a liquid in the form of tiny droplets (like clouds) or collections of these minute droplets (rain) or, if the temperature is low enough, as frozen droplets (snow or hail).

*Humidity* refers to the amount of water vapor in the air. It does not concern itself with the droplets.

There are two modifying terms used with the word humidity which should be understood: *specific humidity* is the number of pounds of water vapor in each pound of air; *relative humidity* is a percentage that measures how close to saturation the air is.

For example, at 70° F the specific humidity of air saturated with water vapor is 0.0157 pounds of water vapor in a pound of air. This is the equivalent of approximately ¼ of a liquid ounce of water in 14 cubic feet of air. A normal room of about 10 feet by 10 feet and 9 feet high would have a total of just about one pint of water in the form of water vapor. Doesn't seem like much does it? But this represents a relative humidity of 100 per cent! Under most normal conditions the relative humidity would probably be around 50 per cent and then the total quantity of water in the form of vapor in your average room would be only half as much—perhaps a cupful!

But the difference between one and two cups of water is very easily noticeable when you are in such a room. The reason is that your body uses the evaporation of water to keep your skin cool. When the relative humidity gets close to 100 per cent the air simply can't absorb any more water in the form of vapor. This means evaporation won't take place and the natural perspiration collects on your body.

The other extreme is just as bad. If the relative humidity gets too low, the air picks up every little water droplet as soon as it appears. This leaves the skin dry and uncomfortable.

Other things suffer from extremes of humidity as well. Adhesives and wood react to changes in the relative humidity by drying out or swelling. Ladies' hairdos, paper, and fabrics all require carefully controlled humidity if they are to look and stay right. Human hair is very sensitive to changes in humidity. As a matter of fact most *hygrometers* (humidity-measuring instruments) determine the humidity by changes in the length of a human hair.

Many experiments have been run to determine the most comfortable combination of humidity and temperature for people, so that air conditioning equipment can be designed to produce these conditions. The problem is complicated by the variability in human preferences. Some people like dry climates and high temperatures, others like high humidities or low temperatures. The current preference, as far as temperature is concerned, seems to be somewhere near 70° F—a bit lower in the daytime, a bit higher at night. In humidities the variation can be wider—as low as 40 per cent, as high as 60 per cent seem to be the limits. Of course, the preferred temperatures and humidities are not independent of each other. The higher temperatures should be accompanied by lower humidity ratios so that the perspiration works well as a cooling agent. Conversely lower temperatures can be accompanied by higher humidities without discomfort.

These relationships have been combined in a *temperature-humidity index* (THI) which is the mathematical relationship of temperature and humidity to comfort. In theory each person could establish his preferred range of THI and when a summer weather report indicated that the THI was above his minimum he could dash to the nearest air-conditioned room.

Before leaving the subject of humidity we should say something about condensation and frost. This is the deposit that forms on cold objects—iced drinks, cold windows, and on the cooling coils in your refrigerator. As we saw earlier, air does not have to be saturated with water. It can carry any amount up to the 100 per cent saturated value for a given temperature. Let's suppose you have a room full of air at 70° F and 50 per cent relative humidity. This means there is ⅛ of a liquid ounce of water in each 14 cubic feet of air. A room filled with this air would be quite comfortable.

We do not have to add water to raise the humidity to 100 per cent. Instead we can lower the temperature, which reduces the ability of the air to hold water vapor, and so the little water there is would end up as the amount needed to saturate the air as some lower temperature. It turns out that ⅛ of a liquid ounce of water in 14 cubic feet of air is the saturation point at just over 50° F.

Now perhaps you see why water condenses on a cold object. Right near the surface of an iced drink the temperature may be as low as 35° or 40° F. The air can't hold as much water vapor at these temperatures as it did at 70° F and so the water condenses on the glass. Similarly windowpanes are cold in the winter, so room air adjacent to the panes gives up its water.

Your refrigerator works on this principle also. It is at very low temperatures. Each time you open the door you permit high-water-content air to enter. As the air cools it gives up its water vapor which condenses on the coils and freezes there.

# I

## IONIZERS

There are still many things we don't know about the human body. One of these is its reaction to ionized air. Reputable researchers have documented amazing recoveries from chronic asthma, bronchitis, and even skin burns, when their patients breathed ionized air. Others were not able to duplicate the results at all.

This much is known: the air we breathe often includes particles of dust, oxygen molecules, and water vapor, which carry positive or negative electrical charges. These are *ions.* When cosmic rays, or X rays, or ultraviolet light from the sun strikes the air at the outer reaches of the atmosphere, an electron can be knocked off an air molecule and attach itself to an oxygen molecule or to a particle of dust or water vapor (see ELECTRICITY). On earth there are places of relatively strong natural radioactivity and ionization of air is also to be expected in these areas.

Normal circulation of atmospheric air, aided by the turbulence of thunderstorms here and there around the world, brings these particles down to earth where they are breathed by you and me. Normally the concentration of ions is very low, but in certain areas, near radioactive spas and in certain parts of the Alps, much larger concentrations are found. And for hundreds of years people have been visiting such places for rest and for health cures.

The reason for the effect now seems to be the higher concentration of negative ions in these areas. Apparently our atmosphere is normally low in ions and having, if anything, a slightly positive charge. But there is evidence that negative ions relieve asthma, bronchitis, and even hay fever. They speed healing of any kind of wound and promote the general health of individuals breathing such air. At least that is what some of the experiments have shown. Positive ions, on the other hand, seem to aggravate fatigue, dizziness, headache, asthma, and sinusitis.

Several manufacturers have attempted to exploit this still-very-much-in-the-testing-stage research by putting home air ionizers on the market. The ionizers consist of a small ultraviolet lamp—much like those in many commercial sterilizers now on the market—and a small fan to blow air past the bulb and into the room. As presently designed and built the ionizers are relatively inefficient at their job. Better ultraviolet sources and targets (the light has to strike certain metals to produce lots of negative ions) could be designed. But no one is certain how much ionized air is good for you; certainly there is a limit beyond which ionization could cause harm.

The problem is complicated by the aura of quackery that surrounds the whole subject. It is concerned with things like the electrical potential of the different organs of the body, the flow of electric currents through nerves and blood stream, and the influence of such currents on health and healing. While such subjects are of great interest to modern physicians who are much more knowing about electronics than their predecessors were, still when phrases like neural current, electrical potential of the blood, or liver voltage are tossed around, the average family doctor is understandably skeptical.

What we have so far is this: certain hospitals and certain doctors using certain ultraviolet light sources in certain fixtures have found that their patients do heal more rapidly or experience relief from some respiratory problems. At first the ultraviolet light was thought to have these effects because of its ability to kill germs, but well-controlled tests have shown similar results when only ions were present.

So now you have the facts. I'd say if you want to experiment, and your doctor approves, try one.

# L

## LAWN MOWERS

One day lawn mowers got their own power and soon there was one on every suburban lawn. And a new one replaces the old model every three or four years—alternating with the family car.

Remember the old boy-pushed models? They had four or five twisted blades mounted in a cagelike formation that scraped

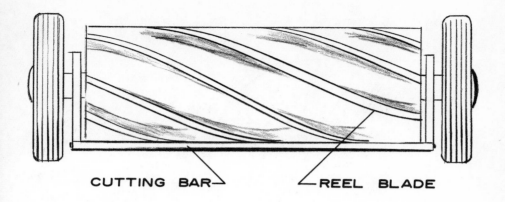

CUTTING BAR → ← REEL BLADE

against a cutting bar underneath. When you pushed the mower the big rubber wheels turned and sent the blades around against the cutting bar like the top half of a pair of scissors.

It was easy enough to add motor power to this design. A small electric motor was added which drove the wheels and the blade cage by gears, by chain, or by belt. Of course, this meant a long electric extension cable had to go to the house outlet, but that wasn't much of a bother.

The next step was the two-cycle or four-cycle gasoline engine. It works exactly as the automobile engine does (see AUTOMOBILE ENGINE) but has only one cylinder instead of six or eight, and the starter is a rope and muscle power. The gas engine is much noisier than the electric motor but it cut the umbilical cord that kept the electric mower within a closely prescribed radius of the house.

These *reel-type mowers* are still around. They give a very smooth cut to putting greens and other carefully tended, close-cropped grass lawns. As mentioned above, they also have power drive to the wheels, which is an advantage.

But over 90 per cent of all lawn mowers now used are the *rotary type*. This is simpler in construction. It consists of a blade like a double-ended scythe attached to the engine and spinning in a plane parallel to the ground. The blade sweeps around so fast that it doesn't have to be very sharp to slice the thickest weeds as neatly as the tenderest new blades of grass.

The rotary mower has several advantages over the old reel type to account for its popularity. The mower can be made more cheaply, and so the price is lower. It works closer to walls and path edges since the wheels don't have to be outside of the cutting edges. They are usually designed so that at least one of the front wheels is placed forward of the blade. The edge of the blade, therefore, can be very close to the side skirt of the housing. The rotary

121

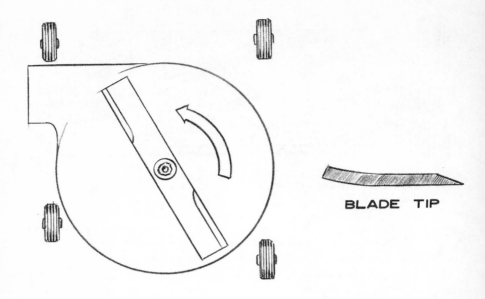

BLADE TIP

motor doesn't care whether the grass is thick or thin and it even chops up the leaves in its path to make a mulch that sprays over the lawn.

The chief disadvantage of the rotary mower is its tendency to throw rocks and clumps of grass or soil out of the exhaust port at pretty high speed. Furthermore, it will chew up careless toes just as easily as grass, which is why newer mowers are made with grills on the underside. The grass stands up into the cutting arc right through the grill, but your foot doesn't get caught so easily.

The back edge of the blade is swept up slightly, rather like the edge of a fan blade, and for the same purpose. The blades suck a draft of air up through the grass from around the mower housing which makes the grass stand straight for cutting. The draft of air also helps carry the cut ends out through the exhaust. Because of sand and stones, these turned-up back edges wear out as quickly as the front grass-cutting edges do. So when the mower doesn't cut as well as it should, you should buy a new blade (they're relatively cheap) rather than to try sharpening just the cutting edge.

A second disadvantage of the rotary mower is its tendency to scalp the tops off mounds and other irregularities. This leaves bald spots if you're not careful. Mow along the slope, not up and down. Mow around the hillocks, not across them. It's better for safety's sake anyway—you won't have to chase after the mower rolling downhill by itself.

Most mowers have a couple of accessories you might be interested in. The first is the starter, and the latest news in starters is

122

the impulse type. You wind up a spring slowly and without too much effort. When the spring is released it drives the engine shaft at twice the speed and for twice the time you could with the old cord wrapped around a shaft. The second accessory is the slip clutch—a release mechanism between the engine shaft and the mower blade shaft designed to permit the motor to turn even though the blade is held fixed, as it would be if it struck a rock or a branch.

Of course you can buy ride-on mowers as well and these have nearly all the gadgets your automobile has—a seat, gear shift, clutch, steering wheel or bars, brakes, a horn and an ignition key.

## LIGHT BULBS

There are two kinds of light bulbs in home use today and a third kind coming up fast. The *tungsten* bulb is the oldest and most familiar. This has a globe of clear or frosted glass sealed to a brass socket. Inside, a glass stem holds up a wire frame with a *filament* (zigzag-shaped or coiled wire) of tungsten. When electricity flows through the filament, it heats up. It finally gets so hot it turns red and then white hot. This is called *incandescence,* and by this light we read, write, work, etc.

The globe of glass is evacuated (all the air is removed) to keep the tungsten filament from burning up too fast. Usually the air is replaced by other, nonreactive gases (nitrogen, for example). When the filament does burn out it breaks, and you can usually hear it flopping loosely against the glass when you shake the bulb.

The second type of light source is the more efficient *fluorescent tube.* This reduces the problem of heat because fluorescent tubes give off the same amount of light with much less heat. It also means that the same light output can be had with lower electric bills.

The fluorescent tube is filled with mercury vapor which acts like the filament between metal contact rings at either end of the tube. The mercury vapor gives off ultraviolet (invisible) light when current flows through it. The ultraviolet rays strike a phosphorescent coating on the inside of the tube which then glows brightly.

The third type of light source is called *electroluminescence.* It depends on the property of certain materials (called phosphors) to glow when exposed to alternating electric voltage.

A coating of metal so thin that it is transparent is sprayed on a glass panel. A layer of electroluminescent phosphor is placed on the metal and a thin sheet of metal foil completes the sandwich.

123

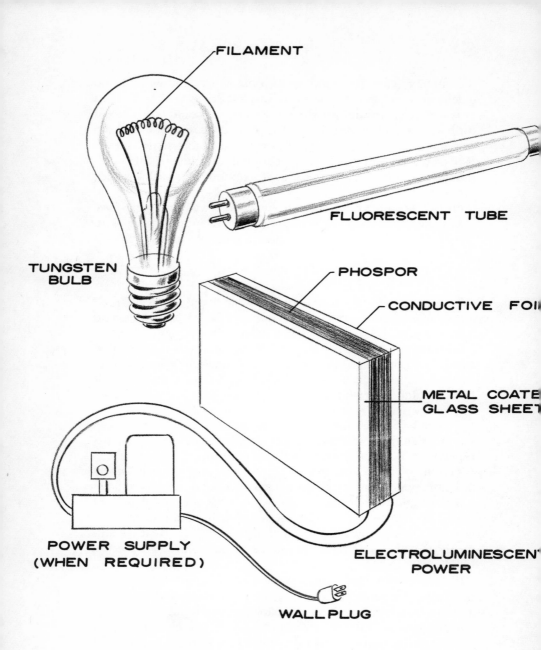

FILAMENT

FLUORESCENT TUBE

TUNGSTEN
BULB

PHOSPOR

CONDUCTIVE FOI

METAL COATE
GLASS SHEET

POWER SUPPLY
(WHEN REQUIRED)

ELECTROLUMINESCEN
POWER

WALL PLUG

When alternating current is connected to the two conductive layers, the phosphor glows.

Electroluminescent light draws relatively little current and the whole flat panel, not just a filament or tube, is lighted. The panel can be shaped, cut out (for auto dashboard instruments) and mounted on ceiling, floor, wall, or stair tread, to put the light just

124

where you want it. It's cool, should last for years, and it is efficient —meaning low light bills.

One important problem still remains to be solved. The amount of light given off by the panel is relatively low. You would practically have to cover a whole ceiling to light a room, and even then it would be too dark to read.

Mass production and further refinements are sure to solve the problems and the next decade should see widespread adoption of these new lights.

# LOCKS

Louis XVI, too shy and self-effacing to take advantage of his husbandly prerogatives with the lovely Marie Antoinette, found solace in locks. Nor was he the first to be fascinated by what a few bits of metal, string, and wood can do to make a rivet-studded oak door impregnable from the outside.

Today you can buy bathroom locks, house-door locks, bicycle locks, padlocks, combination locks, safe locks, time locks, or just about everything twenty or thirty centuries and the inventiveness of a property-conscious mankind could devise.

The simplest is probably the usual closet-door lock whose key is a rod with a little perforated flag of metal hanging from its end. The flag has been cut so as to clear a series of barriers in the door and turn freely through one full turn. This permits it to push a pin sticking up from the bolt and thus force the bolt in or out of the jamb. The trouble here is that "skeleton" keys can be made, one of which is sure to clear the barriers of your door—and practically every other door lock of this kind.

A much more ingenious design is that of your front-door lock which presents the same appearance to all keys yet opens to just one. Your door key is a flat piece of metal with slots and ridges on the sides. The slots and ridges must match corresponding ridges and slots in the key hole or you can't even get the key into the lock. On the upper edge of the key a series of peaks and valleys establish your key and your lock as different from anyone else's. They are designed to match a series of little rods in your lock (see the sketch).

When you insert your key the rods ride up and down the peaks and valleys of your key until it is fully inserted. At this point the lower rod of each pair just reaches the top of the barrel—the part you turn to open the door. Since the rod ends all line up, the barrel can be turned freely and the lock opens.

125

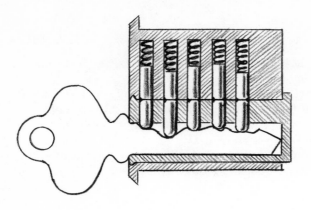

Of more interest perhaps, is the situation when the wrong key has been inserted. Then the rods rise to different levels in their slots and at least one, and probably several, lie right across the dividing line between the barrel and the cylinder surrounding it. Try as you may you can't turn the barrel without being stopped by the blocking rods.

Locksmiths carry a whole stock of different size rods and they can change your lock in a few minutes by changing the rods, or simply by rearranging them in different order in the barrel. Of course a new key is required.

Two other, related, lock types are of interest here: the combination lock and the time lock. The combination lock has the distinct advantage of needing no key. Instead you have a series of numbers to remember. To avoid forgetfulness many people have their wall safes set to open with the numbers of their birthdays, telephone numbers, or house numbers. Clever safecrackers usually try a series of these familiar combinations before resorting to their ears and delicate touch or other, more explosive, methods of getting at the family jewels.

Combination locks work on a principle of alignment. Three disks turn freely and independently on the same axis, side by side. Each has a notch cut into its rim and each adjacent pair have little tongues that stick out toward each other and engage when the disks are rotated. The knob is connected to the front disk of the set and when turned in one direction, the front disk tongue engages first the middle disk which in turn, engages the last disk. Thus the knob eventually turns all three disks at once.

You spin the knob twice around and then to a certain number. This sets the last disk with its notch pointing in a desired direction. Next you reverse the knob for a full revolution to engage the center disk from the other side of its tongue and you continue in this direction to a number setting corresponding to a disk position with its notch lined up exactly with the last disk. Then you turn the knob forward again for a short distance to line up the first notch with the other two.

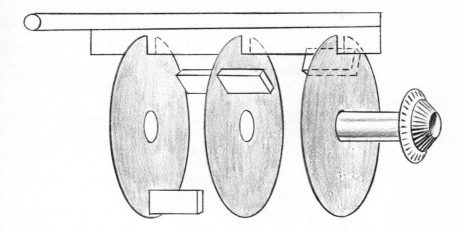

When all three disks have been lined up, the notches free a release mechanism and the safe may be opened.

As you can imagine, the variations on this principle are endless. Tumblers may drop into the notches in turn to clear the lock, though stethoscope-equipped thieves have made these designs unpopular of late.

Probably safest of all, the time lock seals a safe door from anyone, even the owner, during certain hours of the day or night. The clock permits the combination to be used successfully only, say, between 9 and 9:30 in the morning when thieves are least likely to be prowling the banks.

# M

## MAPS

The whole problem with maps is that you have to flatten a sphere (the earth's surface) onto a plane surface (the sheet of paper which is the map). There is no way of doing this without some distortion, either in the areas or in the shapes of the areas to be represented.

Of course for relatively small areas—a city map or even a county or state map—the curvature of the earth is so slight that there is no practical difference between the map shapes and the actual land features. When the areas to be represented get to continent size, however, the distortion is quite noticeable.

No discussion of maps can avoid the mention of latitude and longitude lines, so lets make sure we understand what they are before we start. The world is a sphere (or close enough not to make any differences on our maps) so we divide the *equator* (the waistline) into 360 degrees of *longitude.* Each longitude line runs north-south from pole to pole. By knowing which longitude line you are on, you know how far away you are from Greenwich, England, the place of zero degrees longitude.

*Latitude* is measured north and south from the equator. Imagine that the earth has been cut into slices like a hard-boiled egg. The largest slice cuts through the equator. Smaller slices above and below the equator intersect the surface of the earth in horizontal lines running around the earth. The slices are spaced at equal distances along lines of longitude. So latitude lines intersect longitude lines and provide the second co-ordinate for locating yourself (or an airplane, or a ship) on the earth.

Maps are most easily understood by examining the pattern of latitude and longitude lines. The larger the area represented by the map the more pronounced the curvature of these lines.

The most familiar maps are made by conic projections. The mapmaker places a cone of paper like a dunce's hat on a transparent globe. He puts a light bulb at the center of the globe and traces the outlines of continents projected on the paper hat. He then unwraps the cone, and this is his map of the area.

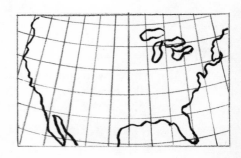

**CONIC PROJECTION**

The larger the distance between a point on the cone and on the globe, the more the distortion and error. To overcome this problem, when relatively large areas must be mapped the mapmakers pretend that many cones—one for each belt around the earth— are placed in contact with the globe for projection. The result is that the longitude and latitude lines have pronounced bends, as shown in the "polyconic" sketch.

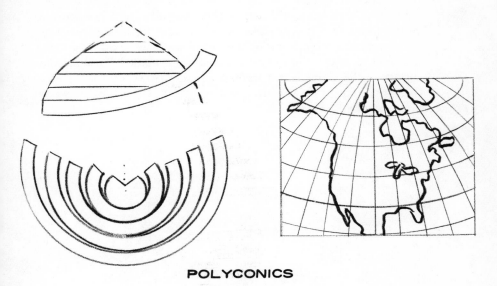

**POLYCONICS**

Sometimes transpolar maps for plane routes show the earth as if latitude lines were a series of concentric circles. The result is pretty accurate for areas near the pole though the distortion of more southerly areas is considerable.

**POLE MAP**

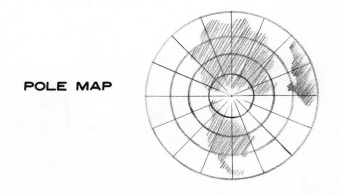

129

Cylindrical projection is made by pretending the earth is wrapped by a cylinder of paper which touches at the equator. With a light placed at the exact center of the earth the image thrown by the light is a Mercator map. This map has the characteristic of highly exaggerated land areas north of the United States. In these maps the upper portions of Canada and Greenland seem tremendous by comparison to other sections closer to the equator.

Obviously the most difficult problem of all is to represent the entire world, a complete sphere, on a flat surface. Several relatively accurate projections of the entire world do exist. The best solutions appear to be the interrupted maps made by pealing the surface of the globe as if it were an orange. However, these suffer from the serious disadvantage of having open spaces between map sections.

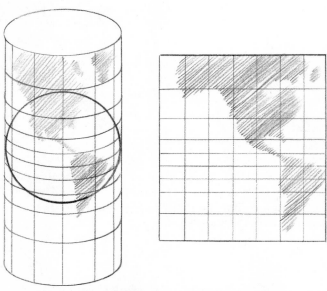

**CYLINDRICAL PROJECTION**

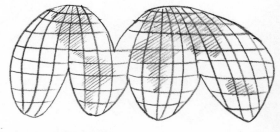

**INTERRUPTED MAPS**

# MEAT THERMOMETERS

The old cookbooks all say to "cook until done" which drives most young homemakers frantic. Almost as bad are the ones that tell you to cook for a given length of time at "moderate" or "high" temperature and then neglect to explain what these are. The reason for this ambiguity is that, until relatively recently, no one knew how to measure a food's progress in the pot without looking, poking, and comparing to previous experience.

Well, science is beginning to lift the veil a little. It turns out that the most reliable gage of doneness is temperature. That is, the temperature of the food itself reveals how well cooked it is. A roast beef, no matter how much it weighs or how big around it is, is pink at the center and crusty outside when the inside reaches 160° F. It's well done at 170°, rare at 140°. Cakes and pies, roast chicken and turkey, and even most vegetables are done when they reach the proper temperature. This is why pressure cookers, operating at temperatures higher than normal for boiling water (see PRESSURE COOKERS), cook so fast; they're hotter.

Meat thermometers and other degree-of-doneness testers are ordinary thermometers shielded by stainless steel from the effects of grease and food acids, and capable of operating up to about 300° F. You want to be sure to place the thermometer in the center of your meat because that's where it gets hot last. The manufacturers recommend the heavy part of the thigh for a turkey (not touching the bone) and in the lean parts of pork, ham, or beef. Fat sections are not likely to give accurate readings.

Incidentally, you can check your thermometer if you're unhappy about the way it's operating. Just fill a pot with water and heat it to boiling. Hold the bottom four inches of the thermometer spear in the water so that it does not touch the pot. The indicator should read within five degrees of 212° F—the temperature of boiling water in all locations lower than 2000 feet above sea level.

# MIXERS AND BLENDERS

The major difference between mixers and blenders and the old-fashioned egg beaters is that the former are motor driven. Most mixers have the electric motor mounted on a pedestal and sticking out over a base plate. From its front end the motor drives the twin beaters. From the rear it drives down inside the pedestal to a rubber wheel which turns the bowl slowly.

Portable mixers are much the same as those with pedestals

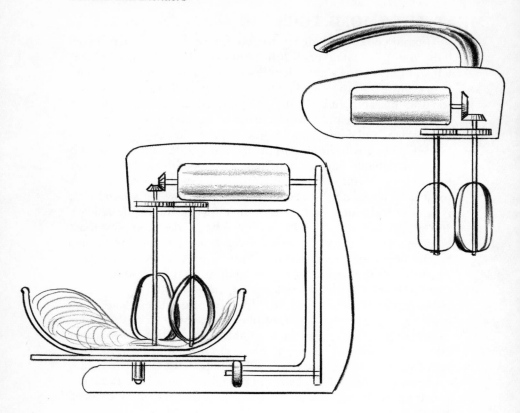

except that the motor and beaters must be held by hand over the mixing bowl—no pedestal is provided—and the attachments are limited to beaters and simple drink mixers.

Most mixers have a speed control. By flipping a switch the electric power to the motor is reduced and it slows down. This is cheaper to make than a gear shift (see TRANSMISSION AND REAR END) but when thick batters are placed in the bowl the motor may not have enough power to run at all. However, higher speed settings are powerful enough for all normal kitchen use.

*Blenders* evolved in a slightly different direction, and at least one mixer manufacturer has followed their lead. The blender has its motor in a heavy metal base. The glass bowl or jar has a beater built in. The beater has a shaft that goes through a watertight hole in the center of the bowl and sticks out the bottom.

You set the bowl on the base. The bowl is held so that it cannot tip or spin when the motor is running. The beater shaft engages the motor shaft so when the motor is turned on it drives the beaters in the bowl. All speed control is in the base of the blender.

You fill the blender and just set it on the base. A flip of the switch starts the motor spinning and the beater cuts, aerates, and blends the mixture because of the fanlike action of the beater blades. The blades force the fluid up and around, creating a powerful circulating current which brings new fluid to the blades all the time.

The most recent design of mixer combines the advantages of mixer and blender. Here the motor is built right into your kitchen countertop. Normally a flat cover hides the motor shaft. When you want to use the blending attachment, you lift off the cover and set the blending jar on the unit. An adjacent control knob turns the motor on and controls the speed. For mixing you replace the blender jar with a mixing bowl that has egg beaters in the center of the bowl. The beaters are driven by a shaft right through the bottom of the bowl just as the blender is.

Meat grinder, grater, and even knife sharpener can be attached to this device just as they are with a standard mixer.

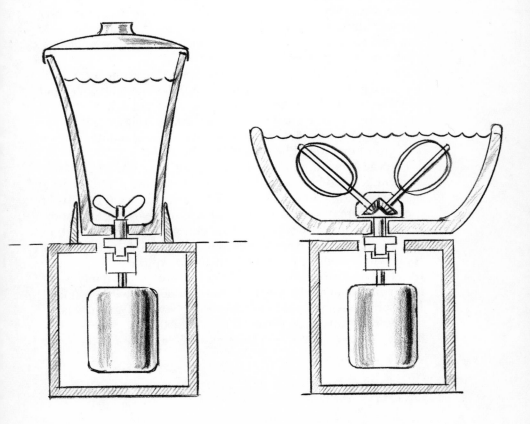

# O

## OVENS AND RANGES

You may take your oven for granted, and probably do, except when cleaning time comes around, but it's not the elementary heating box it appears. Gas-heated ovens must be carefully designed so that the air drawn in at the bottom to feed the flames flows smoothly through the oven compartment and out the top-rear vent. The flow must be regulated, so that it isn't too free—the oven couldn't get hot enough if large volumes of cold air were constantly brought in—yet not too restrained either, since the gas will not burn without a generous supply of oxygen.

Take a look at the bottom plate of your gas oven compartment. You'll find a series of holes or slots along the front edge, but not at the rear. They are there so that hot air coming from the lower burner compartment will flow forward almost to the oven door and rise into the oven at the front, which would otherwise be the coolest place in the oven.

The flue built into the ceiling of the oven compartment conducts the air to a chimney-vent at the top rear of the oven. Put your hand over the vent holes at the back and you can feel the hot air pouring out. Usually the flue turns several corners before it gets to the vent. This slows the flow of air and reduces the amount of vaporized grease that would be carried into the room.

Electric ovens don't need to set up a flow of air. The heating element gets red hot as the current flows through it and no air is necessary to support combustion. The heating element consists of a central core of conductor wire of strong, heat-resistant alloy. This means the wire will not burn out easily though it will, of course, get very hot when the current flows. An electric insulator is packed around the central conductor to protect you from electric shock and from the short circuits that would inevitably occur if a pan accidentally touched the conducting wire. A metal tube surrounds the insulator, holds it in place, and acts as a good radiator of heat when current flows. Exactly the same kind of heating element is used on the top of the electric range except

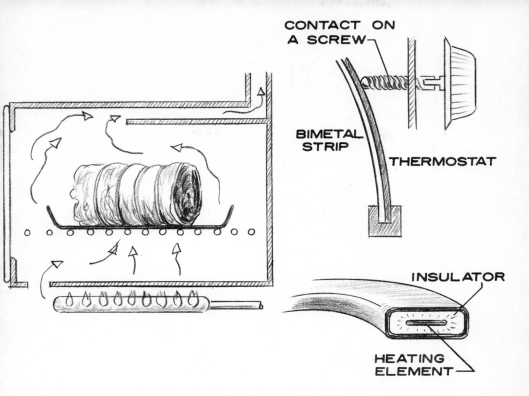

CONTACT ON
A SCREW

BIMETAL
STRIP

THERMOSTAT

INSULATOR

HEATING
ELEMENT

that here the element is coiled into a spiral which concentrates the heat and provides a convenient support for the pot.

Controls for oven and range are getting a lot of attention from designers these days. Let's look at the oven temperature controllers first. You dial a temperature and then confidently walk away knowing that the oven will heat to the desired temperature and remain there. How is it done?

Temperature can be controlled by varying the flow of gas to the burners or electricity to the heating element but the oven must know when it is too hot or too cold. Here's our old friend the thermostat again (see THERMOMETERS AND THERMOSTATS). The thermostat senses temperature by the amount of bend of its bimetallic strip. When the strip bends far enough to move away from a contact (in electric ovens) or to close down a gas valve (in gas ovens) the oven temperature will drop. As the thermostat cools, the bimetallic strip straightens out and re-establishes electric contact or reopens the gas valve.

Note that you call for a desired temperature by moving the contact toward or away from the strip. If you move it toward the strip, it will take a higher temperature (more bend) to break the circuit. If you move it away from the strip, it will regulate to a lower temperature.

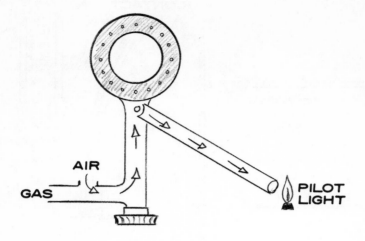

AIR

GAS

PILOT
LIGHT

Gas ranges have an additional controller. It is the gadget that makes them light at the turn of the knob. This is the pilot light in the center of the range section which is a single flame left burning all the time. It only uses a trickle of gas, of course. A metal tube extends from each burner to the pilot light. When you open the control valve by turning the knob of a burner, you start gas flowing to the burner but a small part of the flow of gas also goes down the tube toward the pilot light. When it reaches the pilot light it ignites with a whoosh and the flame races back up the tube to the burner.

You set gas ranges to give the desired heat as judged by the height of the flame and the activity within the pot. The flame can be very closely controlled to give exactly the heat desired. Electric ranges are usually push-button controlled. Any one of four or five heat levels can be selected and they produce exactly the same temperature every time. There is no choice of in-between heat levels.

One word of warning: Don't touch the heating element on electric stoves unless you're absolutely sure it's cold. It doesn't have to glow red to be hot enough to give you a nasty burn.

Electronic ovens are a relatively new development coming as an unexpected by-product of wartime radar. It was discovered by accident—repairmen working in front of the big radar antennas got unexplainable burns on and *in* their bodies. It was finally realized that the ultrahigh-frequency radio waves will heat up just about any nonmetallic object in their path. And the heating isn't just from outside in the way a fire toasts a marshmallow, the waves go right through the object and heat *all* of it at exactly the same rate.

Do you realize how unusual this is? Up to now we've never

dreamed of heating except from the outside in. When a roast beef or a turkey is put into an oven the hot gases or the radiant energy from the heating elements raise the temperature of the outer surface of the meat. Slowly this heat soaks into the roast until the center is warmed to about 140°. When the center reaches this temperature the beef is done (for those who like their beef rare—160° if you like it medium). No, 140° isn't very hot, the steamroom in a Turkish bath is hotter, but to get the beef heated to that temperature the oven had to be 350° for over three hours!

Now you see what is so amazing about the electronic oven. It heats the whole roast through at the same time. This means the oven stays relatively cool. Dishes can be taken out with unprotected hands. Yet it cooks much more quickly than gas ever could. A layer cake can be baked in exactly three minutes, bacon in under 100 seconds.

The only problem is that with such high speed and low temperatures the food doesn't get the lovely brown crust we like so well. So a compromise is made. You sear the meat first in regular electric or gas heat, and then turn on the radar to cook it through.

# P

## PAINTS

We tend to think of paint, varnish, and shellac as three separate and distinct things. This is because your hardware store carries them in different containers and for different purposes. Actually all share similar ingredients.

Let's start with what is most familiar. *Paint* is a mixture of finely powdered solids well blended in a liquid medium which carries and spreads the solids. The powder is usually a pigment—one of many natural and synthetic *oxides*. The fluid may be linseed oil, natural resins, or any of the many synthetic resins now available (see PLASTICS). When the solid powder is omitted the finish ceases to be a *paint* and becomes a *varnish* or a *shellac*.

So paint is always intended as a covering coat. The natural

look and grain of the unfinished base is completely hidden by the powdered pigment. Normally paints are made of the powdered pigment, linseed oil, and a little turpentine. The paint is easily brushed or rolled on because of the clinging, oily properties of the linseed oil, and it is thinned enough by the turpentine to cover well. The volatile turpentine evaporates quickly, leaving a layer of oil with the pigments in suspension. The oil slowly absorbs oxygen from the air and polymerizes, which means that it hardens (see PLASTICS) into a firm protective surface that holds tightly to the small dips and depressions in the original surface.

Paint can be had in a *high-gloss finish* (with a reflective shine to the surface) or *flat* (nonreflective). *Enamels* are usually high-gloss, brilliantly surfaced paints. Flat paint is made up of the same basic ingredients as enamel. The only difference in the formulation is that glossy enamel has very finely ground pigments while the flat paint is less finely powdered. In addition, the flat paint has somewhat more turpentine by percentage, than the gloss enamel has.

*Varnish* is basically a resin, it is mixed with oil for flexibility and toughness, and a thinning, evaporative vehicle is added to ease the brushing. Varnish alone dries to a clear high-gloss coating used on the woodwork of boats and on wooden furniture and floors where scuffing and wear are likely to be a problem.

Varnish can be made of all natural resins (shellac is one) as well as the many synthetic resins and rubbers now available. The thinner is usually turpentine, though some of the newer synthetic rubber finishes are water based so that you can wash your paint-stained hands with water. Once the water-based paint has set, the surface is as waterproof as turpentine-thinned varnish.

*Shellac,* a particular form of varnish, is a resin secreted by an insect that grows and lives in the bark of certain acacia trees. The raw shellac is ground, washed, and filtered and what remains is a resin soluble in alcohol which dries quickly to a thin glossy coating.

Shellac is not to be confused with *lacquer,* particularly that used on Oriental woodwork. Lacquer known in the United States is a spirit varnish which is a solution of cellulose compound mixed in a volatile solvent. Oriental lacquer is entirely different. It is made from the sap of a tree. This lacquer, oddly enough, only hardens in the dark and in humid air. The lacquer is put on in many coats until the deep colored, shell-like appearance of Japanese and Chinese lacquer ware is produced. It is very hard, durable, and lustrous.

So many paints and finishes have been made that there are expert chemists and engineers whose specialty is the prescription of the proper finish to achieve the desired color and durability in a finished product. Today the aerosol spray (see AEROSOLS) is bringing into the backyard (if not the home) the same chemical compounds formerly reserved for automobile paint shops and artists' workrooms. Even the baked enamels—resin-based paints hardened under heat—are becoming available in nonbaking compounds. They set (polymerize) in air to the same hard, glossy finish as their baked cousins.

# PAPER

How do they make paper? With it we can wipe our hands dry, wrap our gifts, write our letters, box our canned goods, get the news, roof our homes, line our walls, stiffen our shirts and pretty soon, if current predictions come true, wear it as disposable clothes.

Paper is essentially a mat of cellulose fiber. The fiber comes from wood pulp and from many of the same plants that supply our textiles (cotton, flax, etc.). *Rag-content paper* is made from old clothes, sheets, and so on because the manufacturers cannot afford to buy the fiber from the farmer directly. Rags are cheap and serve just as well as new fiber would. Rag-content paper does not include synthetic fabrics since these are not cellulose fibers and would cause trouble in the processing.

Whatever the raw material, the papermaking process is much the same. The raw material must first be shredded into tiny fibers, washed and bleached to the desired grade of whiteness. Impurities must be removed by chemical processing and by washing in lots of water. Then chemicals are added to make the finished paper water-resistant, to give it the desired color, or to make it whiter. Clay or chalk fillers are mixed in to reduce the porosity and help make a smooth-surfaced paper.

This pulped material is cooked in great vats, sometimes under pressure, with lime or caustic soda to help reduce unwelcome greases, waxes, oils, and just plain dirt that accompanies the rags and the carbohydrates found in the wood.

The mix is then poured into a large tank that has a long thin slit along one bottom edge. The water-soaked fibers pour out of the slit and onto a wire-mesh belt which carries a thin layer of mixed fibers away in an endless stream. Water drips through the wire belt and a light squeezing by rollers takes more of the water out, so when the matted fibers reach the end of the wire-mesh belt they have been pressed into a fairly strong sheet. Watermarks are applied just before the paper leaves the wire-mesh belt. Raised designs on a roller produce a dense area on the sheet which never disappears. The belt then feeds the sheet to a series of hard rubber rollers that squeeze the fibers tightly into what we now may call paper.

The paper strip is then dried by passing through a steam-heated oven. It is given a final pressing between steel rollers and wrapped around a roller or cut into separate sheets ready for printing.

This whole process is almost as old as civilization. But today high-speed paper mills are about as complicated as modern machinery can get. A machine to make newsprint is as long as a city block and as wide as a city street.

Today paper is made in thousands of grades. It is coated with adhesives for labels or with special finishes to make it glossy smooth. Some papers are porous—cigarette paper has a carefully controlled porosity so that just the right amount of air will accompany the smoke. Creped paper is wrinkled up when it is still wet so that it dries into the ridged pattern that stretches across party ceilings.

In all cases the raw material (rags, woodpulp) combined with the processing method (how finely shredded, how carefully bleached or cleaned) determines the strength and appearance of the finished product. Since these materials vary a good deal in chemical make up, color and so on, the paper manufacturer can only promise a *relatively* uniform product. Yet how consistent and beautiful the results generally are!

Americans today produce and consume nearly 400 pounds of paper per person each year. Some of this is as costly as gold— $35 per ounce is cheap when you add the cost of cutting, printing, folding, and mailing of a company annual report, for instance. But the paper towel you find in a restaurant or office washroom is cheaper to use and throw away than the laundry charge on a towel would be.

We can't leave the subject of paper without saying something about *parchment.* Parchment is made from the skin of animals (sheep and goats for the most part) and the younger the animal the better the parchment. The skins are scraped, washed, pared down to a uniform thickness, dusted with chalk and rubbed with pumice to smooth the surface and prepare it to take ink. Much of the old literature preserved for us today we owe to the long life of parchment.

*Vellum* is parchment also—originally made of the skin of a calf. Today you can buy vellum which is really a very good paper imitation of parchment.

# PENCIL SHARPENERS

They're so familiar, yet the operation of a pencil sharpener is far from a simple thing. You're probably aware that the sharpener has two striped rollers that move around the pencil point. What makes them move that way and why does the movement result in a sharpened pencil?

Let's work from the outside in. The crank turns a sort of yoke that carries end pivots for the two rollers. The rollers slant away from each other in a sharp Vee. One end of each roller carries a gear and the gears mesh with another larger gear built into the housing of the sharpener. This is an *internal gear*—one in which the teeth point toward the center rather than away from the center, as ordinary gears do.

Now we have enough to see how the peculiar spinning motion of the rollers is created. As you turn the crank you turn the yoke carrying the two rollers. The rollers are carried around the pencil point but at the same time the gears at their ends are also turned as they roll in mesh with the internal gear.

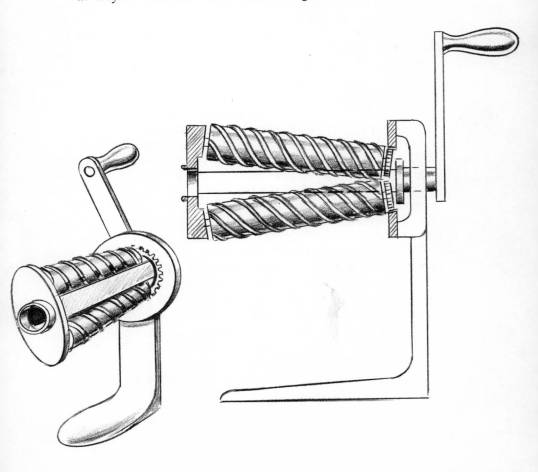

Pretend for a moment that you are very small and that you stand in the center of the sharpener, much as your pencil does. If the crank were rotated slowly you would see the rollers move around you as the moon turns around the earth. At the same time the rollers turn on their own axes and so the stripes seem to climb along the roller just like the stripes on a spinning barber pole.

The stripes are actually raised and sharpened welts spiraling around the rollers. The sharpened edge of the stripe cuts forward as the roller turns and makes a spiral cut around and back on the pencil point. Each edge takes off a thin sliver of wood and lead. Since there are four or five edges in contact with the tapered point of the pencil, four or five such slivers are removed in neat, tapered spirals, leaving a rounded needle-sharp point on your pencil.

## PENS AND PENCILS

Here's another deceptively simple-looking gadget which we tend to ignore because of familiarity. Yet quill pens were used for 1300 years (between the sixth and nineteenth centuries) before steel nibs became popular. Thirteen hundred years is a long time for man to stick to one writing instrument, and geese, swans, and crows must have grown tired of having their feathers plucked in springtime, just when the flying was good.

The trick in all ink-writing instruments is to conduct the ink to the paper just when and when pen and paper touch. The line so formed should be fine and smooth. The answer is capillary action, and this is an interesting effect worth some explanation.

*Surface tension* is a common characteristic of fluid surfaces. Take a glass of water and note that thin bits of wire, needles, and even light coins will float on the surface if you can keep the water from wetting them. Water bugs skitter about on the surface as if it were a gigantic, slippery, but slightly flexible sheet. These all demonstrate the relatively firm skin that water has if you don't let it wet and cling to objects thus bringing the objects *inside* the skin.

But water has a tendency to wet surfaces, unlike mercury which seems to draw away from the very bottle that contains it. Note how water climbs up the sides of a glass. It clings to the glass and the surface tension pulls more water up, wetting areas above the water level. It would climb indefinitely if it had no weight.

If the glass is very small, its mouth only as big around as a hair, the water will climb several inches up the sides. This is called *capillary action* and is demonstrated by dipping a tube of glass, with a tiny hole in its center, into a larger container of water. You can actually see the water rise in the tube. This principle explains why water soaks up into a piece of fabric or towel when one end is dipped, why melted wax rises in the wick where it is vaporized and burned (see CANDLES), why blotters soak up ink, and why paper takes ink from a pen.

A capillary tube connects the reservoir of ink in your fountain pen with the nib. The tube stays full of ink until you write a few words, this draws some of the ink from the tube. The ink is then replaced by ink from the reservoir at the other end.

The split nib acts as a flexible capillary channel. It conducts ink to the paper, and the flexibility permits the point to spread when you press it against the paper. Spreading broadens the line so as to give the letters character. Pen points are cut away at the sides to add flexibility, and slits in the sides are sometimes added for the same reason.

Fountain pens often have "combs" cut into the plastic under the pen point. These are used as storage areas for ink when it is forced out of the reservoir. This happens when changing air pressure or temperature makes the trapped air pocket expand. The comb will take care of all normal atmospheric changes, but if you're planning to take an airplane ride be sure the pen has been guaranteed by the manufacturer to take the ride without leaking.

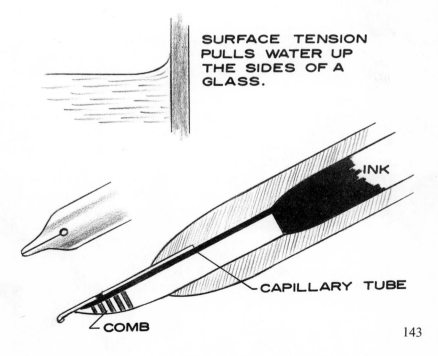

SURFACE TENSION PULLS WATER UP THE SIDES OF A GLASS.

INK

CAPILLARY TUBE

COMB

143

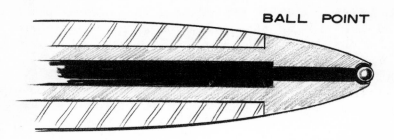

**BALL POINT**

Ball-point pens are not a new invention, but they couldn't be made until we were able to manufacture the tiny, perfectly round balls for their tips. A thick ink is used which constantly bathes the upper surface of the ball. As you roll the ball on paper it carries a layer of ink around and to the paper. The ink has to be just the right thickness—too thin and it will run out, too thick and it won't flow. The balls have to be round but not necessarily glassy smooth or the ink will have trouble clinging to the surface and the ball will skid on the paper.

The problem with ball-point pens is that if the pen is not used for a while the ink on the exposed surface of the ball dries and keeps the ball from rolling. Note that fountain pens have a similar problem. Even when covered with a nearly airtight cap the ink at the tip finally dries, and it's a nuisance to get the pen writing well again.

Pencils use a form of carbon called *graphite* to mark the paper. Graphite has the useful characteristic of coating just about any surface it contacts. It is rather greasy to the touch and for that reason is often used as a lubricant between rubbing surfaces when oil might dry out or freeze, as in automobile door locks.

Now graphite is not the same as coal or coke or diamond—though they also are carbon. It was first discovered as a natural mineral and it is still mined in England. It is now made out of coal in special electric arc furnaces. The graphite in your pencil is probably made from anthracite coal. The chunks of coal are exposed to massive doses of electric current to turn them into graphite. The blocks of graphite are then pulverized, mixed with water and certain clays, pressed in a huge hydraulic press, and squeezed out through small holes in a steel plate to make a long thin rod. The rods are dried and then heated in a furnace where the clays bake and stiffen the leads. The leads are encased in cedarwood to make wooden pencils and thinner versions are used in mechanical pencils.

# PERCUSSION INSTRUMENTS

As a class, these are probably the simplest of all instruments. They may be divided into two broad groups—those having a definite pitch so you can play a melody however crudely, and those having no definite pitch intended primarily as rhythm accompaniment for the other instruments.

The *tuning fork* is a Y of metal whose arms vibrate toward and away from each other producing a single pure tone when struck. The pitch is dependent only on the size and weight of the arms. You can amplify the sound of a tuning fork by setting its handle on a table or box. This puts a lot more air into motion than the relatively thin arms can.

*Xylophone, marimba*, and *glockenspiel* have wood or metal bars. Each is carefully shaped and thus tuned to give off a particular

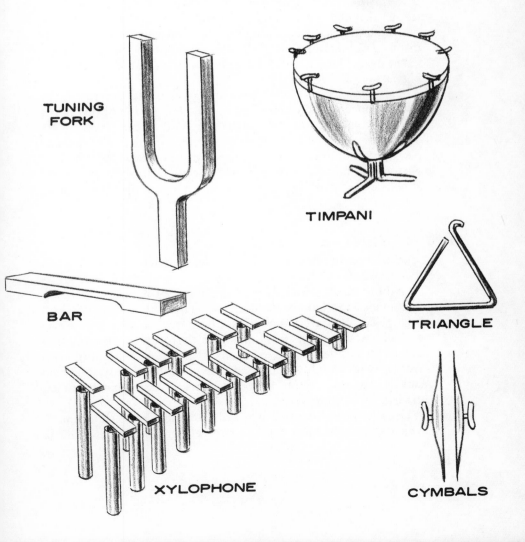

TUNING
FORK

TIMPANI

BAR

TRIANGLE

XYLOPHONE

CYMBALS

DEFINITE PITCH: TUNING FORK, XYLOPHONE, MARIMBA, CHIMES, GLOCKENSPIEL, CELESTA, TIMPANI (KETTLE DRUMS), BELL, CARILLON

INDEFINITE PITCH: SNARE DRUMS, BASS DRUM, GONG, TRIANGLE, CYMBALS, TAMBOURINE, CASTANETS

note when struck by a hammerlike mallet. The sound is sometimes amplified by placing a tube of metal or wood under the vibrating bar. The column of air in the tube adds a soft clear tone to the relatively sharp sound of these instruments.

*Kettledrums* or *timpani* are changed in pitch by tightening the leather drumhead across the open end. You've probably seen the performer hurriedly adjusting the knobs spaced around these big drums and then tapping the drumhead lightly, with his ear close to the drum. This is to check the pitch of the drum before his next big passage.

*Snare drum, bass drum, triangle,* and *cymbals,* to name just a few, produce sound of indefinite pitch. These are not just noise-makers, you have to have a perfect sense of timing, excellent co-ordination, the ability to do different things with each hand and perhaps a foot or two, and you need nerves of steel. Nothing is so obvious as a mistake in the percussion section. Have you ever heard a pair of cymbals go clattering down upon the floor during a concert?

## PERMANENT WAVES

To understand how permanent waves work it is necessary first to have a general idea of what hair is and how it grows. Hair grows straight or curly, depending on the hair root or *follicle.* The follicle makes the hair cells which elongate and harden into stiff bristle. The cells are joined by a kind of glue at their contacting surfaces, and it seems to be this glue that provides the point of attack for permanent wave lotions. If the hair is round in cross section, with evenly distributed cells, it will grow straight and lank. If it is oval, with one side growing a little faster than the other, the hair will curl or wave.

Usually the wave lotion is based on thioglycolate—a chemical which softens the links between hair cells and permits the hair to

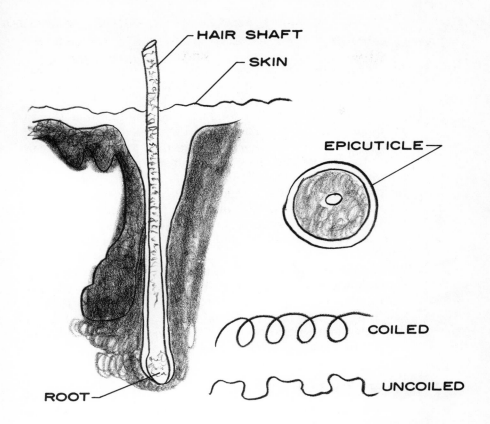

HAIR SHAFT

SKIN

EPICUTICLE

COILED

UNCOILED

ROOT

be molded just as a sculptor molds clay. The wave lotion is applied to the hair and when it has had time to work a bit the hair is curled into the shape the hairdresser wishes it to take. This curling operation consists of wrapping and pinning individual locks around "rollers" of various sizes.

Note that a hair wrapped in this way will, when released, take the familiar wave form. Try straightening a coiled telephone cord and you'll see the same shape develop. The tightness of the curl depends on the strength and resilience of the hair, diameter of the roller and, of course, the strength and application time of the wave lotion.

When the hair has been thoroughly saturated with the softener and curled into the desired shape the hairdresser applies a "neutralizer" which returns the hair to its original stiffness. That is, the cells are fixed into their new arrangement (conforming to the curlers) by chemical hardening of the cell connecting links.

When the hair has been hardened the hairdresser releases it from the curlers and "combs it out" which means he finds out whether his sculpting produced the shapes and swirls he hoped

147

for. The hair has had a "permanent"—and it *is* permanent, make no mistake about it. The curl will stay in the hair unless it is resoftened and shaped again.

The strength of the wave lotion, or the length of time it must be applied seems to depend on the resistance of a thin layer of protective tissue that surrounds the hair from root to end. All hair is covered with this *epicuticle* layer, and apparently thin hair with a proportionately smaller body is less amenable to softening than thick hair is. This is why a child's hair does not take a permanent easily and specially strong lotions must be used. Conversely, bleached and dyed hair seems to have lost its protective layer and so it responds well, almost too well, to the hairdresser's wave lotion.

The reason permanents have to be repeated at frequent intervals is that hair grows at the rate of six to twelve inches a year. The curls grow out—with straight hair coming from the roots. Soon you have a head of curly ends and straight roots, and apparently this is not always desirable. So off to the beauty parlor again for another treatment.

## PHOTOENGRAVING

The method used to print all tones of gray between black and white is really ingenious. Pick up a newspaper and look at the photographs very closely with a low-power magnifying glass, if you've got one. Do you see how the image is made up of hundreds, even thousands of small dots? In light areas the dots are tiny and surrounded by large areas of white paper. In dark areas they tend to block up and may fill in as solid black in places. But in either area the number of dots per square inch is the same!

The reason for the dots is that the printing press, either letterpress or lithography, cannot produce a gray area with black ink. It either prints black or it doesn't print at all. The brilliance of the invention of the half-tone screen came from the use of the white paper as the "mixer" to dilute the black into shades of gray.

The photographic original, which includes all tones, is rephotographed with a special engraver's camera through a glass screen that has thousands of lines scribed in crisscross pattern. Newspaper screens are usually about 55 lines per inch—giving a relatively coarse image. High-quality magazine printing uses as many as 130 lines or more per inch.

The result is a negative in which the screen dot pattern is superimposed on the original photograph. Where there were dark areas,

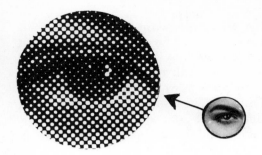

tiny dots of occasional light reach the negative to turn into small black dots. Where there were light areas, the screen is flooded with light and the negative produces a dense black area with fine lines of white faintly crossing it.

This negative is the reverse of what the printed image will be. It is placed on a sheet of copper or zinc which has a coating of sensitized emulsion much like that on photographic film (see FILM). The clear areas on the negative transmit light to the plate, the dense areas protect the plate from the light. When developed, the exposed areas (remember, these were the dark areas on the original picture producing clear areas on the negative) have a coating of acid resist; the shielded areas are left with bare metal.

An acid bath is then used to etch away the bare metal areas. The coated areas remain as raised reliefs on the plate. The raised areas will carry the ink to reproduce the black areas in the original photograph, the etched areas will leave the white paper untouched.

This whole process is called photoengraving, and the engraver can produce relief plates of just about anything that can be photographed. He can even reproduce full color pictures just as you see them in slides or paintings because the principles of full-color reproduction are the same.

Mixtures of inks of the three primary colors, plus black, are enough to convince the human eye that it sees the full range of colors. Yellow and red make orange; yellow and blue make green; red and blue make purple. All of the colors can be mixed with proportions of white paper (as above) to produce paler colors. Add black for dark shadows and you have the most versatile reproduction means you could want.

For full-color pictures the engraving photographer places his screen in the camera and then puts a colored filter over the lens to hold back all the colors in the picture except the yellow. This negative will be used to produce the yellow printing plate. A similar plate is made from a negative exposed for red and one for blue and one for all three, leaving black. Thus four slightly different plates are etched. You can print each of the four in black ink and see the small differences or you can print the four plates on a special four-color printing press in which each plate prints the color for which it was designed. The result is an amazingly good reproduction of the original.

No, this is not the method used for art reproduction. Here six colors are often needed to duplicate the many subtle tones and shadings, but even six plates to print six colors are cheap in a printing process that will produce thousands or even millions (for *Life* magazine, for example) of identical art reproductions.

# PLASTICS

It seems difficult to believe that the whole plastics industry started with a substitute for billiard balls, but that is exactly what happened. The problem was that ivory, of which billiard balls were made, had become increasingly scarce as the herds of elephants were ruthlessly killed for their tusks. In 1863 Phelan and Collander, a firm of billiard ball manufacturers, offered $10,000 for a workable substitute, and plastic was the result.

It was very soon realized that the plastic used for billiard balls (a cellulose compound later called Celluloid) could serve in other ways as well, and soon it was appearing in dental plates and as the famous Celluloid collar of the twenties.

That was the beginning and the end is not yet in sight. Plastics have such widespread application that it is difficult to conceive of life without cigarettes wrapped in cellophane, photographic film, foam rubber, fast-drying paints, nail polish, glue, electric switches, knobs and dials, luggage, airplane windows and safety glass, television and radio sets. All of these and a thousand more could not exist in their present forms if not for this invaluable product.

Plastics refers to a large, loosely defined group of chemical compounds made of very large molecules. These molecules are combinations of many smaller molecules (called *monomers*) joined into long chains and networks whose exact shape and chemical formulas are closely controlled by the chemist. The combination process is called *polymerization*—the making of *polymers* out of monomers—and the polymerization process is what makes plastics.

The original plastic used for billiard balls comes from wood pulp. *Nitrocellulose* (Celluloid, cellophane) was used in dental plates, combs, brushes, eyeglass frames, later as the base for photographic negatives, and lacquer for automobiles to replace old-style paint as a strong, easily applied and quickly dried finish. Nitrocellulose was also the first plastic used in safety glass (see SAFETY GLASS) though it was soon replaced by other plastics less likely to discolor in sunlight. Nitrocellulose was spun into fibers and the first artificial textile, rayon, was the result.

*Cellulose acetate* followed closely on the heels of nitrocellulose. It is the "dope" used to coat the old fabric-covered airplanes. It is still used in model airplane glues (acetone soluble) and nail polishes.

Both of these plastics are based on a natural product—wood pulp—but soon the synthetics came along and before going into these we should define the important difference between thermoplastic and thermosetting compounds. The *thermoplastic* group melt at relatively low temperatures (not much above that of boiling water) and so they can be warmed and molded into any desired shape. They can't later be used near heat, of course, since they would only lose their shape and droop discouragingly. But there are many applications which do not require heat resistance and for these the thermoplastic compounds are versatile and colorful materials.

*Thermosetting* compounds are made of heated mixtures of two or more chemicals. The chemicals react with each other and once the chemical reaction is finished the plastic stiffens—even though it is kept hot. These are the molded-once compounds as far as manufacture is concerned, but once set they have amazingly high heat resistance.

For example, *phenolic* (Bakelite) is a thermosetting compound. You can heat it up but it will not soften. Its good electric insulating qualities make it a natural for radio tube sockets, terminal strips, radio knobs, dials, and the like.

Some other thermoplastic compounds include: The *urea* derivatives used in adhesives and finishes, zippers, buttons, and other dress accessories, radio and television housings. *Melamine*—highly resistant to boiling water and to food acids—is made into dishes, the handles of knives and other kitchen implements. The *polyesters* are combined with Fiberglas in the light, strong plastic automobile body, with the color built in—no painting, no waxing, and very little care other than washing to keep it looking like new. It is still a bit too expensive to compete with lacquered steel but eventually a process will be devised to take advantage of plastics for this application.

The *thermoplastics* include all of the *vinyl* compounds used as adhesives, insect screens, and even chewing gum. Many fabrics are now woven, at least in part, from vinyl fibers. (Saran is a vinyl.)

*Acrilic plastic* is the Plexiglas of airplane windshield fame. It is now used in boxes for milady's cosmetics and shoes, and as transparent furniture parts. It is very strong and as clear as glass. It won't age, or change in color, either. It's expensive. *Orlon* and *Acrilan* are also acrylic derivatives.

*Nylon* comes from polyamide, discovered almost by accident by a Du Pont chemist studying polymerization. Nylon stockings are only a little over twenty years old. The first nylon was made into toothbrush bristles and a year later it was woven into a heavy stocking. This was in 1940 and only three years later women were standing in line to get the few pairs made in a war-production economy.

*Dynel* is partly vinyl, partly acrilic. It is used in pile fabrics, socks, certain woven fabrics used in industrial products. It is mixed with wool or cotton for men's and women's clothes to combine the feel and warmth of wool, the strength and crease resistance of plastic.

*Dacron* was the first polyester fiber generally available in consumer products. It was the first of the "nonwrinkle, wash-without-ironing" fabrics and it mixed so well with wool and cotton that the mixtures have become very popular substitutes for natural fibers.

There's no real end to this list. Hundreds of plastic formulations are now available and industry is making good use of them. A few years ago a plastic product was regarded as a cheap substitute. Today plastic is sought after for the qualities no natural material can duplicate.

# POTS AND PANS

Let's go back a step or two before we get involved in the materials from which these implements are made. Pots and pans are used to transmit heat from burner to food and so we really should know what heat is and how it is transferred.

Most ranges have electric or gas heaters (see OVENS AND RANGES). The electric ones have metal coils of flat ribbon, the gas burners have grates separating the pot from direct contact with the burner. Both designs are intended to distribute the heat as evenly as possible over the bottom of the pot or pan. Needless to say, this is nearly impossible. And so one of the important criteria of excellence in choice of a pot material is how evenly it distributes localized heat on its bottom to the food within.

To distribute heat evenly the material must have high heat conductivity. Copper is the tops in this respect with aluminum running a close second and cast iron and stainless steel poor thirds.

Next you have to consider thickness of the pot wall. The thicker the wall the more likely it is for the heat to spread evenly over the inside surface of the pot.

Last you want to be careful about the chemistry involved. Are food acids or soap alkalis likely to stain the pot? How hard is it to clean off cooked foods? For these we look to the experience of professional cooks (and dishwashers) plus the findings of the various specialty manufacturers.

Here are their recommendations:

1. No single material is best for all purposes. You must choose your pots and pans individually, and vary the materials to suit the particular task.

2. No material is more beautiful than any other. Stainless steel probably shines the most; copper and cast iron have the most impressive Old World look; the various enamels have a wide range of colors.

3. Package sets of pots and pans generally are a waste. The price is not significantly lower than the cost of individual pots you will want and need. In the set, you always get an extra pot or two that you never use and would never otherwise buy. Shop for each utensil with care knowing exactly the uses to which it will be put and how it will fit in with the rest of your collection.

Here are some things to remember when shopping:

Has it a flat bottom? It won't stand easily or fit well on the burners or heating elements if it doesn't—and that wastes electricity, gas, and time.

Choose straight-sided pots over fancy sloped ones—except for omelet fry pans which are sloped on purpose. This conserves space on top of your range and provides a better flow of heat between burner and food.

The pot surfaces should be smooth, with rounded corners inside and out, for easy cleaning. Hammered and dimpled surfaces may look interesting but they can be a nuisance by trapping burned food and grease. Sharp corners are impossible to get at with scouring pads or steel wool.

The bottom diameter of the pots should match the diameter of the burner or heating element on which it is placed. This is simple economy—larger elements will throw heat away to the kitchen if there is no pot directly above, and they will overheat the sides and handles. Elements smaller than the pot will heat only the center and increase the likelihood of burns and scorches. (If you're stuck with a small burner keep the pan moving all the time so as to spread the heat as evenly as possible.)

The pot wall should not be so thin as to dent or bend easily, nor should it be so thick as to be too heavy to pick up. This is simple common sense. Pots and pans should have firm handles— preferably the kind that stay cool, like wood or plastic—and they should not turn in your hand or you'll never be able to pour out of the pot. Make sure that the handle isn't so heavy that it tips the pot over when empty.

A word about sizes: pots are rated by the liquid volume when filled to the brim; frying pans are usually rated in inches of diameter at the rim. Now let's look at some of the materials available, their characteristics and best uses.

*Aluminum* is lightest—even in the thicker sections. It heats quickly and evenly, and holds heat well, especially in the heavier weights. It has a durable surface (chemically) though the metal is relatively soft and so must be fairly thick to be bump-and-bang resistant. Aluminum is recommended for baking pans and sheets, roasters, saucepans, frying pans, Dutch ovens, and teakettles.

Aluminum will be stained by alkaline foods, such as eggs or potatoes, by hard water, and even by soap and detergents. The stain is a darkening film which is removed by scouring with steel wool. Occasionally boil one tablespoon of cream of tartar mixed in one quart of water in the pot for five or ten minutes and then wash the pot out in light suds.

Poor grades of aluminum, made of cheaper alloys, may pit from salty foods. Thinner pots will be burned through pretty easily and they will dent at the slightest touch.

Cast aluminum is generally heavier in section but its rougher surface may be difficult to clean. It is used for electric fry pans because of its light weight (it has to be thick enough to bury the heating element) and even heating characteristics.

*Stainless steel* is more expensive and the easiest to keep brightly polished. It is strong, even in thin sections, and won't warp or dent. However, stainless steel heats slowly and unevenly, creating hot spots in frying pans—a disaster for omelets or French pancakes. To counteract this the manufacturers have bonded stainless steel to aluminum or copper, combining the heat distributing advantages of these metals with the easy cleaning of stainless.

Excessive temperatures will discolor stainless steel but it can be cleaned with a stainless steel wool pad if not too serious. Salt and acids may also discolor the surface in the same way.

Stainless steel makes good double boilers, pressure saucepans, coffeepots, and teakettles.

*Cast iron* is still the favorite of many diehards. It heats evenly and holds the heat well. It's very durable, of course, and actually improves with age and use. Add low cost and you have a formidable set of advantages.

However, cast iron is relatively heavy—the larger pots are almost impossible for a woman to pick up. It rusts easily so you must be sure to dry it thoroughly after each washing. Incidentally, don't wash cast iron in detergents—they dissolve out the oil that penetrates this relatively porous material and gives it its excellent frying qualities. To "season" a new cast-iron pot or pan scour it clean, dry thoroughly, and brush with unsalted vegetable oil or shortening oil. Place in a 300° oven for four hours, brushing on a layer of oil every hour. Wipe clean at the end of four hours and repeat the whole process.

Cast iron makes excellent frying pans, Dutch ovens, and griddles.

*Tin* is usually used as a coating for steel, aluminum, or copper. When the bright finish has darkened somewhat tin changes into an excellent pot material. It heats rapidly and fairly evenly, is light in weight, easy to clean, and relatively inexpensive. Of course, when the finish is worn through by scouring or general use you have the core material to deal with.

Tin plate makes good pie pans, cookie sheets, roasters, and racks.

*Copper* is rarely used by itself but very often combined with stainless steel. The combination heats about as well as good aluminum, but it is expensive. The copper bottoms are, of course, an attractive addition to any kitchen. However tarnished pot bottoms do need regular attention with one of the new cleaners (see SILVER POLISH).

Copper plate makes good double boilers, saucepans, frying pans, and coffeepots.

*Enamelware* usually is made of an enamel baked on a steel base. It heats quickly (because of the metal) and is easy to clean—don't scour it or use steel wool, just let it soak a bit and then rub with a sponge. Enamelware chips easily however, and once chipped it isn't really safe for further use. Enamelware makes good teakettles, double boilers, roasters.

*Glassware* has the great advantage of making the cooking food visible—for those who can't resist peeking. It's easy to clean and holds the heat well though the food heats more slowly than in metal pots. Watch for breakage—cold water in a boiling pot and the like.

Glass makes excellent casserole dishes, double boilers, pie pans, coffeepots, and teakettles.

*Earthenware* heats slowly but holds the heat well through a long dinner. It is excellent for slow cooking at moderate temperatures in the oven. Earthenware is usually glazed on one or both surfaces. The glaze is smooth and easy to clean (watch for cracked glaze).

Earthenware makes good casseroles, bean pots.

*Pyroceram* is the newest pot material. It gets its fame from previous application in the nosecones of missiles. Pyroceram is really an especially heat resistant form of glass. It can go from the freezer to direct flame without damage (though this should be a relatively unusual requirement). Otherwise it shares most of glass's advantages and disadvantages. It is relatively expensive.

## PRESSURE COOKERS

Pressure cookers didn't walk off with all of the home-cooking chores, much to the manufacturers' regret. Many foods normally cook in too short a time for any real advantage in using these gadgets. Further, a few mishaps have added a healthy measure of caution to many housewives. Many of us can still remember, ruefully, the pot of beans that splattered explosively all over the kitchen—ceiling, cupboards, behind the stove, and neatly patterning the freshly scrubbed linoleum.

Carelessness? Of course. You probably never had pressure-cooked beans again.

But for many long-cooking foods you can't do better. The cooking times are reduced by a third in most cases—a very useful saving.

How does a pressure cooker work? How does that dangerous-looking machine manage to get the food inside cooked so fast?

It all goes back to air pressure and the temperatures at which water boils. The miles-high layer of air that surrounds the earth is not as weightless as you might think. As a matter of fact it exerts a pressure of almost 15 pounds on every square inch of earth surface.

It acts on us just as the ocean acts on the fishes underneath. Imagine yourself underwater at a depth of about 34 feet. If you turned an ordinary teacup upside down on a saucer, sealed the edges with grease, and then sucked all the water out through a hole in the bottom, you'd have a pretty tough time lifting the cup off the saucer.

Similarly, if in open air you sealed the teacup to the saucer and sucked all the air out you'd have a hard time lifting it off the saucer. Suction cups work in exactly the same way. All that weight of air is pressing cup and saucer together in an effort to crush and fill the vacuum inside.

This same weight of air is pressing down on the surface of an open pot of water as if to keep it from boiling off when heated. Eventually the water gets hot enough so it can't be held back. At 212° F it bubbles freely, that is at sea level where the pressure is 14.7 pounds per square inch. On the tops of mountains—where the weight of air, hence its pressure, is markedly lower—water boils at 205° F or even 200° F. Conversely, in areas below sea level, where the pressure is higher than normal, the water boils at temperatures above 212° F.

Vegetables and meats cook in an open pot at 212° F and no hotter, no matter how high you set the flame. But if you seal the top of the pot and turn up the flame, the trapped vapor has no place to go. It raises the pressure inside the pot higher and higher. If there were no relief valve the pressure would finally explode the pot, and the beans as well. Which is why pressure cookers are all built with valves that open and relieve the pressure long before the pot will explode.

In any case, pressure builds up to a set value—usually around 15 pounds per square inch (that is, 15 pounds per square inch *above* the normal 15 pound-per-square-inch air pressure acting on the outside of the pot). At this point you are instructed to reduce the flame under the pot and maintain the pressure as read on a little dial or extended rod or similar gage. The temperature inside the pot is about 250° F (corresponding to the 30-pound-per-square-inch pressure acting on the food and water in the pot) and this higher temperature is what speeds cooking time.

You may wonder why ovens couldn't be used to cook foods this fast—or faster since temperatures can be raised to 500° and 600° F if desired. The answer is that vegetables must be cooked in water, otherwise they dry out and are unpalatable. Whenever water is used, the maximum temperature it can reach is the 212° F boiling temperature—except in pressure cookers.

Incidentally, double boilers are also limited to a maximum temperature of 212° F. No matter how actively the water is boiling the upper compartment stops at 212° F so you never have to worry about burning the sauce.

When the pressure cooker has been up to pressure for the required length of time, you turn off the flame and *wait until this pressure drops to* ZERO. This means inside pressure equals outside pressure and it is safe to take the top off.

Remove the cover too soon and you'll get a face full of boiling hot steam.

You can hasten the cooling-off period by wrapping a water-soaked towel around the pot.

## PRINTED CIRCUITS

Actually the printed circuit isn't really "printed" though it does look as if it had been. The goal was to simplify the complex wiring in radio and television sets. You must be familiar with the crazy jumble of interconnected wires in the bottom of most radios—it is doubly impressive when you realize that every wire and part had to be soldered in place by hand. The wire is cut to size, the insulation stripped off the ends, and the bared wire hooked into the terminal of the tube socket or terminal strip. Then a hot soldering iron raises the temperature of the terminal and wire so that when the soft solder is touched to the terminal it melts and forms a tight electrical connection.

Mass production techniques could operate with this system for only a limited time before trying substitutes. The printed circuit is a prefabricated substitute—an assembly of the wires, not the components like tubes or resistors—that go into the radio. Instead of mounting the different components wherever it is convenient and then stringing wires between them, you make an insulating plastic board with thin strips of conductive metal laid on as if with a paintbrush. The strips represent the wires, and they interconnect different points on the insulating board. The various electrical components are attached directly to the board by poking their wires through holes provided and by melting solder to fill the hole. This can even be done automatically which eliminates the slowest and most laborious task of radio manufacture—hand wiring.

There are two basic methods of making printed circuits. In one method a prepared insulating board is dipped in a plating bath so that metal conductors are built up in the desired places. In the second method the insulating board starts out with a thin sheet of metal bonded to it and the undesired portions are acid etched away to leave the desired pattern of interconnections.

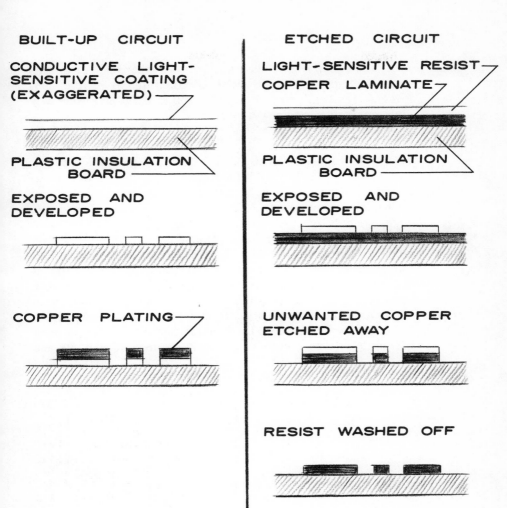

**BUILT-UP CIRCUIT**

CONDUCTIVE LIGHT-
SENSITIVE COATING
(EXAGGERATED)

PLASTIC INSULATION
BOARD

EXPOSED AND
DEVELOPED

COPPER PLATING

**ETCHED CIRCUIT**

LIGHT-SENSITIVE RESIST
COPPER LAMINATE

PLASTIC INSULATION
BOARD

EXPOSED AND
DEVELOPED

UNWANTED COPPER
ETCHED AWAY

RESIST WASHED OFF

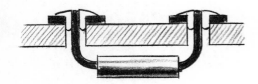

What are the advantages and disadvantages of printed circuit boards? The most obvious advantage is ease of repetitive manufacture. Automatic machines have been designed to take over practically the entire task of manufacture of radio and television sets. The machines don't get tired and make a badly soldered joint every now and then. They don't make mistakes in wiring, and

159

every radio or TV set is identical to every other set. This means easier final adjustment and more consistent quality of reception. Printed circuits are ideal for mounting transistors and other new ultraminiature electronic components.

The big disadvantage seems to be that maintenance men have a hard time tracing the circuits when they have to repair a set. Television or radio repair has always been a complex job, part art, part experience, and part intuition. Often repairmen have to guess at what is wrong from the symptoms and then explore to see if their guess is accurate. Once they know what is wrong, a simple change of tube or component will set things right. But to check the guess they must poke around from component to component, taking instrument readings and making tests. The poking requires that each wire be traced from part to part to see what happens electrically at dozens of junctions. The printed circuits are such crazy jumbles of interconnecting strips that the maintenance man has a hard time finding his way from point to point. This criticism has been largely answered by manufacturers' careful marking of the various parts of the board with printed on symbols and colored paint.

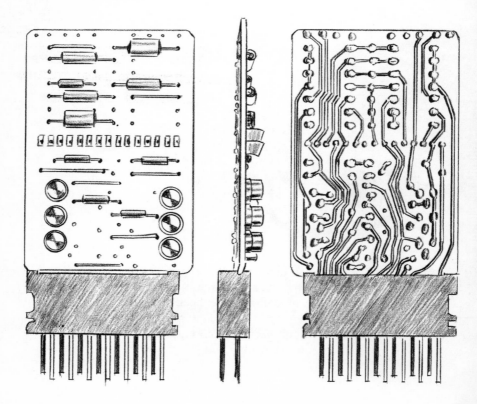

# PRINTING

The history and development of printing is a fascinating, though enormous, study that closely parallels man's rise out of the dark ages. We will limit ourselves here to the basic principles of printing words. See PHOTOENGRAVING for a discussion of the reproduction of photographs.

All printing (that is, the putting of ink on paper) is based on four essentials: the *type,* or *plate,* which carries the reversed image to be printed; *ink; paper;* and a *press.* Printing, however, has dozens of different methods of putting the ink on the paper. The two most important are *letter press,* oldest and still most popular, and *lithography* or *offset* printing, now faster and somewhat more adaptable to the latest photographic methods.

Letter press is usually used for books, magazines, and newspapers. You start with typewritten copy, for example. The manuscript goes to an operator who sits at a large machine that has a keyboard like the one on a typewriter. He types out eight or ten words. As he touches the key for each letter a *mat* (short for matrix) drops down a chute and into a slot within easy reach of the operator. At one end of the mat there is a recessed image of the keyed letter in the style of type being set. When all the letters of a single line have been collected they are spaced apart between words just enough so that a fixed line length is produced. This is called a *justified line* and gives book or newspaper printing its neat look.

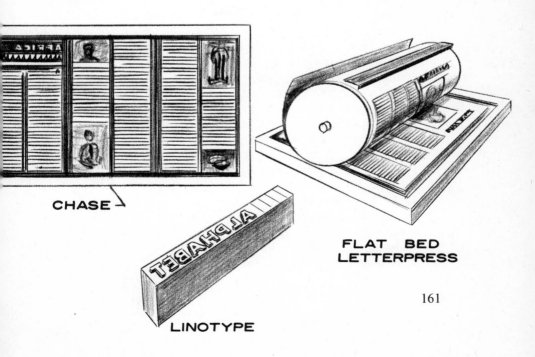

CHASE

LINOTYPE

FLAT BED LETTERPRESS

The assembled and spaced group of mats goes to a casting section of the machine where the entire line is cast in metal as a single unit. This line of type is quickly cooled and carried to the delivery rack on the machine. The matrices are then automatically lifted to the top of the machine where they are redistributed to their proper bins.

This machine is a Linotype machine and it is used to produce the large amounts of reading material that makes up the body of books, magazines, and newspapers. The lines so cast carry raised reverse images of the letters and words to be printed. The lines are stacked, combined with larger display type (for headlines and so on) made on other machines working on similar principles, and then "locked up" in a metal picture frame called a *chase* on a *stone,* a flat granite or steel table, by the *compositor.*

The *pressman* mounts the chase on the bed of the press where inked rubber rollers run over the raised type and put a coat of wet ink wherever the type stands high. A sheet of paper is clamped at one end and wrapped tightly around a drum. The drum rotates on its axis and the inked chase of type passes under the drum. In this way the ink is transferred from type to paper in one quick pass.

The paper is then removed from the drum, passes over a flame or through a spray to dry the ink, and is delivered to a growing stack of printed sheets. Each sheet is printed on both sides. The finished sheet then goes to a machine which folds the sheet into *signatures* ready for binding (see BOOKBINDING).

Lithography is similar. The original from which the lithographic printing plate will be made carries all the letters and pictures as they are to appear on the finished page. The page is photographed and the photographic negative is then placed on the lithographic plate—a thin sheet of aluminum or zinc with a special chemical coating—and exposed to a powerful arc light. The exposure and later development makes a change in the surface of the plate—in places where ink is to be carried the plate takes on a slightly greasy coating. All other areas remain smooth, clean, and shiny.

The thin plate is wrapped around a drum in the lithographic press. It is wetted by a water-covered roller and later an ink roller. The ink is repelled by the water and sticks only to the greasy areas. The drum presses the plate against a rubber "blanket" which picks up the ink and transfers it to the paper in a mechanical process similar to that of the letter press.

Sounds complicated? Well, it is, and a great deal of art and plain old-fashioned working experience is necessary if you want to be a good offset (lithographic) pressman.

162

Just remember that letter press requires that each word and line to be reproduced in the printed version must be cast in metal for the press. In lithography the original will be photographed so you can work from sketches, photographs, and proofs of type previously set or pages previously printed. Of course, letter press can work from photographs too. A description of the method can be found under PHOTOENGRAVING.

# PROJECTORS

With the birth of photography came the lantern slide. Originally the "lanterns" were true oil-burning light sources that weren't too bright and generally smoked up the place. More modern light sources are powerful tungsten light bulbs, and projectors in theaters use electric arcs to throw their images many hundreds of feet across the auditorium.

But what we shall be concerned with here is the familiar home projector, either for slides or for motion pictures. To project a transparency—that is, a rectangle of film whose image must be seen by light that passes through the film rather than by light reflected off the opaque surface of the print—you must throw a strong, evenly distributed beam of light on the entire surface of the film. The beam then goes through a focusing lens which throws the image, much enlarged, on a screen across the room.

The sketch shows how this is done. The lamp and reflector are the light sources for the projector. The light strikes the first of a pair of condensing lenses whose purpose is to collect as much of the emitted light as possible and spread it evenly over the surface of the slide. However, the heat rays also carried in the beam of light would strike the film and probably melt it if a thick section of heat-absorbing glass was not placed as a shield somewhere between slide and lamp—in this case between the two condensing lenses. This glass will stop most of the infrared rays from reaching the slide.

Even this is often not enough protection. Slides probably won't burn, but the heat that gets through the shield makes the emulsion side of the film expand more than the uncoated side and so the slide "bellies" out (pops), throwing the center section out of focus while the edges of the slide stay sharp. One answer to this is a glass slide holder in which the film is kept from buckling by a sandwich of two closely spaced squares of glass that press tightly on either side of the film and keep it flat. The glass has the additional virtue of protecting the film from scratches.

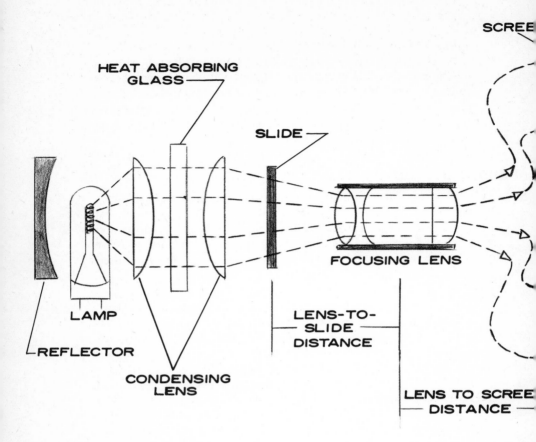

HEAT ABSORBING
GLASS

SLIDE

LAMP

REFLECTOR

CONDENSING
LENS

FOCUSING LENS

LENS-TO-
SLIDE
DISTANCE

LENS TO SCREE
DISTANCE

Of course glass mounts are expensive and so an alternate solution—relatively successful for home projectors—has been the addition of a small motor-driven fan which pulls cool room air into the projector and passes it at high speed over the slide. This cools the slide and keeps it from bellying.

Note that focusing lenses come in different focal lengths just as camera lenses do. Focal lengths are not "better" or "worse" as far as the quality of the lens is concerned; the differences are only a matter of convenience for the user. The shorter the focal length of the lens, the larger the image will be for a given projector-to-screen distance. If you want a full screen image and must project in a relatively small room with the projector within ten feet of the screen, a 35-mm projector will need a four-inch lens. If you want to push the projector to the back of a longer room to get it out of the way of the viewers (as in a theater), a lens with longer focal length is necessary. Manufacturers know this and they try for a best compromise.

More recently a variable focal length lens has come on the market. This (called the Zoom lens) permits you to set your projector anywhere in the room. You bring the image into focus by moving the lens toward or away from the film and then, by varying the focal length of the lens, increase or decrease the size of the image until it just fills the screen.

Movie projectors have the same basic optical system, though all but one of the dimensions must be scaled down to movie-frame size. This can be quite a scaling down since the 8-mm frame is only one sixteenth the area of the 35-mm slide yet, for convenience, the projector-to-screen distance must be roughly the same as that with the 35-mm slide projector.

However, the optics of the small film projector are no problem. Actually they are cheaper and easier to make since they are so much smaller. The difficulty in the movie projector is the added need to pull the film off the supply reel in a series of jerks that places one frame at a time in front of the projection light beam. In between times the light is cut off by a revolving disk with holes that pass in front of the light beam just as each film frame takes its place. Sprocket wheels guarantee the correct position of each frame as it moves into position and a take-up reel winds the film up after it has passed through the projector.

All this is accomplished with a single motor driving the various elements with gears and belts. The more expensive movie projectors have a control that permits slowing or speeding the motor and even stopping it completely so that you can view a single frame at leisure if you like.

## PUMPS

Fans, compressors, and pumps all do approximately the same thing; they move fluids. Fans have been covered under the own heading. They are intended to blow a gas (usually air) from one place to another for the purpose of ventilating, exhausting, cooling, or heating. Compressors are also intended to move air but in their case the air is shoved into a confined tank and since air is compressible, the compressor packs more and more air into the tank, raising the pressure to some desired value. Compressed air is used in air brushes, paint sprayers, or through nozzles to clear away stubborn dirt in factories. Compressed air powers many tools—pneumatic drills, screw drivers, and hammers break up our streets and mine our ores.

Except for minor variations in sealing and valving details, the compressor is much like a pump. The only difference is that the pump is usually used to move a fluid, such as water or oil or gasoline, which is relatively incompressible. The pump usually moves fluid to a greater height (as the water pump that elevates tap water in tall buildings to the tank on the roof—see FAUCETS AND VALVES).

In any case, the function of the pump is the same. Fluid must be moved from a tank of relatively low pressure and pushed into a new location against a higher pressure. To do this the pump sucks a small quantity of the fluid into a compartment. It then closes off the inlet, opens a passage to the high pressure side, and forcibly squeezes the trapped fluid out of the compartment and into the high pressure passage. The principle is always the same, but the specific methods vary enormously and we can consider only a few of the most popular methods here.

Perhaps the most familiar is the *piston pump.* You use one to charge up the tires on your bicycle. The bicycle pump consists of a cylinder, a tight-fitting piston that slides back and forth along the length of the cylinder, and a couple of valves in the end of the cylinder. One of these valves permits air to flow into the cylinder. Let's call this the inlet valve. The other permits air to flow out of the cylinder. Let's call this the outlet valve.

These one-way valves are called *check valves.* Imagine a flexible rubber flap which covers the opening into or out of the cylinder. When air goes out through the hole the flap is pushed aside and the air flows freely. When it tries to return, the flap is pressed tightly against the hole and seals it.

If the valves connect the cylinder to the atmosphere on the inlet side and to the tire or tank on the outlet side, you have all the elements needed to pump air. By working the piston back and forth, a fresh charge of air is drawn in from the atmosphere at each back stroke and the air is then forced into the tire on the forward stroke.

Engineers have taken this same basic idea and mechanized it for great volume and less effort. Instead of a single cylinder the *axial piston pump* has a number of cylindrical holes bored so that they make a circle of holes in the stator block. Each hole has its own piston sliding back and forth, driven by the *wobble plate—* a circle of metal with a slanted cut on one face. As the wobble plate turns on its axis, it pushes the pistons into and out of the cylinders one at a time. The valving is connected at the far ends of the chambers.

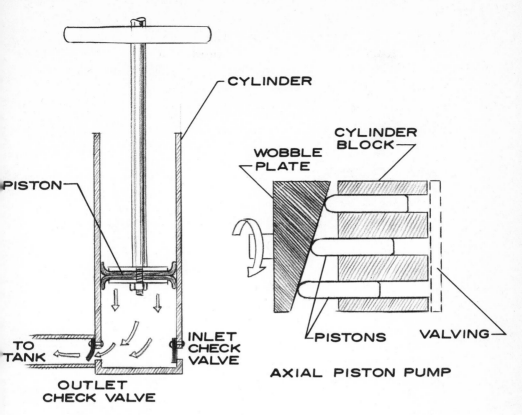

CYLINDER

CYLINDER BLOCK

WOBBLE PLATE

PISTON

TO TANK

OUTLET CHECK VALVE

INLET CHECK VALVE

PISTONS

VALVING

BICYCLE PUMP

AXIAL PISTON PUMP

Piston pumps of this kind work at hundreds of revolutions each minute and force gallons and gallons of water or oil up to pressures of thousands of pounds per square inch.

The *gear pump* is much simpler. It has only two moving parts—two meshed gears revolve in a specially fitted housing so that the spaces between the teeth and the housing carry the fluid around from one side of the pump to the other. Note that only one of the two gear shafts has to be turned by the motor since the one gear will automatically drive its mate.

A third type of pump often used is the *vane pump*. Here a rotor runs in a housing of larger diameter, but the rotor is offset to one side so that it nearly touches the housing at one point. Sliding vanes move in radial slots cut into the rotor. They are held in tight contact with the housing by springs. As the rotor turns, the spaces between the vanes trap slugs of liquid and carry them around to the delivery side.

Sound simple? Well they are really, in principle. But consider

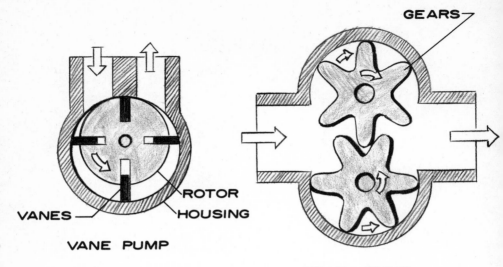

VANES — ROTOR HOUSING

**VANE PUMP**

GEARS

**GEAR PUMP**

some of the problems in these pumps. The front and back surfaces (in the plane of the page in these sketches) must be tightly sealed so that liquid doesn't slip around from the outlet to the inlet side. The shafts, which connect the driving motor to the moving rotor, must also be sealed so that fluid won't leak out around the bearing and spill on the floor. And both of these problems become more critical and less easy to control as the pressures go higher. Maybe it is difficult to group the magnitude of 10,000 pounds per square inch. Just think of a pump that had to drive liquid up to a pressure *seven hundred times* that in your pressure cooker.

# R

## RADIO

Most people accept the fact that radio "waves" travel through the air, through certain buildings, and even through the vacuum of outer space. But what are radio waves and why are they transmitted this way? The physicists don't even know the answer. However, we do know a great deal about *how* radio waves may be used and if you promise not to ask *why* this secion will show how really ingenious the original inventors of radio were.

You're familiar with the 60-cycle per second alternating current available in most houses. The current flows first one way and then the other, through the two prongs of your house lamp plugs, 60 times each second (see ELECTRICITY). This current changes direction very quickly, it's true, but it is possible to send electricity through wires reversing thousands and even millions of times each second. Such very high frequencies have peculiar characteristics. The most important for purposes of the radio is that the wire carrying the current radiates an electromagnetic wave into the space surrounding the wires, and this wave travels on for hundreds of miles, getting weaker all the time. Another wire strung up some miles away will intercept the passing wave and a weak electric signal, identical to the original will be created in the intercepting wire.

So the radio station uses an antenna—a specially shaped wire held up as high as possible—which radiates the wave your radio receiver "picks up." The signal sent out is coded in a special way to carry the music or words that your receiver decodes and amplifies and uses to operate its speaker (see HIGH FIDELITY).

Two coding systems are used: one is called AM for amplitude modulation, the other called FM for frequency modulation. Let's talk about amplitude modulation first.

Imagine the transmitter sending out a constant high-frequency (called *radio frequency*) signal at 1000 kilocycles per second. (A *kilocycle* is 1000 cycles so this is a shorthand way of saying 1,000,000 cycles per second.) A graph of the electric voltage received at your radio antenna would look like this.

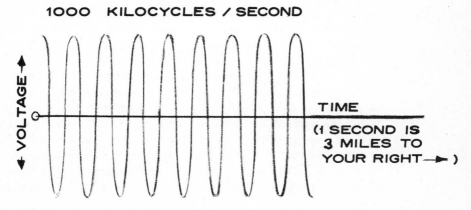

**1000  KILOCYCLES / SECOND**

VOLTAGE

TIME

(1 SECOND IS 3 MILES TO YOUR RIGHT→ )

a

Now sound waves audible to the human ear range from 40 or 50 to 15,000 cycles per second (see SOUND). On a somewhat smaller scale than the first graph, these pressure waves would look something like this.

**b**

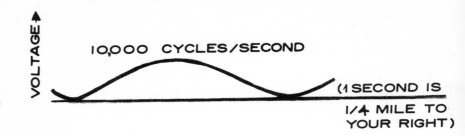

VOLTAGE → 10,000 CYCLES/SECOND (1 SECOND IS 1/4 MILE TO YOUR RIGHT)

The difference in the number of up-and-down lines in these drawings comes from the fact that the radio waves are 1000 times more frequent—they move up and down 1000 times, on average, for each single sound wave.

Suppose you combined the two waves in your transmitter by superimposing the sound signals (transformed into electric signals in a microphone) on the high-frequency radio signal.

**c**

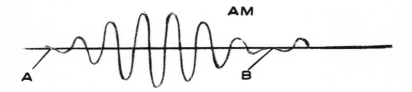

AM

A                                                                    B

Actually this sketch is much exaggerated because of the relatively few radio-frequency curves drawn for each sound wave—if this were a middle-of-the-piano note (500 cycles per second) superimposed on a 1000 kilocycle radio wave, there would be 2000 radio frequency peaks between points A and B.

Your AM radio receiver senses this strange signal and separates out the radio frequency. This is called *demodulation*. What remains is a replica of the original sound performed in the studio. It is amplified and reproduced in your home by the speaker.

Each radio station is assigned a specific radio frequency by the Federal Communications Commission. The station transmitter sends on that frequency (550 kilocycles per second, 1030 kilocycles per second, etc.) and only that frequency, so when you want to change stations you "tune" your receiver to a different spot on the dial and your radio then only responds to the new station's sending frequency.

The problem with AM is that it is extremely sensitive to radio interference. Every time a light switch is flipped or an automobile passes by, the radio signal gets bumped out of shape and you hear a click or pop. To avoid this, frequency modulation was invented.

Just as amplitude modulation meant you changed the amplitude, or height, of the radio wave to send a signal, frequency modulation calls for changing the base frequency somewhat. A frequency-modulated curve, mixing the two curves shown at the top of this section, would look like this.

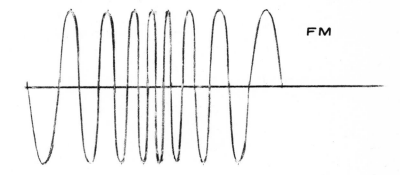

FM

d

Here the high part of the sound signal serves to crowd up the radio frequency signal. The low part of the sound signal spreads the radio frequency curves out. Just how much crowding or spreading depends on how high and low the sound signal goes. Raising the pitch of the sound signal calls for more such crowdings in a given period of time. Lowering the pitch calls for fewer.

The average FM station sends at about 100 megacycles per second (100,000,000,000 cycles per second!), at its mean point. At its most crowded (loudest) point during a particular broadcast, it may increase in frequency to 100,000,075,000 cycles per second; at the widest spread point, 99,999,925,000 cycles per second. This may seem like a small percentage of change but it is ample for all practical broadcasting purposes and FM stations today are known as the high-fidelity stations throughout the nation.

Your FM receiver "tunes" to the center frequency of a desired station and *demodulates* by sensing frequency changes from this center. The sensed signal is amplified and drives your speaker. Note that the amplitude of a frequency-modulated signal does not change with changes in the signal. Thus light switches and automobiles are much less likely to interfere with an FM broadcast.

## RAIN, THUNDER, AND LIGHTNING

The earth is surrounded by moving masses of air (another name for wind), which interact when they meet. Sometimes they mix; sometimes they climb on each other's backs; sometimes they strike head on and roll, tumble, and boil in violent storms.

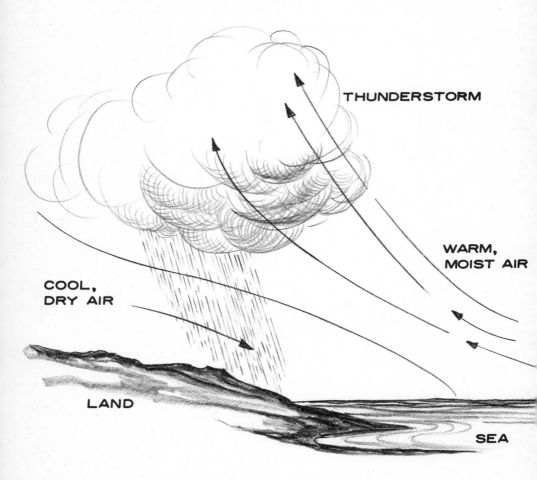

If a mass of warm, moist air (coming from the sea) meets a mass of cool, dry, land air, it rides up over the dry air and this sudden rise in altitude quickly cools the air below the temperature at which it can hold large amounts of water vapor (see HUMIDITY). If the temperature drops far enough, the water vapor condenses out in minute droplets which are visible. Clouds are just such collections of tiny water droplets floating in air.

If the air continues to rise, ice crystals form and these are the *seeds* from which rain eventually comes. The cloud by itself, no matter how wet, cannot form rain. The water droplets just don't collect into drops heavy enough to fall to earth until a few ice crystals form and then the crystals seem to collect droplets just as a snowball grows by rolling down a snowy slope. The water droplets grow to mature size and then fall as rain.

Cloud seeding to induce rain is based on these principles. If the cloud is ready you can start it raining by throwing tiny crystals of dry ice or sodium iodide into the cloud from an airplane, at least so many people believe. The trouble here is that the right conditions have to be present beforehand and the right conditions can't be made by man.

Any continuing drop in temperature of a warm, moist mass of air will eventually produce rain or snow or sleet. The slow, steady winter rain comes from a gradual cooling of warm moist air. The spectacular thunderstorm is the result of a more rapid cooling process.

Lightning is actually a rush of electric current between cloud and ground or from cloud to cloud. The electric potentials (voltage differences between cloud and ground) are created by the uprushing warm air and downfalling rain. The droplets carry minute electric charges away from the clouds and the charges eventually accumulate to the point that the balance must be restored by a gigantic discharge in the form of lightning.

Just before the discharge a path is created in the air between cloud and the nearest contact with the ground. The path is searched out by a thin *leader* and then followed by a gigantic flow of current. The current is the lightning. It produces a bright flash of light and the rent air causes the thunder heard as much as ten miles away. Both thunder and lightning are produced at the same instant but because sound travels more slowly than light, the flash of lightning precedes the thunder by a measurable amount of time. This is the rule of thumb used to measure how far away the lightning is: You count the number of seconds (one-thousand-one, one-thousand-two, etc.) between the time of the lightning flash and the time you hear the first rumble of thunder. Each second means one fifth of a mile traveled by the sound to your ear. If ten seconds elapse between lightning and thunder, the storm is two miles away.

173

Lightning will find the easiest path for the current to flow between cloud and earth. The higher the building the more attractive it is as a path. Thus the Empire State Building in New York is struck dozens of times during every thunderstorm.

Lightning rods do not ward off lightning strokes—they attract them and provide a safe electrical path for the current to go down through the house and into the ground. The lightning rod is placed above the roof level so that when lightning is attracted by the building it will strike at the rod rather than at the TV antenna or the chimney.

In flat country the tall tree is the attraction, which is why you are advised to stay away from trees when caught in the open during a thunderstorm. Further, if you lie down on the ground you yourself become less attractive as a path for current to ground.

The damage caused by lightning is exactly what you would expect from very high currents (thousands of amperes) flowing for short periods of time (average about one hundredth of a second). People so struck can often be revived by artificial respiration and they may have to be treated for burns and shock. Trees are split and burned; cement or brick homes are disintegrated in the path of current. Thin, insulated wires are sometimes left as hollow tubes with their metal conductors boiled right out of them.

Thunderstorms are by no means unusual occurrences, though you may see only two or three a year. In the tropics, storms often come every day and sometimes many times every day. It has been estimated that there are some 50,000 thunderstorms on the surface of the earth every day.

## RAZORS

Men have been scraping their beards off almost as long as they have been walking upright. Despite all this time for invention there are still no really satisfactory methods for shaving the bearded chin.

What we have are three methods: the straight razor, the safety razor, and the electric razor. All have their merits; all irritate the skin to some extent.

The *straight razor* is a strip of hardened and tempered steel with a pivoted handle and a hollow-ground edge. The hollow grinding helps the blade keep its sharpness longer. The edge is ground and honed on oiled stones and then stropped on a leather surface to bring it to the feather edge that characterizes the best blades. Note that the thickness of a sharp edge is only a few molecules of metal. It can't last long, and it doesn't even when

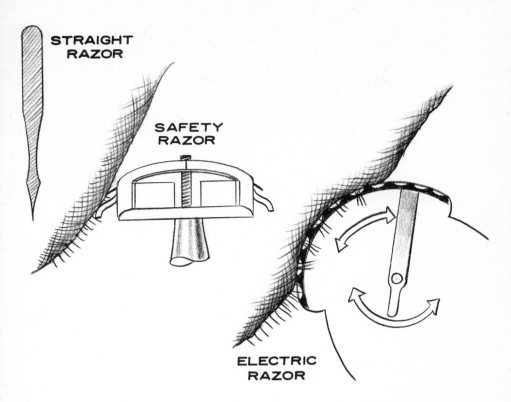

STRAIGHT
RAZOR

SAFETY
RAZOR

ELECTRIC
RAZOR

cutting something as soft as human hair. And so straight razors require frequent stropping and honing to keep them keen.

*Safety razors* are only about half a century old. They were designed to protect the chin from the lethal cuts a misdirected razor could inflict. The idea is to place a metal bar between the blade and the cheek so that deep cuts or gouges are not possible.

At first the protecting bar was added to the straight razor. Later, with advances in the steelmaker's art, disposable blades became economical. Today the safety razor is the most commonly used method of shaving.

*Electric razors* were developed in an attempt to eliminate water, lather, strop, disposable blade, and aftershave cream and lotion. The electric razor consists of a very thin perforated shield which is placed against the cheek so that the individual hairs extend through the perforations. A moving scraper, held tightly against the underside of the shield, shears off the hairs sticking through by scraping them against the surface of the shield.

The scraper is driven at a very high speed by a tiny electric motor—thousands of scrapes each minute—and so there is little pulling of the hairs. The shield is moved over the surface of the beard so as to present the uncut areas to the scraper.

175

There are dozens of variations of electric razor. The shield may be made up of several relatively small round cylinders (called *heads*) side by side on the top surface of the razor, or it may be a single large cylinder with a straight scraper sweeping across the entire shield surface like an automobile windshield wiper.

No matter what the details, electric razors, with the thickness of the shield between scraper and skin, can never cut as closely as the straight or safety razors. The hairs will always be left a little longer. Of course, this is easier on the skin too.

## RELAYS

The relay is just a fancy switch—a switch operated by electric current rather than the flip of a toggle. The current goes to a *solenoid* (see ELECTRICITY) which is simply a coil of wire wrapped around a rod of soft iron. When current flows in the solenoid coil, a magnetic field is created which turns the soft iron rod into a relatively strong magnet. This magnet attracts the second component of the relay, the *armature*. The armature is also made of magnetic

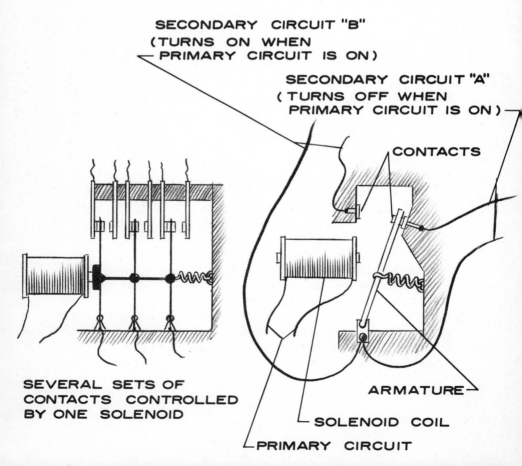

SECONDARY CIRCUIT "B"
(TURNS ON WHEN
PRIMARY CIRCUIT IS ON)

SECONDARY CIRCUIT "A"
(TURNS OFF WHEN
PRIMARY CIRCUIT IS ON)

CONTACTS

SEVERAL SETS OF
CONTACTS CONTROLLED
BY ONE SOLENOID

ARMATURE

SOLENOID COIL

PRIMARY CIRCUIT

iron. It is pivoted so as to swing freely toward or away from the end of the solenoid rod. Thus when current flows through the solenoid coil the armature is attracted. When current is cut off, a spring attached to the armature pulls the armature away from the solenoid.

Contacts are mounted on the end of the movable armature, and on fixed stops at either end of the armature travel. When the armature is pulled toward the solenoid it touches one contact. When it is released it touches another. Thus the relay contacts can open or close a circuit depending on how that circuit is attached to the contacts and depending on whether or not current flows through the coil.

The circuit containing the solenoid coil is called the *primary circuit,* the circuit containing the armature contacts is called the *secondary circuit.* The primary circuit is the controller—it determines whether power goes or doesn't go to the secondary, or controlled, circuit. Ordinarily the primary circuit operates on much less electric power than the secondary circuit and so the relay is actually a power amplifier as well as a control device.

Relays are used extensively in automatically controlled equipment such as those operated by electric eye (see ELECTRIC EYES). They are the backbone of telephone switching apparatus and they can do many simple decision-making operations. For example, a relay armature with several sets of contacts can interconnect some circuits and disconnect others at a single signal through the solenoid coil, as when several sets of lights must be controlled from a single switch.

In general, relays will be buried in the web of wiring of any appliance you are likely to meet. It is a circuit component, and like the vacuum tube, does its job silently and efficiently. Like all such devices the relay occasionally breaks down. At that time it's better to call the serviceman to fix things than fiddle with them yourself.

## REMOTE CONTROLLERS

These are most familiar in television sets, though we'll be talking about remotely operated garage doors later on. The principles can be applied to any electrically powered device that you want to control from a distance.

Let's look at remote controllers for TV sets first. Some are extremely simple devices which shut the set off or turn it on from chairside, others are complex gadgets that adjust volume, change

177

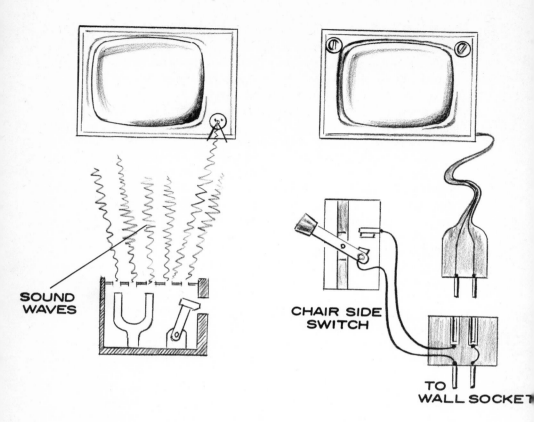

SOUND
WAVES

CHAIR SIDE
SWITCH

TO
WALL SOCKET

stations, or even adjust picture contrast or brightness. If there is a wire going from the controller to the television set or to a socket plugged into the wall outlet to which the set is connected, you have one of the simpler controllers. A special plug fits in the wall socket into which, in turn, the television set is plugged. It is wired so that the current doesn't proceed directly to the television set, it has to make a detour through an extra pair of wires that lead to your chair (see sketch). A switch placed in this line will interrupt the flow of current to the television set, or restore it.

The circuit is simple, convenient, inexpensive, and relatively safe. One disadvantage is that you have an extra pair of wires to contend with. The other is that such a switch can only turn the set on or off. There is no middle ground, such as the muting of sound. Thus if you wish to avoid the commercials, you have to turn the entire set off and each on-and-off cycle reduces the life of the various vacuum tubes and requires an annoying warm-up delay.

The next best thing is to have a controller for volume as well as a switch to turn the set on or off. For this, a second set of wires

178

can be taken from the television volume control to a controller at chairside. By turning a knob on the controller you reduce the current to the speaker and so cut or increase the sound level. This also works well, but it adds still another set of wires to an already cobwebbed room.

Engineers went one step further. They figured that direct wire connections had to be eliminated completely. That leaves either sound or light as the means for signaling the set to turn on or off, loud or soft. They first tried light—an electric eye installed in the front face of the set. The eye reacts to light striking its face by creating a weak current. The current can be amplified and used to flip a relay (see ELECTRIC EYES). The relay then opens or closes the circuit to the television set.

To control the set you just point a flashlight at the electric eye. Each time the light strikes the electric eye it reacts and the relay alternatively turns the set on, then off, and so on.

A second electric eye can be mounted on the set to control the sound. Each time the light beam strikes this eye a relay turns a switch one quarter of a revolution. The first position turns the set on at lowest volume. The second and third positions progressively increase the volume. The fourth position is the off position.

Note that all you need is a flashlight to operate the system. However, the electric eye must have a small amount of electric power for itself. There is no point in wasting this power during times when the set will not be used and so a "standby switch" is supplied which turns the electric eye circuit on to be ready for your signals.

The most sophisticated of these systems works on sound rather than light. Flashlight batteries wear out and have to be replaced, and the electric eye can be fooled by strong sunlight or other electric lamps.

To get around these objections engineers replaced the electric eye with a sensitive microphone and the flashlight with a small tuning fork. The fork is set to ring with an extremely high-pitched sound well beyond the ability of people, and even dogs, to hear (see HIGH FIDELITY). This sound is up around 40,000 cycles per second. It is heard by the microphone which produces a weak electric signal that is amplified (made stronger) and used to operate a relay so as to change stations, or turn the sound on or off, or turn the volume up or down.

Note the devilish ingenuity of this system. The microphone is tuned so it is sensitive only to certain closely controlled sound frequencies. Each frequency signals a different relay to control a different function on the television set—this is especially important on color television which has a multitude of controls needing adjustment after each station change. Each frequency is created by its own tuning fork mounted in the controller. By pushing one of four buttons you snap a tiny hammer against one of four tuning forks. The fork rings with an inaudible sound that doesn't even have to be aimed accurately at the microphone since the sound spreads as it approaches the microphone and it bounces off all hard surfaces like ceilings or floors. The microphone hears the sound, determines which of the four frequencies is being sounded and signals the appropriate circuit in the set to obey your command.

Once again, the microphone uses electric power and so a stand-by switch must first be turned on for the system to be put into action, but once turned on, you have the set in complete control from anywhere in the room.

Garage door controllers can be operated remotely by any of the methods outlined above. But garage doors have an additional requirement—they should be burglarproof. This complicates the problem considerably because now you must signal with a key or a code to start the door opening.

Normally the door is locked shut by an electric latch, a locking bolt on the inside which is retracted when electric current is permitted to flow through a special releasing solenoid (see ELECTRICITY). When the bolt is withdrawn the main door-driving motor starts and lifts the door. The drive motor is automatically turned off when the door is all the way open. Later you close the garage door by flipping a switch inside the garage.

But how do you signal the latch to open and the door motor to start? There are several ways. For example, an auto ignition switch can be attached to a post at the end of the driveway. You stop the car, insert the key and turn it just as you would in an automobile. This signals the garage door to start opening and it will continue to open even though you remove the key.

Or an electric eye can be used which signals the door to open when it is hit by the light from a special lamp in the car. The lamp has to be special so that the electric eye won't open the door with any light. Usually the "code" is in the form of a high-speed flashing of the lamp, too fast for anyone to imitate.

Ultrasonics can be used, of course, just as it is for the television sets. The problem here is that jet planes and police or fire truck sirens often produce sounds in the ultrasonic range so they too may open your garage door.

Most popular, and reliable, is the radio-controlled garage door. In these a signal is emitted from a tiny transmitter in your car. The signal is specially tuned so no other radio transmitter is likely to produce one like it. The signal is received by a loop antenna buried in the concrete of the driveway (see RADIO). You transmit from the car when you are parked right over the antenna. This makes a very weak transmitter practical. It is just strong enough to reach out the few feet from car to roadway.

The transmitter is operated by push button in your car. You pull up the driveway, pause over the antenna, and push the button on the dashboard. This starts the garage door up and you drive right into the garage. It's a great convenience on rainy days.

# S

## SAFETY GLASS

All U.S. automobile windshields and side and rear windows are made of safety glass (sometimes called *shatterproof glass*). It isn't absolutely shatterproof, of course, but compared to the ordinary variety of plate glass used in houses and stores it is much less likely to break into sharp flying pieces.

Safety glass is actually a sandwich. You take a sheet of ordinary plate glass, lay a thin sheet of vinyl plastic on it and cover the two with a second sheet of glass. You put the sandwich in a press and heat and squeeze them together. The plastic flows slightly and bonds itself tightly to both panes of glass.

When struck by a stone, the glass may crack but the pieces are held in place by the vinyl so they don't fly. Even when small stones go through the pane completely they break away only a few small vinyl-held pieces of glass and leave the majority of the pane cracked but held firmly in place.

Those armor-plated trucks you see near banks have *bulletproof glass* in the peep holes. This is a sandwich too, except that it is 1½ inches thick. Bulletproof glass is made up of several layers of glass and vinyl and the 1½-inch thickness will stop just about anything but a small cannon.

Two other extra-strong glasses should be mentioned here. *Wired glass* is made by embedding a wire net in a solid sheet of glass.

The glass is actually poured around the wire net while it is still molten. The glass cools and hardens with the wire in its center which strengthens the glass enormously. Wired glass is used in skylights, ground floor windows, in ship portholes and in the lenses of some automobile parking lights. Certain city ordinances require wired glass in public passageways like halls or railroad stations since it will not break and fall during a fire as safety glass will.

There is also a hardened and toughened glass called *tempered glass.* It is made by cooling hot glass quickly with a blast of air. The tempering makes the glass eight times stronger than normal window glass. This glass is used in most European automobiles as windshields and side windows. When it breaks it shatters into many relatively small and harmless pieces.

## SAILING

The most amazing thing about sailboats is that they can move against the wind. No matter which way the wind blows, an expert sailor can move his boat in just about any direction he likes on the lake or, indeed, on the sea.

This is possible because of the shape and action of the sails combined with the stabilizing influence of a deep, weighted keel. Most people forget how important the keel is to sailing because it is under water. Its broad area resists sidewise drift and the heavy weight concentrated at the bottom helps resist overturning when a strong wind blows against the sails.

The sails act like wings standing on end (see AIRPLANES). They are actually most efficient when heading into the wind. There is a strong pressure on the inside of the sail when it drives into the wind (a "lifting" force) and a smaller "drag" pulls toward the trailing edge. The lifting effect tends to drive the sail and the boat, sideways. But the keel won't let it drift to the side and so the boat is forced to move forward. The drag opposes the forward push somewhat, but usually not enough to stop the boat. Thus you sail forward, against all apparent reason.

Of course there are limits. The more directly the boat is faced into the wind the less force there is to push the boat forward. A fast, trim racing yacht can sail much "closer to the wind," that is, facing more directly into the wind, than a big, slow cargo boat can.

To sail his boat to a spot immediately upwind from where he is, the yachtsman makes a series of zigzag courses. Each zig or zag brings him closer to the desired position. The "closer to the wind"

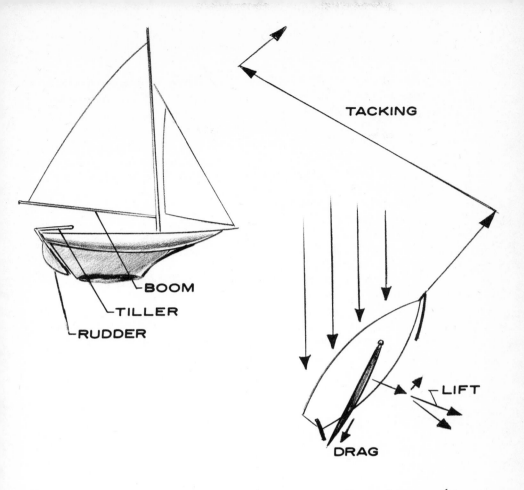

BOOM

TILLER

RUDDER

TACKING

LIFT

DRAG

his boat can sail, the fewer zigs and zags necessary to cover the distance.

These zigs and zags are called *tacks,* and the great explorers of the world were forever struggling over where their starboard (right) and port (left) tacks took them. They were always *coming about* (turning from one tack to the other) with much collapsing of sails and snapping of canvas. This is because when changing from port to starboard tack, or back again, the boat first turns to face the wind and then continues around to bring the wind on the other side of the sails. This means that there is a moment when the sails will be limp, then the wind comes from the opposite side of the boat filling the sails from the opposite side.

*Running with the wind* rather than against it would seem much simpler, but such sailing has its problems as well. Most boats have more than one sail and the rear (aft) sails may block the wind from the front ones. Sailing with the wind also tends to drive the prow of the boat down into the water. A too-quick turn or an unexpected gust can bury the prow and then overturn the boat completely.

The *rudder* is a pivoted board that extends down into the water at the rear of the boat. By swinging it left or right you interfere with the flow of water past the hull. The displaced water forces the boat into a turn.

The rudder is controlled by a *tiller* or a *helm*. Smaller boats (and smaller rudders) can be manually controlled with a tiller which extends forward into the boat over the back rail. Larger ships with big rudders weighing hundreds of pounds cannot be held by hand against the strong water forces. A wire rope or motor-driven gear system is then used and the helmsman turns a spoked wheel to move the rudder left or right.

To help control the driving forces on the boat the sailor tightens or loosens his sails and changes their position relative to the ship. Most small boats having swinging booms that extend back from the mast and stretch along the bottom of the largest sail. By moving the boom left or right he can change the direction in which the sail bellies, and this plus the position of the rudder are all he needs to control his boat.

## SCALES

These are the simplest looking, yet probably the most complex of all household appliances. The Scales of Justice or the elegant balance we used for our first chemistry experiments are truly beautiful linkages whose origins are nearly as old as civilized man. But the design of linkages to achieve weighing accuracies in the order of millionths of an ounce needs all the precision and sophistication of modern-day science. Your doctor's scale and even your bathroom scale are marvels of complex levers, fulcrums, springs, weights, and balances. They're far more complicated than their simple exterior would indicate.

Let's start with the *balance*. A straight beam is pivoted at its center. Two pans are suspended at equal distances on either side of the center fulcrum. When the pans hold unequal weights the balance tilts and one or more of a standard series of weights may be added to or subtracted from one side of the balance to return it to level. By totaling the number of weights you put in the pan you know how much the object in the opposite pan weighs.

Note in the sketch that the suspension points for the pans are located slightly below the center fulcrum. When the pans are nearly in balance the beam tilts at an angle proportionate to the amount

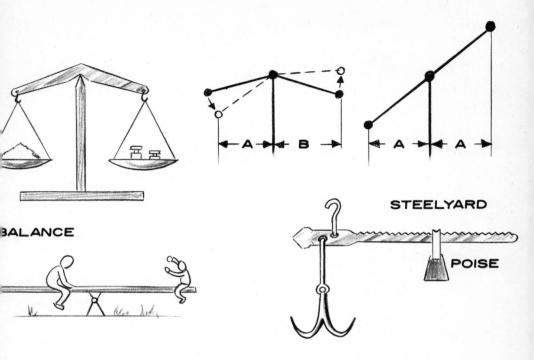

BALANCE

STEELYARD

POISE

of unbalance. As the beam tilts the rising pan moves away from the center (B), the falling one moves in (A). This movement compensates for the difference in weights much as the lighter child moves out on the seesaw to balance the heavier one.

The *butcher's steelyard* is a modification of the balance requiring no auxiliary weights for weighing. Instead, a movable *poise* is adjusted along the arm until its weight just counters the weight hung from the hook. The heavier the object the farther out along the arm the poise must be moved. Sometimes an adjustable poise of this kind is combined with a standard set of poises that hang from the farthest tip of the arm. Each poise weighs perhaps only a pound, but it adds as much as 100 pounds to the indicated weighing range. For example, a steelyard working in the 0 to 100 pound range would, with a single auxiliary poise added, weigh between 100 and 200 pounds, and so on.

Most complex of all are the *platform weighing machines* used for trucks, cars, over-the-counter store goods, and people. These are complex because the object being weighed may be placed anywhere on the platform without changing the indicated weight.

185

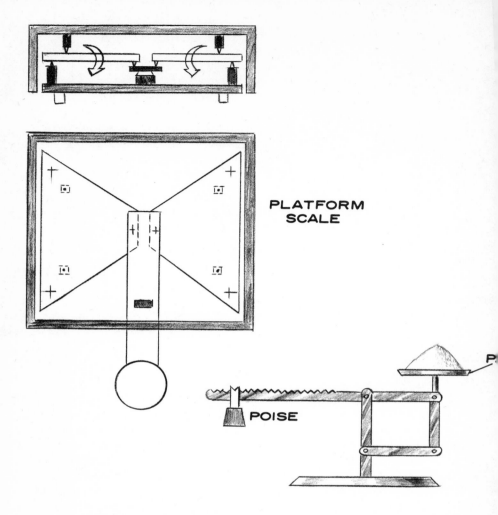

PLATFORM
SCALE

POISE

P

The rectangle of links and pivots under the pan is called a *parallel linkage* because the pan may move down or up but it will always stay exactly parallel to the ground. Therefore no matter where the object is placed on the pan the scale will read the same.

Doctors' scales are platform scales. Here two triangular plates in the base of the machine take the load from the four corners of the platform. They both tend to lift a lever whose far end pulls down on a steelyard hook. Because of the relative lengths of the linkages, only a very light poise is needed to balance people weighing 10 to 300 or more pounds on the platform.

*Bathroom scales* work in a similar way—triangular plates transfer the load to a single point but then one or more springs balance the weight. As the spring is compressed a dial rotates indicating the load on the platform.

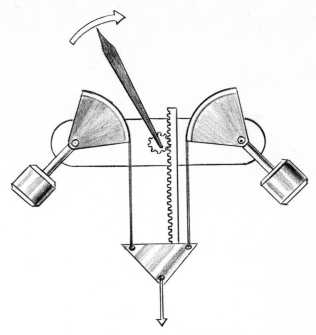

**PENDULUM SCALE**

The "honest-weight-no-springs" school of platform scales are balanced by swinging pendulums. The pendulums start out hanging vertically and as the platform load increases they swing out, applying more and more of their weight to resist the platform load.

In all of these scales meticulous attention to detail is essential. The design of the pivots, the rigidity of the links and the stability of the springs under all conditions of temperature and vibration are vital factors in the accuracy of the indicated weight.

## SCREWS

There's no question about it, the invention of the screw was nearly as important as the invention of the wheel, and it came a lot later in human history. It is based on a pretty complicated mathematical curve called a *helix* which is the path taken by a point rotating around in a circle at the same time that the circle moves forward along a line through its center. More familiarly, a helix is a driving forward and turning at the same time. All these words fail to create the simple picture in your mind that the sketch here produces.

If you take a round rod and wrap around it a length of cord so that each turn of cord just touches the last turn, you have a tight

## MACHINE SCREW AND NUT

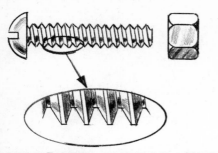

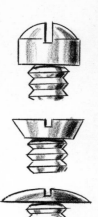

## STANDARD THREAD FORM

## WOOD SCREW

## SOME OTHER THREAD FORMS

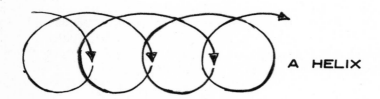

## A HELIX

helix built up around the rod. If you substitute steel wire for the cord you have a pretty close approximation of the standard machine screw.

The cord or wire is called the *thread* of the screw and most often it is not added to the rod as described above; the material of the screw is itself cut or formed into the thread shape.

Note that the sketched helix turns clockwise as it moves forward, or away from you. This is called a *right-hand thread*. Left-hand threads can be made as well—they would turn counterclockwise as they advance. Left-hand threads are used in certain special applications today, but for most designs screw threads are cut right-hand. This standardization is very important to servicemen and assemblers who develop the habit of tightening all screws with a clockwise rotation of the screw driver and loosening them with counterclockwise rotation.

Screws are used to fasten parts together, to clamp them, to hold parts in position (as with the adjustment screw) or to change their position (the lead in a mechanical pencil). In all cases a *nut* is necessary as the mate and matching part to the screw. For machine screws, the nut is simply a square or hexagon of metal through which a hole has been drilled and a thread cut in the exact matching, but negative, shape of the screw thread. When mated the screw will drive forward into the nut as it turns.

This is what happens when two metal plates are drilled through, the screw put in the hole, and a nut placed on the end of the screw. As you turn the screw it can't advance since the head already butts against the metal plate. You keep the nut from turning with a wrench or with your fingers and as the screw turns it draws the nut up tightly against the metal plate.

*Wood screws* make their own nut threads in the wood. The wood fibers are flexible enough to move aside and mold themselves to the screw-thread shape. The same clamping action takes place between wood and screw head.

Note that there is nothing sacred about the triangular shape of screw thread. Square threads, and even saw-tooth threads are used in special-purpose machines like lathes and drill presses.

We have talked about threads and how they are used but perhaps you have asked yourself, Why? What is the real advantage or principle of the screw thread? The thread is, in reality, a wedge. The wedge that is used as a door stop is a perfect example. The long sloping surface pushes up on the door with tremendous force when it is jammed in the space between door and floor. This is called *mechanical advantage*. You push lightly with your toe on the

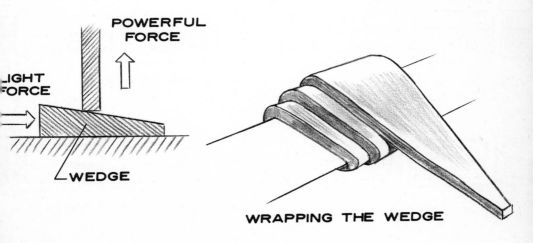

POWERFUL FORCE

LIGHT FORCE

WEDGE

WRAPPING THE WEDGE

short edge and the sloping surface magnifies this force greatly in the clamping action.

A screw thread is a wedge that has been wrapped around a cylinder. By turning the screw you are tapping gently against the short edge of the wedge and the top surface of the thread acts as a long sloping surface engaging the nut. That is why a light tightening action on the screw driver gives you tremendous clamping force between nut and screw head. The wedging action is all in your favor.

## SEWING MACHINES

Machine sewing is different from hand sewing in two important ways. First, the needle itself is different. A hand needle has a long point with its eye at the rear, a machine needle thickens rapidly right back of the point and the needle eye is about an eighth of an inch from the point. The needle then thins slightly toward the heavy shoulder at the back end.

The second important difference between hand and machine sewing is that most home machines operate with two threads rather than one. Let's look at the difference in stitches and then at the exact process the machine uses to form the machine stitch.

The most familiar hand-sewing stitch, and certainly the simplest, is the *running stitch*. The needle dips into and out of the cloth in a regular pattern and when drawn tight the thread follows in a regular series of stitches (see sketch).

The most popular machine sewing stitch is the *lock stitch*. Here two threads are used, one runs along the top surface of the material and dips down into the material at regular intervals, the second runs along the bottom surface of the material and rises to engage the loops in the upper thread. The threads link within the width of the material and hold tightly. All you see from above

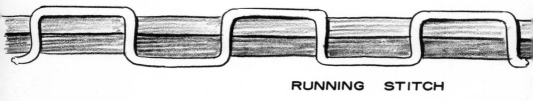

**RUNNING STITCH**

**MACHINE LOCK STITCH**

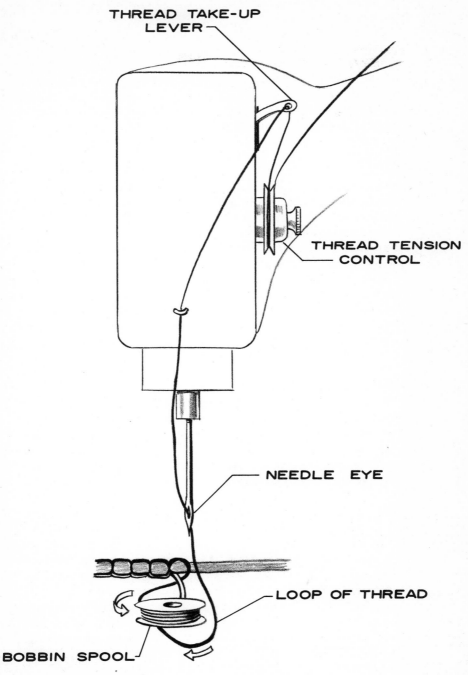

THREAD TAKE-UP
LEVER

THREAD TENSION
CONTROL

NEEDLE EYE

LOOP OF THREAD

BOBBIN SPOOL

or below is a regular series of short stitches, each starting where the last left off.

Try to imagine a machine to produce a lock stitch. Not so simple is it? And yet sewing machines are well over a hundred years old. The trick was to take a lesson from the textile weaver's shuttle. In sewing machines this is called a *bobbin*—a small spool on which you wind a length of the thread and which will provide the thread for the under part of the lock stitch. The needle eye carries the upper thread fed from the main supply spool.

At each stitch the needle pierces the material, carrying a loop of spool thread right through the material. Underneath a hook catches the loop of needle thread and draws it out into a large loop. The length of thread to make this loop is provided by the downward sweep of the thread take-up lever—the rod that swings up and down in at the top left end of the machine. The loop so formed is spread and guided around the entire bobbin hidden underneath the base plate. The loop is then withdrawn by the return swing of the thread take-up lever.

When the needle leaves the material the saw-toothed gadget in the base plate rises up into contact with the material and draws it forward by a set amount to bring the material into position for the next downward sweep of the needle. By varying the amount of feed you can regulate the length of the stitches.

## SILVER POLISH

Both silver and brass lose their bright metallic finishes and darken when exposed to air. They darken faster when moisture and certain food chemicals are present. This tarnish is confined to the outer layer of the metal and so it can be removed either by abrading away the surface to reveal a new, clean layer of the metal, or by chemical or electrolytic applications which react with the tarnish products and leave the surface clean again.

Silver polishers, like pastes, liquids, and polishing cloths, have an abrasive. When rubbed on the silver, the abrasive takes off a microscopic layer and leaves a shiny polished surface. There are dip and electrolytic solutions that remove oxidation products completely or reverse the oxidation process. Let's see what the consumer testing organizations have found about them.

The *pastes* are all good. They consist of a clay, chalk, or diatomaceous earth abrasive ground into a powder and mixed with a liquid carrier (usually water) which turns the solution into a paste. You take the paste, rub it on the silver and then wash it off. The result is a brightly polished surface. Note, however, that the crevises and deeper tooled shapes are not so easy to clean with paste.

*Liquids* are about the same as pastes except that they have a greater proportion of liquid carrier. The carrier is likely to be a fast-drying solvent rather than water. The problem here is that fast-drying fluids are usually combustible, and this creates an unnecessary fire hazard. Liquid cleaners may have chemical cleaners added, and these assist in, and speed, the polishing job.

Polishing cloths or papers usually have jewelers' rouge (powdered iron oxide—rust) impregnating the cloth or paper. Jewelers' rouge is a fine polishing agent and may be used either wet or dry. In either case the silver is cleaned quickly if the tarnish is light, much more slowly and with more effort if the tarnish is deep. Papers and cloths are relatively expensive for the amount of silver that can be polished, and they are soon soiled by the black tarnish products and make your hands messy.

*Dip cleaners* are purely chemical solutions. You take the silver and dunk it into a jar of liquid for a few minutes and pretty soon the silver comes out clean and lustrous. It's a fast, effortless way to clean silver but two problems may exist. First, the silver doesn't have the same high polish that the abrasive polishers give it. This is simple common sense since no rubbing or polishing at all is involved in the dip cleaning. The second problem is that the entire exposed area of silver is going to get cleaned. If clefts or engraved marks in the silver have a three-dimensional antique effect that you like, you'll have to buy an artificial tarnishing agent to replace the black after a cleaning in the dip.

Dip cleaning produces a dull, low-luster surface. After many cleanings the silver takes on a yellowish tone which can't be removed except by polishing with an abrasive.

*Electrolytic cleaning* is the cheapest and easiest of all because you don't have to buy anything special. However, it suffers from the same disadvantages that the dip cleaners do—deliberate antiquing will be removed and the finish produced is dull rather than highly polished (though this may be preferred by some people).

Here's how you do it: scour an aluminum pot so that the surface inside is quite clean. Add hot water, and one tablespoon of a strong detergent for each quart of water. Drop the silver in and within a few minutes all the tarnish will have disappeared. How does it work? An electric current is set up (very small—don't worry about shocks) between the silver and the aluminum. This carries the tarnish products away from the silver and distributes them over the pot surface. To eliminate the pot-staining problem you can use aluminum foil and then throw the foil away. Not all foils will work—some have varnish coatings and others are made of relatively inactive alloys.

There is a foil on the market especially designed for this purpose. It is made of magnesium and so it is slightly more active and effective than the aluminum would be. You can use an aluminum pot or even a glass or enamel pot in this case. Just be sure that all the silver pieces either touch the foil or another silver piece that touches the foil.

We shouldn't leave this subject without mentioning brass and copper polishers. Here too the commercially available polishers are abrasive and chemical—usually in combination.

Most brass and copper originally comes polished and then coated with a thin layer of protective, transparent varnish (see PAINTS). The varnish keeps the metal bright and shiny until it is worn off. Then the metal begins to look spotty and something has to be done about it. What you do is remove the varnish with a solvent (acetone, amyl acetate, or even nail polish remover will often do this handily).

Now use the commercial cleaner. Don't touch the metal with your hands after it begins to get clean. Wash it carefully in warm water—quickly since the polish hastens the tarnishing process as well—and then dry thoroughly. Now coat the metal with a wax furniture polish, or better yet, with one of the canned transparent plastic sprays, for a long-lasting bright finish.

Don't put the spray coating or the wax on the bottom of a pot directly exposed to flame. They will probably burn and they certainly won't last beyond the first few seconds.

# SOUND

Remember how, as a kid, you tied a rope to a doorknob and whipped the other end sharply to make a bump of rope travel the length of the rope? They call this a *wave*—because of its similarity to an ocean wave. Sound is a wave, or a series of waves, too. Imagine first a long, soft, coiled spring (like the "Slinky" you can buy in toy shops) instead of the rope. You give one end a sharp pull, spreading the coils at the near end of the spring, and the spread coils seem to travel down the length of the spring just as the bump of rope did. Conversely, you can give the spring a sharp push and the coils will close up momentarily, then the closed-up coils seem to travel down the length of the spring.

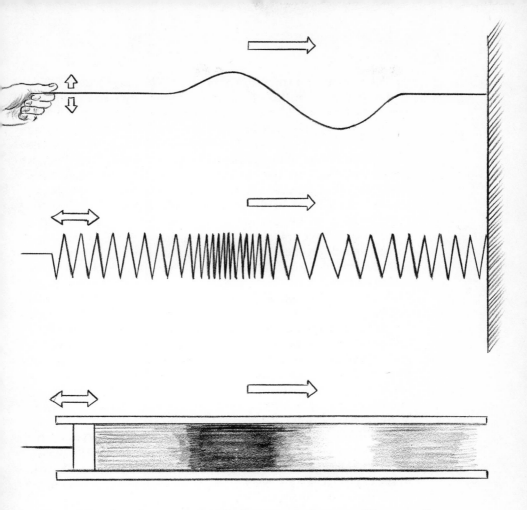

The closed-up wave is called a *compression wave*. The spreading, thinned-out or rarified, wave is called a *rarefaction*.

You can make a train or series of waves in your spring by alternately pushing and pulling on the end. The spring will then carry a series of compressions and rarefactions following one another down the length of the spring.

Let's replace the spring with a long tube of air open at one end and with a movable piston, rather like the piston in a bicycle pump, at the other. Like the spring, air can be compressed or expanded and you do this by pushing the piston sharply in or out. By oscillating the piston back and forth in the end of the tube you will start a train of waves in the air running the length of the tube. In this case the compression part is where the air molecules are pushed more closely together. The rarefaction part is where they are spread more widely apart.

This is sound—a train of waves in air. The *pitch* is determined by the *frequency* of the waves, that is, how often you swing the piston back and forth in a second. The lowest sound you can hear —deep organ notes for example—are near 30 cycles per second (each cycle is one compression followed by a rarefaction). The highest sounds are ultrahigh-pitched whistles of near 15,000 cycles per second. Dogs can hear whistles of even higher frequencies (up there it's called *ultrasonics*) and so dog whistles of the "silent" variety are made to operate at these high frequencies.

To go back to the analogy of the spring for a moment. The compression wave travels down the spring at a fixed speed. The speed depends on the softness of the spring and the weight of the coils. No matter how often or how fast you push and pull at the spring end, each wave travels down the spring at the same speed. The faster you oscillate the end the more crowded the waves will be.

Similarly, compression waves travel in air (which has a measurable "softness," and weight) at a fixed speed. The sound which you originate at one end of a room takes a measurable amount of time to reach the other end. This is independent of how loud the sound (which varies the degree of compression and rarefaction, but not its speed) or how high the pitch (which varies the number of compressions and rarefactions in each second).

For air at sea level conditions, the speed of sound is very nearly 1100 feet per second or close to 750 miles per hour. In these days of jet airplanes and rockets, 750 miles per hour is not so fast. Actually airplanes have been going faster than this for some time, hence terms like *supersonic aircraft* and breaking the *sound barrier.*

We have been talking about what sound is, but not about how we know it's there. Actually your ear has a narrowing passage which concentrates the train of sound waves on a small thin membrane called the *eardrum.* This membrane vibrates back and forth in tune with the sound waves striking it, and transmits the vibration through an ingenious series of links to nerve cells which send appropriate signals to the brain—and so you hear.

## SPEEDOMETER AND ODOMETER

How fast? How far?

By law you can't drive without one and you probably couldn't sell your car without the other.

You may never have wondered how they worked, but chances are you'll be a little incredulous and disappointed to discover how simple the whole process is.

The circumference of a wheel of your car is measured and then it is calculated how many turns of the wheel it takes to roll a mile. A special *flexible shaft* transmits the number of wheel turns to a little counter on the dashboard. This flexible shaft is an ingenious gadget consisting of a relatively thin, braided wire which turns inside a woven metal sleeve. The combination is easily bent around corners and if you hold the sleeve fixed and turn the braided wire at one end, its other end is similarly turned through all the sleeve's bends and twists.

The counter is a series of wheels with numbers 0 through 9 printed on the rims. As each turns through a full revolution it clicks the adjacent wheel over one number. Tenths, units, tens, hundreds, thousands, etc., of miles are thereby registered on this *odometer.*

New cars have their odometers sealed at the factory so that you can't disconnect them.

The *speedometer* consists of a disk of aluminum which has a pointer attached and a wire spring tending to turn the pointer and disk toward the zero mark.

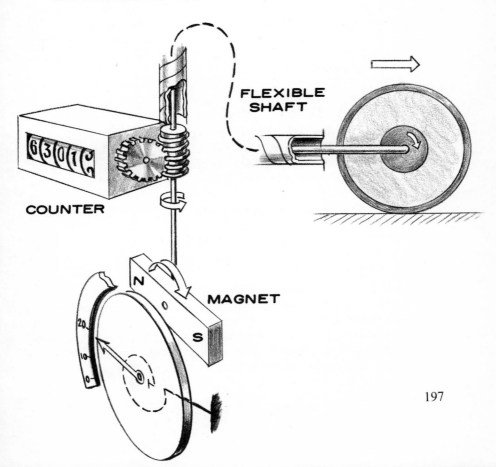

FLEXIBLE SHAFT

COUNTER

MAGNET

Right behind the disk, and turning on the same axis, is a permanent magnet geared to the same flexible shaft, mentioned above, that turns the odometer. The faster the car goes, the faster the flexible shaft turns, and the faster the magnet spins on its axis.

The spinning magnet creates electric currents in the aluminum disk (see ELECTRICITY), the currents set up a second magnetic field in the disk which is pulled by the spinning magnet and so the disk tends to turn the pointer and disk away from zero. The faster you go the faster the magnet spins and the stronger the pull against the pointer spring.

That's all there is to it. A few tests establish the relationship of speed to pointer position, and motorists have been following their guidance ever since.

Actually speedometers are far from accurate measures of an automobile's speed. They're usually set to read high from two to five or ten miles per hour—especially at the higher speeds. This protects the motorist who thinks he's going faster than he is, and the manufacturer who never knows just how the speedometer will read and figures to err on the side of safety.

Change your tires, or the load in the car, or the air pressure, and your speed will read differently by as much as one or two per cent. But don't try to argue with policemen. They use specially designed speedometers to clock you, or radar, or the time it takes you to whiz over a measured distance.

## SPINNING AND WEAVING

Here's another one of those techniques that is almost as old as man and the wheel. Apparently soon after humans climbed down from trees and discarded hides as clothing, they started making cloth and experimenting with the different patterns woven cloth could make.

But before man could weave he had to have thread and thread required spinning. So let's start with spinning first, find out how thread is made from fibers, and then follow with a quick look at how these threads combine to make the thousands of fabrics we know today.

Spinning is just what it sounds like. A mass of fiber—cotton, flax, silk, synthetic, etc.—consists generally of a tangled bundle of short lengths of extremely thin and weak fibers all intermixed in a spongy mass. A few of these fibers are pulled out of the mass and attached to a *spindle*—a length of wood or metal. The fiber mass is then pulled away from the spindle and so a relatively thin string of fibers stretches out in a thin string between the spindle and the fiber bundle.

The stretching action is combined with a high-speed spinning of the spindle. The spinning spindle winds the stretched-out fibers into a coiled thread. The individual fibers are interwined and tightly held by the twist. The tension on the stretched fibers and the tightness with which they are wound plus, of course, the strength of the original fibers determines the strength of the resulting thread and its fineness.

In primitive hand-spinning operations the wound length of thread was then coiled on the spindle and a new length of fibers drawn from the unspun mass. Modern machinery draws the fibers and twists them in a continuous controlled operation.

Once he had thread, primitive man could make cloth. His early attempts were probably not very different from this: take a picture frame of wood—as large as your patience permits. From one pair of facing sides of the frame string a series of threads so that they make an even series of lines, not unlike the strings of a harp, across the open frame. For simplicity you can tie the ends to an evenly spaced series of nails at each end. Let's call this first series of threads the *warp*. Now sew a thread through the warp threads in a simple over-and-under pattern. When you have come to the end of the warp threads just turn around and go back. Call this second series of threads the *weft*. As each weft thread is added it must be pressed tightly against the last to make a closely woven pattern. After the entire frame is filled with the woven cloth you can cut the ends, tie them and take the rectangle of cloth to your wife who will immediately insist on color and pattern to lend a fashion note.

This is weaving. With minor variations it produces a cloth as fine as the finest damask or crude as the coarsest burlap. Let's see how weaving machines make this process simpler and faster.

First, the threading of the weft (cross) threads is a miserable, tedious operation. How would you speed it? Well, if the odd threads of the warp could be lifted and the even ones lowered you would have a wedge-shaped passage running across the width of the fabric for the weft to go through in a quick straight line rather than in the over-and-under path. That would save plenty of time, and work. To do this you mount a series of wires so that they run perpendicular to the plane of the cloth. Each wire has a tiny loop at its center and each warp thread goes through a loop on its way from one end of the frame to the other. The vertical wires are attached in groups called *healds* at their tops and bottoms. Each of the odd

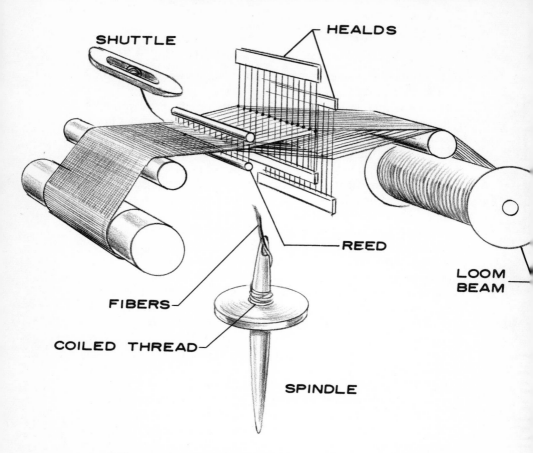

SHUTTLE

HEALDS

REED

LOOM
BEAM

FIBERS

COILED THREAD

SPINDLE

wires, carrying the odd warp threads, belongs to one heald. Each
of the even wires carrying the even warp threads belongs to
another heald. Now you can separate the warp threads by lifting
one heald and lowering the other. When the next weft thread is to
be added you simply lower the first and raise the second heald to
create the over-and-under pattern in the warp threads.

Next problem: The weft thread is awkward to pull across with
a small needle. Wind a length of thread on a *shuttle* and "throw"
the shuttle across between the separated warp threads. The
shuttle is a rounded piece of wood or metal with a spool of
thread at its center like the passenger in a rowboat. The shuttle
has the necessary weight and shape to slide freely on the web of
separated warp threads. The spool unwinds weft threads without
tangling or losing thread tension.

Next problem: To wedge each weft thread tightly against the
cloth so far formed takes time and is uneven when done by hand.
To solve this add a series of wires much like those of one of the
healds but make this set (called a *reed*) movable along the length

## PLAIN WEAVE

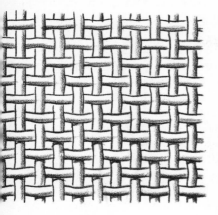

## CHECKS

## CANVAS WEAVE

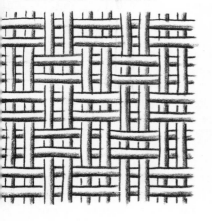

## TWILL

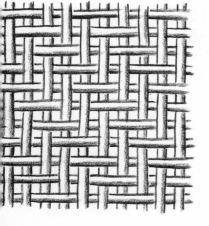

of the fabric and the warp threads. Each wire fits between warp threads and after the shuttle has passed the reed can be pushed against the collected cloth adding the most recent weft thread tightly to the rest of the cloth.

Next problem: We've got to make cloth of much longer lengths than that provided by a simple picture frame. To do this the warp threads must be first wound on a large cylinder called a *loom beam*. A separate thread is wound for each warp thread to be in the cloth. If the cloth is to be 36 inches wide it might need 500 or more threads in the warp and each thread might be 600 yards long. That's an awful lot of thread to get tangled up in, but there are machines to wind the beams. After the loom beams are wound they are then placed at the back of the loom and the individual threads taken through the proper heald loops, through the reed opening and then hooked to another cylinder at the front of the loom which will be used to hold the finished cloth as it is woven.

Proper tension must be kept on the warp threads at all times and the beams must turn slowly to wind the finished cloth away from the reed making room for new weft threads.

That about covers the most troublesome problems. With a little imagination you can see how cloth may be woven in many different patterns (see sketches). There needn't be only two healds but three or four or more may be used to lift and lower different groups of warp threads in complex sequence. Further, there can be more than one shuttle, each carrying a different color or thickness of thread. The warp threads may be of different colors or thickness, too.

And to complicate things out of all understanding, many fabrics are not woven of just one set of warp and weft threads. Imagine two completely separate cloths lying face to face, in which certain threads from one loop down into the other—not deeply enough to show on the outside surfaces, but deeply and frequently enough to hold the two fabrics together. In this way you have a compound fabric that might be completely different on each side. Or the two fabrics might be so closely interwoven to give patterns of different weaves in a sort of patchwork—neither side really different from the other.

# SPRINKLERS

Before we get too deeply engrossed in the exact way these gadgets spread water, let's look a little into the water needs of a lawn. All growing things need water. If the water is supplied naturally by rain, so much the better. But if a long dry spell comes along, you have to supplement the rain with artificial irrigation. The amount of water needed varies with the soil. Light, sandy soil should have about ⅜ inch every four or five days. Average loam needs ¾ inch every seven to ten days. Heavy clay needs 1¼ inch of water every 12 to 18 days.

You also have to know how much water per hour a sprinkler spreads. It is possible to spray water faster than the soil can absorb it and the result is run-off and waste. Light, sandy soil will take up the ⅜ inch in about 15 minutes. Average loam will take the ¾ inch in a little over an hour. Heavy clay needs a full three hours to soak up 1¼ inch of water.

These dimensions (inches of water) refer to the height of water thrown on the lawn. You can measure the amount of water your sprinkler throws by placing three straight-sided cans in the area being sprayed. Put one can about three feet from the sprinkler, the second out at the edge of the sprinkled area, the third about halfway between the two. Let the sprinkler run for exactly one hour, measure the height of water in each of the three cans, and average them. The result is the inches of water per hour your sprinkler spreads on the lawn.

The amount the sprinkler sprays must be matched to the amount of water the soil can absorb. That is why heavy clay, for example, cannot be well soaked in less than three hours—it simply won't absorb more than ½ to ¼ inch of water per hour. If your sprinkler throws water too fast you'd be wise to close the nozzle down a bit.

Incidentally, all sprinklers depend on the water pressure to establish their maximum throw and volume. The higher the pressure the faster the water is spread. Most home type units are designed to operate with around 25 pounds per square inch water pressure. If your water pressure varies markedly from this value you might consider a special sprinkler or one with a very great range of adjustment.

Now for the sprinklers themselves. There are four main kinds of sprinkler. The simplest is the one with two spinning jets that throw the water out in long spirals and simultaneously spin around like the tips on a whirling baton. The spin comes from the reaction to the spraying water in just the same way that a released balloon pushes itself through the air.

In its simplest form the spinning-jet sprinkler is set on the lawn and the water turned on for the necessary length of time. Then you shut off the water, move the sprinkler to a new location and turn on the water again to do the next area.

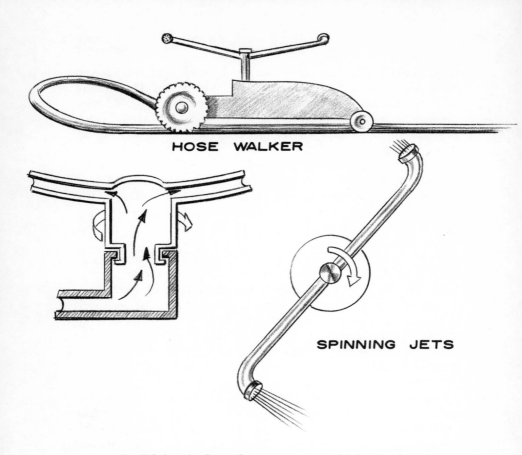

HOSE WALKER

SPINNING JETS

It didn't take long for someone to think of using the rotating jets to take over the moving problem too. The spinning shaft has a gear attached to it so as to turn a pair of wheels slowly making a *hose walker*. The walker rides the hose like a railroad track; you lay out the hose in any shape necessary to cover your lawn, then turn on the pressure and forget it. An hour or two later you return to find the walker has traveled down the entire length of the hose, sprinkling all the way. A modification of this same idea operates the *tape winder*. A metal tape is stretched out and staked at some convenient distance from the sprinkler. The sprinkler slowly winds the tape in from the other end, and the sprinkler moves slowly across the lawn.

Spinning jet sprinklers have been challenged by two other kinds. The first is the *fan sprayer* which covers a rectangular area rather than a circular area. The "fan" is a tube of aluminum with a series of holes drilled along the upper side. The tube is pivoted at both ends so that it can swing around its own axis in a short arc. The swinging action is produced by a short link that alternately pushes and pulls the fan tube (see sketch). The links are adjustable so that the swing can be controlled to work both ways or just one.

You may wonder what makes the short link rotate. The answer is the water itself. A small water wheel (called a hydraulic motor) is built into the sprinkler and this drives the short link as long as water flows.

The last sprinkler to be considered here is called the *impulse type*. Here the jet of water shoots out from a sprinkler head and strikes a weighted bar set just in front of the jet. The bar is pivoted so that it swings freely about a vertical center line and it has a light spring attached tending to hold it in against a stop on the nozzle. When the jet strikes the bar it swings away from the stop. It swings back under the force of the spring, cuts right through the jet and strikes the stop with a sharp blow. The blow swings the entire sprinkler head around a little bit and sets the bar into position to receive the jet again. This is repeated again and again with the nozzle stepping around the circle in a series of short jerks.

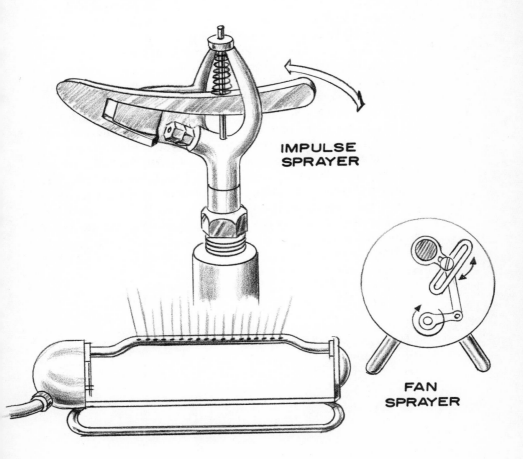

**IMPULSE SPRAYER**

**FAN SPRAYER**

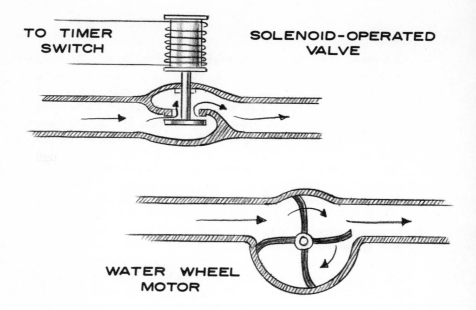

TO TIMER
SWITCH

SOLENOID-OPERATED
VALVE

WATER WHEEL
MOTOR

An attachment can be added to this impulse sprinkler which makes it turn in the opposite direction too. You put a second stop on the back end of the sprinkler head which is tapped by the bar on its outward swing rather than on the return.

Note that automatic sprinklers of this kind lend themselves to permanent installation and completely automatic starting and stopping. Clock timers (much like those used in the automatic washing machine or the clock radio) can be set to turn electric power on and off. The power can be used to operate a solenoid (see ELECTRICITY) and open or close the water valve to the sprinkler.

There are lots of advantages to automatic control. You won't forget to water—the system takes care of itself. The lawn always gets the right amount of water, not too much nor too little. The system can be set to go on during the late night or early morning hours when pressure is high and the air is cool, so less water is lost in evaporation. Also this gives you the freedom of the lawn during the day.

## STAPLERS

You can buy any one of a dozen different staplers in any office supply shop. They range in price from a few cents to many dollars and in size from a tiny pocket-sized affair no larger than your little finger to monstrous toothy machines that will ram a heavy wire staple into a wooden crate.

All staplers work on essentially the same principle. A staple is

206

pre-formed in a squared C shape and guided into a slot wide enough to take the thickness of the wire and just long enough to accommodate the length of the back of the staple. A ram rests on the back and drives it, points down, into the wood or paper. If the staple goes into wood that's all there is to it. If it goes into a sheet or two of paper the arms of the staple must be bent over to hold.

Most staplers have anvils beneath the stapler ram on which the paper rests. The anvil has two depressions just under the staple points. When the ram forces the staple through the paper the points strike the ends of the anvil depressions and are bent in (or out) and up toward the ram. In this way the staple clamps the paper tightly.

Loose staples would be a nuisance to handle and almost impossible to load into the stapler and so stacks of staples are glued together with a light plastic glue just strong enough to hold the staples during loading yet not so strong as to interfere in any way with the operation of the ram. The stack of staples is held in posi-

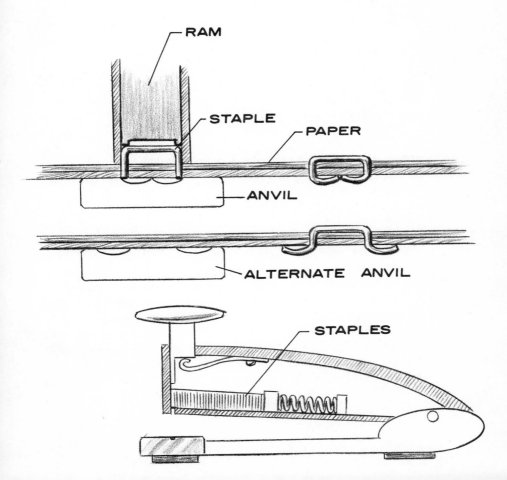

tion by a spring. The end staple is rammed into the paper. When the ram lifts the stack moves up so that the next staple can take its position.

Industrial stapling machines are available which have the stapler actually built into the business end of a large hammer. You swing the handle just as if you were hammering a nail and the staple is driven forcibly into the wood.

There are also staplers that do not need preformed staples. They work with a spool of wire and each action of the ram cuts off a measured length of wire, shapes it into the squared C form, and then drives it home on the anvil.

## STEREO

Have you ever wondered why it is that we have only one mouth for tasting, one nose for smelling, but two eyes and two ears for seeing and hearing. The answer is *stereo*—the perception of depth. Practically every other living being shares these characteristics with us because it is necessary for survival. It is not sufficient that we see—we must be able to estimate distance with our eyes, locate a sound source with our ears. And you need two for this.

It's easy to prove, if you'd like to try. Close or cover one eye and ask a friend to stand facing you at a distance of about ten feet. Tell him to point the forefingers of both his hands straight up side by side and about 18 inches in front of his face.

Now ask him to move his left hand forward toward you and his right hand back away from you maintaining both in line with your eyes. He should move his hands back and forth very slowly in this sawing motion, and you tell him to stop when you think the fingers are closest to each other.

Then open your other eye.

Amazing isn't it? You just can't tell. The fingers appear to be opposite each other when actually they're several inches or maybe even a foot or more apart. Further, it's very easy for him to deceive you if he slows down slightly when his fingers are far apart and speeds up when they approach. You won't see the difference in speed and you'll far more probably stop him during the slow part of the motion than the fast.

The point behind all this is that you need two eyes to perceive depth. Actually your eyes, set apart by about 2½ inches, see different scenes. The closer the object to your eyes, the greater the difference. (Try looking at this page at a distance of about four

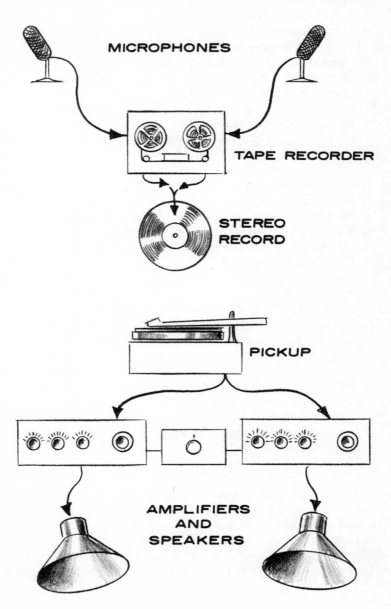

MICROPHONES

TAPE RECORDER

STEREO
RECORD

PICKUP

AMPLIFIERS
AND
SPEAKERS

inches, first from the left and then from the right eye in quick alternation.)

More distant objects look almost the same from each eye, and at distances of 50 feet or so the eye loses its depth-sensing ability and relies on the apparent height of known objects to estimate distance.

Many attempts have been made to reproduce pictures in depth by simulating the difference in what is seen by the two eyes. In early movies, two pictures were taken simultaneously by two cameras whose lenses (eyes) were about 2½ inches apart. The two films were projected through red and green filters on the same screen. In the theater you were given a pair of glasses. One lens had a green filter and the other red. You saw one picture through the red-filtered eyeglass, the other picture through the green-filtered glass. Thus, each eye saw what one of the camera lenses saw to give you an astonishingly realistic feeling of depth.

More recently Polaroid filters on cameras and projectors have been combined with Polaroid glasses to make very realistic 3-D films. They didn't catch on because wearing glasses in movies is a nuisance. Further, the pictures tended to be class B horror types banking on the exaggerated 3-D impression to attract an audience.

In an exactly analagous fashion, the ears are both necessary for you to identify accurately the direction of a source of sound. To enhance the realism of recorded sound in your living room, sound engineers first experimented with two microphones placed on either side of an artificial head in the recording studio. The orchestra played and was "listened" to by the two microphones, each of which separately recorded its impressions. (Original experiments were with disk records, but the invention of magnetic tape enormously simplified the problem since each microphone's signals could be recorded on half the tape width, see TAPE RECORDERS.)

Each recording was then played back through an earphone to make an almost unbelievably realistic recreation of concert sound. You could sit in your living room, close your eyes, and actually imagine you sat in the center of the concert hall.

Successful as this sound was, the equipment left something to be desired in convenience. Headphones are too small for the really effective reproduction of sound—you need a 10- or 12-inch speaker in a specially designed enclosure. Further, people don't much like being tied down to a pair of earphones.

Today's *stereophonic* sound is recorded by microphones placed about six feet apart. The resulting recording (first on tape, and then transferred to special stereophonic records—see HIGH FIDEL-ITY) is played back by a stereophonic pickup which separates the two channels and sends each signal to a separate amplifier, each with its own speaker. The two speakers are placed about six feet apart along one wall of your living room and, in theory at least, that wall becomes the whole orchestra spread out just as it was in the studio.

As you can see, there are approximations in the system which argue strongly against a true reproduction of a 60- or 80-piece orchestra in your living room. The whole illusion becomes much too dependent on your room, the placement of speakers and furniture, as well as the excellence of the equipment. Still, the illusion of depth, of spaciousness in the source of sound, cannot be denied. When it is very good, echoes and reverberations seem to fill a great volume of air out there beyond the wall.

Note the requirements here. A special record, a special pickup, *two* amplifiers (and preamplifiers, if they're not built in), *two* speakers and enclosures. It's an expensive pleasure.

## STORE WINDOWS

They're called "invisible" windowpanes, and with good reason. You really get the impression that there is absolutely nothing between you and the mannequin in the window. Yet you know this can't be and it is very interesting to see how the illusion is accomplished.

Ordinarily the flat glass window is set perpendicular to the window floor. This creates a problem in reflections because some of the light that strikes the glass from outside is reflected and these reflections are visible to the passer-by. Remember how you see street lights, other pedestrians, cars and buildings reflected in the shop window? All of these reflections are bound to interfere with your view of what is *in* the window and they make you very conscious of the fact that you are looking through glass.

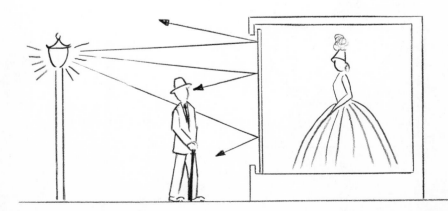

Look what happens when the window pane is tilted forward (see sketch). Now the same reflections are bounced downward, out of your line of sight. The window has become "invisible" to you unless you lean down and make a special effort to see the reflections. However, the disadvantage with this store window is that the tilted glass takes up so much display space that it is almost not worth the trouble. At least half, and maybe more of the window floor area is cut off by the pane.

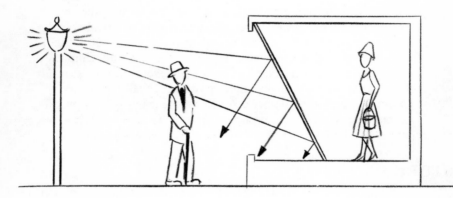

An interesting compromise is a curved glass pane. All reflections are still bounced down out of your line of sight, but more than half of the original floor area is available for display. Of course, the curved glass is expensive and difficult to mount, so these panes are not very popular, but the effect is truly amazing.

Note that curved, tilted, or straight, the glass must be kept very clean. Dust spots and smears are easily visible no matter how the glass is placed.

# STRING INSTRUMENTS

The three important kinds of musical instruments are strings, winds, and percussion. The elements of sound transmission are similar for all three: A volume of air must be set into a series of compression waves (see SOUND) of controllable pitch (number of waves per second) and volume (how high the maximum pressure of each wave). The instruments differ quite a lot in how they produce the sound, and so tone quality varies greatly between piano and bugle, for example, or even between violin and cello.

**PLUCKED STRINGS:
LYRE, LUTE, HARP,
ZITHER, GUITAR,
UKULELE, MANDOLIN,
BANJO, HARPSICHORD.**

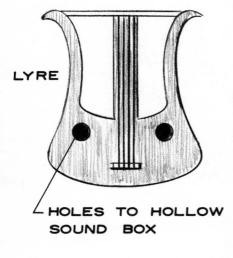

LYRE

HOLES TO HOLLOW
SOUND BOX

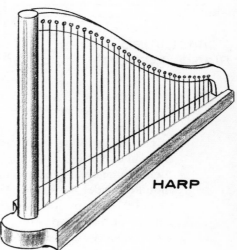

HARP

String instruments are sounded by the vibration of a steel or gut string pulled tight and either struck, plucked, or rubbed by stretched horsehair. Vibration frequency (pitch) depends on the length of the string, its weight and tautness. The loudness of the sound depends on how large the vibrations the string makes.

213

A string alone, held at its ends and caused to vibrate, will make only a barely audible sound since it cuts through the air causing only a mild local disturbance. To get large quantities of air into motion you add a sounding board or box. The string transmits its vibrations to the board or box through a bridge—so called because it usually stands up off the board very much like a real stream-crossing bridge. The strings run in the direction of the stream over a straight section of this bridge to attachment points on the other side. At the far end of the sounding board, the strings are held by rotatable pegs used to tighten, therefore to tune, the string.

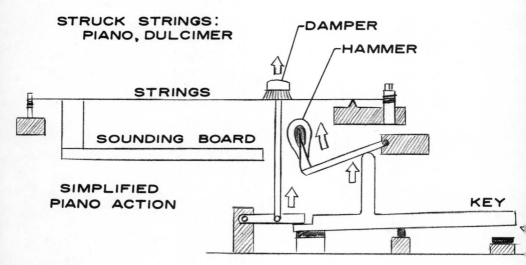

STRUCK STRINGS:
PIANO, DULCIMER

DAMPER

HAMMER

STRINGS

SOUNDING BOARD

SIMPLIFIED
PIANO ACTION

KEY

The piano is the most familiar string instrument. Most of us have, at one time or another, peeked inside to see the large, sturdy metal frame holding neatly lined-up strings. The sounding board is mounted under the strings, usually a pale unfinished-looking slab of wood. Perhaps you thought that you saw the unfinished inner surface of the piano. Actually the board determines the character of sound far more than strings, case, or even delicate touch on the keys by a skilled performer.

The key action is a complex system of levers, leather strips, wire and felt cushions. It is adjusted so that a small movement of the key results in a sharp impact of the hammer on the strings. As the hammer rises a damping pad is lifted off the strings so the sound is sustained as long as the key is held down. An auxiliary pedal also lifts the damper so that keys can be released without stopping the sound. A much simplified sketch, on this page, shows something of this action.

The *violin* family has four strings stretched along a neck or fingerboard then down over the sounding box to the bridge. The box encloses a strangely shaped volume of air. Front and back (called belly and back) are coupled by a sound post near the center of the box, thus both surfaces of the instrument contribute to the sound amplification.

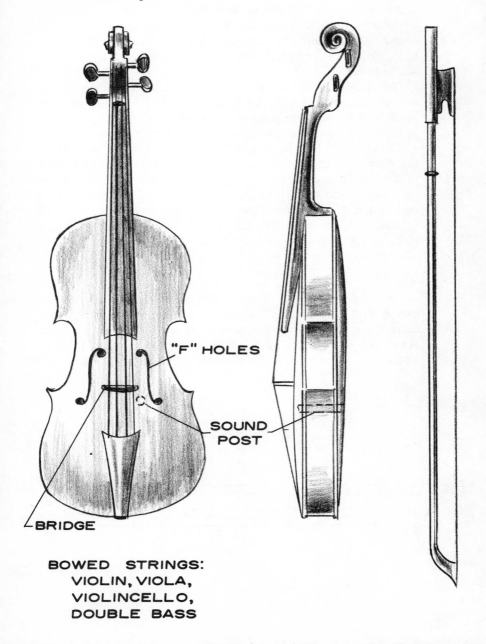

"F" HOLES

SOUND
POST

BRIDGE

BOWED STRINGS:
VIOLIN, VIOLA,
VIOLINCELLO,
DOUBLE BASS

Sound from each of the four strings may be raised in pitch by holding the string against the fingerboard. The shorter the freely vibrating length of string, the higher the pitch. The violin differs from some other string instruments in that its string is sounded by a bow. The bow is a thin rod of wood with horsehair strung tightly between the raised ends. The horsehair is rubbed with *rosin* to increase its friction when rubbed against the strings.

The shape of the instrument, the wood from which it is made, and most particularly the varnish used to seal and preserve the wood constitute the violinmaker's art. Many of the greatest violins of the sixteenth and seventeenth centuries cannot be duplicated today. We don't know just what went into the varnish or how it was applied.

The violin is a difficult instrument to play since you must guess —or know from thousands of hours of practice—exactly where to place your finger to get the note you want. An error in placement of only a fraction of an inch will make the sound sour.

*Guitars* and *banjos* and *mandolins* are much easier to learn in this respect, because they have *frets*—thin metal rods embedded in the fingerboard at exactly the right place for each note. When the string is held against the fingerboard by a finger placed between two frets, it stretches from fret to bridge in exactly the right length to produce a true tone. The string is plucked by fingertip or by a piece of shaped plastic, ivory, or metal called a *plectrum*.

## SWITCHES

The essential purpose of any switch is to connect or disconnect two metallic conductors. When the conductors touch, electric current can flow from one wire to another—the circuit is *closed*. When the conductors are separated, an air gap remains, and electricity can't flow between the wires—the circuit is *open*.

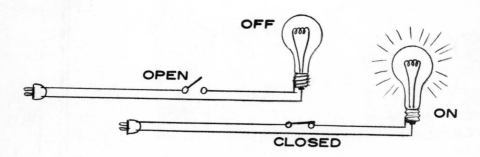

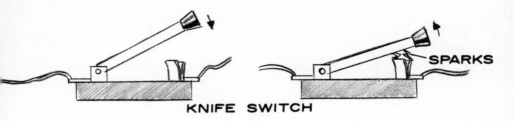

SPARKS

**KNIFE SWITCH**

All switches, therefore, open or close the electrical connection between two or more of their terminals. The simplest form is the *knife switch,* so named because of its cutting action as the blade is pulled down between two springy contacts that are wired to one terminal on the switch. The pivoted end of the blade is wired to the second terminal. The conductive parts of this switch must be mounted in plastic or wood or other nonconductive material so that the switch does not *short out,* that is, provide an alternate path for the current to flow around the open switch contacts. In addition, the knife blade itself must have a nonconductive handle so that you can open or close the switch without touching any of the conductive parts.

This design is fine for certain laboratory work on low-current and low-voltage circuits. The trouble is that too many of the conductive parts are unprotected—a careless finger or tool would bring the electric voltages and currents into dangerous contact with the human operator. And so a switch for home use must be completely enclosed—no conductive parts open to prying fingers at all.

A second requirement for the household switch is that the contacts open and close at high speed. The reason for this is that electric current has a form of inertia—once started it hates to stop. If a large electric current were flowing through a knife-blade switch and you slowly lifted the knife blade, current would continue to flow from contact to contact even when they were physically separated. It would flow in the form of a bright spark jumping across the gap between contacts. This is dangerous—the spark is exceedingly hot and it can easily start fires in wire insulation, and in the plaster-and-wood walls of our houses.

The normal household wall switch satisfies these requirements. It is completely enclosed, has fast closing and opening action, and

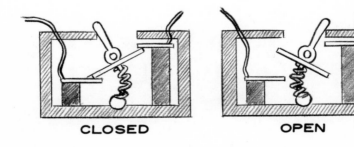

CLOSED                    OPEN

**SNAP-ACTION SWITCH**

it is enclosed in a small metal box embedded in the wall so that even in the unlikely event of a spark, as between exposed broken wires, the flame would be contained by the box.

The snap action of a switch gives it its high speed. In the household switch the toggle you push is forced by a spring to swing fully down or up—no middle position is possible. As the switch toggle is slowly pulled away from one position it approaches the point of no return. Once past the center balance point the spring snaps the toggle over the rest of the way. The contacts are arranged so that one position of the toggle brings them into close contact, the other position separates them.

Another style of switch takes advantage of the buckling characteristics of a saucer-shaped disk of spring metal. When you push down on the convex side of the disk it resists until you raise the pressure beyond its buckling point. At that point the dish inverts so that the convex side becomes concave, and vice versa. When inverted, the contacts are brought together; when in normal unstressed condition, the contacts are held apart by the curved shape of the disk. There are dozens of variations of this design.

One last kind of switch should be mentioned here. The *mercury switch* is called a silent switch because it doesn't operate on the snap action of a spring and so it is much quieter. Mercury is a metal that stays liquid (molten) even at the room temperatures that are comfortable for people. Actually it "freezes" at $-38°$ F. Since it is a metal, it is a good conductor, and two wires dipped into a jar of mercury will act just the same (electrically) as if a solid bar of copper had been welded between them. Of course when the conductors have been lifted out of the jar of mercury the current will cease to flow.

This makes it possible to design a switch using mercury as the contactor. A little capsule of glass contains a good-sized droplet of mercury. The glass capsule is pierced at both ends by wire conductors that end in flattened contacts just inside the capsule.

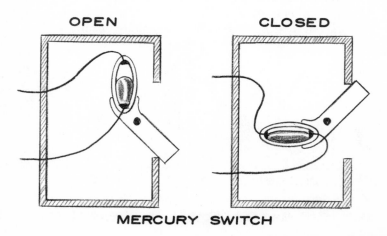

OPEN CLOSED

**MERCURY SWITCH**

When the capsule is placed in a horizontal position the mercury flows down and simultaneously contacts both conductors, completing the circuit. When the capsule is tilted up the mercury collects at one end and the circuit is opened.

Your mercury house switch is mounted in a position such that when the toggle is pulled down the capsule stands upright breaking the circuit, and the lights go out. When the toggle is pushed up the capsule is held horizontally in the switch and the lights go on.

Note that if the switch is mounted upside down (turn this book upside down) the switch still operates just as it did before though the mercury collects at the opposite side of the capsule.

What we have been describing here so far is the two-pole switch—that is, the switch has two contacts that are either connected or disconnected when a toggle is thrown. Note that several switches can be ganged together so that when you flip the toggle many different pairs of contacts are opened or closed at the same time, or even so that some are opened when others are closed. These are multipole switches: two-pole, three-pole, four-pole, and so on are very common in electrical work. Terminal connections can also be added to the center (moving) pole to give another degree of switching control.

For example, have you ever thought how the pair of switches at the head and foot of a flight of stairs are wired? Remember how they work. You can control the stair light from either of these switches. The wiring diagram is shown in the sketches, with arrows showing the flow of current. With the bottom switch in either position the top switch will turn the light on or off.

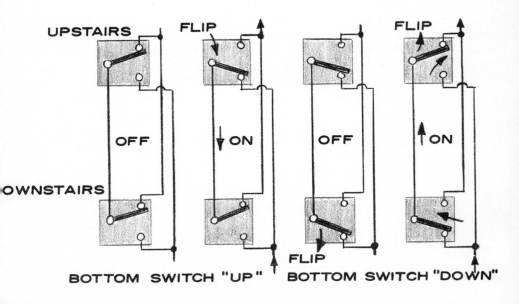

UPSTAIRS    FLIP                    FLIP

OFF        ON          OFF        ON

DOWNSTAIRS

BOTTOM SWITCH "UP"    BOTTOM SWITCH "DOWN"

FLIP

This gives you a hint of the complexity that is possible in switching circuits. Actually a whole new mathematics had to be devised, based on theories of logic that began with the Greeks, in order to permit engineers to design and check the complex switching systems in telephones, radios, automatic manufacturing machines, and missile controls.

# T

## TAPE RECORDERS

The tape recorder is an example of a development that jumped from a hazy idea to a full-fledged industry in less than five years. The principle of recording with magnetism first achieved commercial feasibility shortly after World War II. Like the early disk recordings, the results were disappointing at first, not to say inadequate, for anything other than a dictating machine. The "fidelity" was atrocious.

But the fact that magnetic recording was possible at all led to improvements and soon magnetic tape came spewing from process plants in unending ribbons.

Today you can buy a tape recorder for less than $100—the surest test of commercial success. You can also spend something like $30,000 for one (to record TV programs for rebroadcast). Computer manufacturers record numbers, names, and addresses on tape. Executives record letters. Students practice languages. "Pen pals" exchange recorded messages. Music lovers play back their favorite concert performances. Mothers listen to Junior's first gurgles. The combination of film and magnetic tape entertains the world's moviegoers with four-channel stereophonic sound.

These are just a few of the applications already in widespread use. Charge-account cards for stores, gas stations, round-the-world air travel could have magnetic codes rather than raised or printed names and addresses so that the card could be "read" by a computer and the entire transaction handled automatically. Banks have installed magnetic check readers (to read checks printed with magnetic ink); the U.S. Post Office is thinking about magnetic letter sorting and routing. You'll probably be able to buy a TV set with a magnetic recorder built in to record the programs you want to see

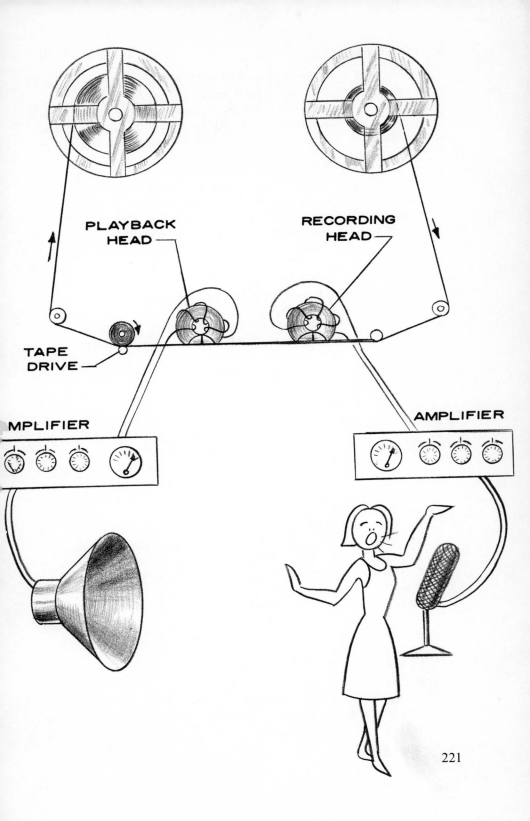

PLAYBACK
HEAD

RECORDING
HEAD

TAPE
DRIVE

MPLIFIER

AMPLIFIER

221

when you want to see them, and you'll be able to save the records for reviewing at a later time if you like.

Today's tape recorder is based on two components: a strip of plastic tape coated with a smooth even layer of iron oxide, and a tape *head*—a small C-shaped electromagnet about the size of a 25¢ piece.

Take your electric signal, representing sound (as it comes from the microphone) or picture (as it comes from the TV transmitter) or any arbitrary electric code at all (representing letters or numbers), and use it to power the electromagnet. The magnet's pole ends are very close together, but not touching; the gap is approximately one ten-thousandth of an inch in present equipment. As the electric current pulses through the coil of the electromagnet it produces a magnetic field between the pole ends (see ELECTRICITY). The field spans the tiny gap between the poles, spreading slightly into the air near the gap.

Picture the magnetic field pulsing in space just in front of the gap. The strip of tape moves through the pulsing magnetic field at a fast, even rate of speed. The pulsing field magnetizes the iron oxide particles in the tape in pulses of magnetism and this constitutes the recorded signal.

This tape carries a magnetic record of the original electric signal and by passing the tape in front of another tape head you can generate a weak electric signal closely duplicating the signal originally used to make the recording.

That is all there is to it. Of course this beautiful simplicity is complicated in practice by the need for a very even tape drive. Moving the tape across the head at constant speed is a lot more difficult than it may seem at first. And, of course, there are electronic amplification and reproduction problems that seem easy to solve now but were formidable challenges in the beginning. For example, you must be able to *erase* a signal from a previously recorded tape so that the tape can be reused. An equalization curve is necessary for tape as well as for records (see HIGH FIDELITY) to solve certain recording problems. Good fidelity at low tape speeds is a challenge since a full cycle of a very high frequency (say 15,000 cycles per second) would be only half of a thousandth of an inch long on tape traveling at 7½ inches per second. It would be desirable if the tape speed could be cut in half to 3¾ inches per second or even slower without compromising reproduction quality.

Fantastic as these difficulties may seem, they have been solved with ingenious electronics, reliable tape transports, and tape heads with impossibly narrow gaps—and all at reasonable price. So this explains the runaway success of tape recorders and their application to every entertainment and most business media.

Just review the advantages of magnetic tape as a recording medium for a moment. You can edit by cutting the tape with a pair of scissors and splicing the sections as you please. Tape is reusable. Once a particular recording has lost its value it can be erased automatically before re-recording the next message. The tape never wears out. Practically unlimited playbacks can be had from a particular tape and the tape itself, if kept cool and away from stray magnetic fields, will faithfully retain and reproduce its message after years of storage. Tape costs are dropping—they approach those of recorded disks on a dollars-per-minute-playing-time basis and now that four-tracks on ¼-inch tape widths and 3¾ inches-per-second tape speeds are becoming practical, recorded tapes may begin to compete directly with recorded disks.

Until stereo disks became a reality, tape was the only practical means of achieving stereophonic sound in the home. Today, recording engineers still use tape as their original recording medium and the purist sound enthusiasts still cling to tape as the best playback method.

# TEACHING MACHINES

We're running out of teachers, and with an ever-increasing school-age population it looks as if we'll never have enough. The only hope seems to be in teaching machines. A lot more progress has been made in this area than most people realize. The machines may be as complicated as a large-scale electronic computer or as simple as a soft-cover pocket book, but all have one set of principles in common. It is these principles which will concern us here.

Learning is a step-by-step process. At each step you are given a bit of information to absorb, then the teacher determines by question or test whether you have understood the new information. If you have, you go on to the next step. If you haven't, the teacher presents the information again in a new way.

In large classes and lectures the teacher must aim at the average or slightly below-average student. This means that no student progresses at his natural speed. Half the class finds the pace too slow; the other half finds it too fast. Solution? The teaching machine.

The machine works in this way: A small bit of information is

presented to you. Generally this is a paragraph or two plus, perhaps, a sketch or small photograph. You read the printed information and study the sketch for as long as you like. An hour is
not too much, a minute is not too little. Once satisfied that you
have grasped the facts or ideas, you read a question and choose
what you think is the correct answer.

The machine tells you immediately if the answer is right or
wrong. This is considered very important and one of the serious
lacks in normal classroom teaching. Psychologists feel that the
longer the delay between the test and the report of test results, the
more likely you are to remember the wrong answer than the right
one.

If your answer is correct, you are given the next bit of information. If the answer is incorrect, you are told it is wrong and why.
The machine repeats the information in a new way and a new
question is presented. This systematic repetition eventually gets
the idea across and the student is sent on to the next piece
of information.

Note the ingenuity of the system. As a student, you establish
your own speed. You can take as much time on each step as you
like and move on to the next step whenever you are ready. The
slower student has several chances at the ideas without forcing the
quick student to wait for him.

Let's see what the machines are actually like. The most complicated one is a good-sized combined projector and computer. It
contains bite-sized chunks of information on microfilm. Each
frame, when projected, displays one step followed by a question
or problem. At the end there are four or five answers. Each answer
has a code number. You choose an answer by pushing the coded
number on a push-button panel in front of the machine. The computer automatically selects a new microfilm frame to project on
the screen. If the answer was correct the next frame reads, "You
are correct. The next thing you need to know is . . ." If the answer
was incorrect the called-for frame reads, "You didn't take into account the fact that . . ." and then presents another question.

*Scrambled books* are written in a similar way. You start out on
page one. There the first ideas of a subject are presented and the
test calls for, say, one of four answers. Each answer is followed by
"see page so-and-so." The first page reference might be for the correct answer. You turn to this page and it says at the top, "You are
correct . . ." The other three page references start out, "No, you
misinterpreted . . ." and go on to present the information in a new
way.

You progress through the book in this way until all the information is absorbed. Of course, this method wastes space and paper, but it doesn't waste a student's time, and which is more important?

Many modifications of this same principle are possible, and you can see that it takes a really good teacher to write one of these books (or *programs,* as they are called). But no subject seems to be too complex for the system. It's a natural for mathematics, physics, and chemistry, but you might not realize that history, language, and even philosophy can be taught with machines. Invariably the students learn faster and more thoroughly than they could in large classrooms.

## TELEPHONES

What an amazing thing the telephone is! Think, for a moment, of what it must do:

(1) Note that you want to make a call;
(2) Connect the operator or central switching system to your line;
(3) Find out what phone you want to be connected to;
(4) Select a wire path to that phone;
(5) Determine whether the target phone is busy;
(6) If busy, signal you; if not busy, ring the target phone;
(7) Note when call is ended; and
(8) Turn off all equipment.

All these are really additions to the original invention by Alexander Graham Bell. His contribution was to convert sound into electricity and send the electricity down a wire to a receiver where it was turned into sound again. Let's see how this transformation takes place.

Sound, you'll remember, is a series of compression waves moving through the air (see SOUND). It is like a ripple disturbing the surface of a pond. When the succession of compression waves strikes a flexible diaphragm the diaphragm moves in and out. Bell realized that this motion could be used to vary an electric voltage in several ways. The one he finally settled on (and the basic system is the same one in your phone today) uses a small round box filled with powdered carbon. One face of the box acts as a flexible diaphragm. The powdered carbon is packed more tightly when the diaphragm moves in; it is loosened when the diaphragm moves

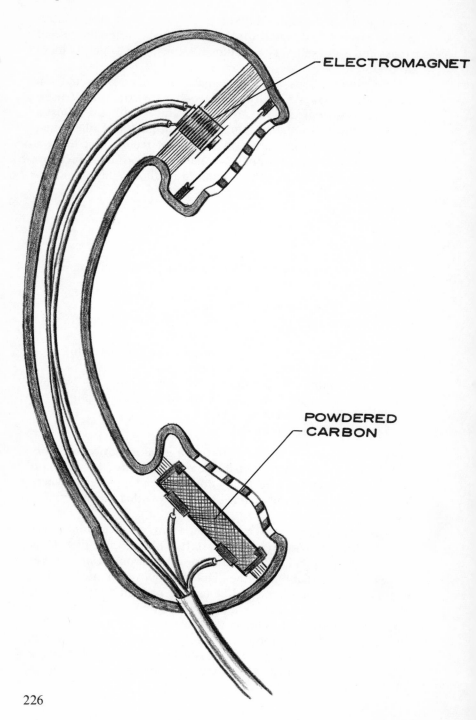

ELECTROMAGNET

POWDERED
CARBON

out. This varying density changes the electrical resistance of the carbon.

If an electric circuit is connected through the carbon, the current will vary just as the air pressure striking the diaphragm varies.

In this same circuit Bell put an electromagnet—a coil of wire wound around an iron core (see ELECTRICITY). As the current increases, the magnetic field in the core gets stronger; as it decreases, the field gets weaker. The receiver has this electromagnet with a magnetic metal diaphragm spaced a short distance from the iron core. The metal diaphragm moves back and forth toward and away from the electromagnet as the field strength increases and decreases.

The motion of the metal diaphragm duplicates closely the motion of the diaphragm on the box with carbon powder picking up the sounds. The metal diaphragm sets the surrounding air into a series of pressure waves like the ones originally picked up.

In this way the sound of your voice is transmitted through wires to any other telephone in the world. Of course, the transformation from air pressure waves to electricity and back to pressure waves is not perfect. The degree of imperfection (called *distortion*) determines how much change there is in the sound of your voice. Still the distortion is kept low enough so that a voice is easily recognizable.

The wonder of the telephone extends far beyond the simple reproduction of sound. The sequence of steps connecting you to another telephone is now handled automatically in most cities and even long-distance calls can now be dialed in much of the United States.

Picture a vast network of wires—the one from your phone joining those of your neighbors and converging on a local office. Trunk lines interconnect all the local offices and special long-distance lines interconnect the major cities.

There are several accessories to the basic phone circuit that might be mentioned here:

Microphones and speakers can be attached to your phone so that you don't have to lift the receiver when a call comes in. You throw a switch and talk as if the other party were sitting at the other side of the desk.

Amplifiers may be built into a receiver so that the volume can be increased for the hard of hearing.

Recording and automatic answering services are available. In one the recorder plays a message to the caller and then gives him a minute or so to record his message to you.

Coin-operated phones are familiar, but don't let the familiarity fool you into thinking they're simple. They have to be able to reject counterfeits. They have to add up what you put into those slots and return your dime when the line is busy or there is no answer.

Eventually telephones will transmit pictures as well as sound and you'll be able to see as well as hear the caller. Transistors will make this possible at reasonable cost and size. They'll make the telephone smaller as well, and even the wrist telephone, no bigger than a watch, is on the drawing boards.

## TELESCOPES AND BINOCULARS

The telescope has two optical parts or *lenses.* The *objective* is the lens at the large end of the telescope, the *eyepiece* is at the end you look through. The two elements are separated by a relatively long tube of blackened metal made in two sections so that one section nests inside the other. This permits the telescope to be *focused.* You slide one section in or out of the other to change the distance between objective and eyepiece, until a distant object is made to apear clear and sharp.

The astronomical telescope used for photographing stars is slightly different. It usually has a mirror instead of a lens as its objective. The shaped mirror serves exactly the same function as the lens—it creates an image just in front of the eyepiece. The eyepiece is a magnifying glass used to enlarge the image. Simple eyepieces are made in the form of a single convex (bellied on both sides) lens. More expensive and sophisticated eyepieces, used in most telescopes and binoculars made today, have two to four glass elements making up their eyepieces.

We should examine briefly the various characteristics that make for a good telescope or binocular (which is just a two-eyed telescope). First, image brightness is controlled by the diameter of the objective lens or mirror. This is usually expressed in millimeters (it takes about 25 millimeters to make one inch), and it is the second figure in the pair of numbers usually used to describe a particular instrument. For example, an 8 x 20 telescope has a 20 millimeter objective lens (0.8 inch in diameter); a 6 x 35 binocular has two 35 millimeter objective lenses (1.4 inches in diameter). Obviously the larger the objective the brighter the image because it gathers more of the light rays coming at the instrument. However, a large objective weighs a lot more than a small one and so a compromise is reached which balances weight against image brightness. In astronomical telescopes where light-gathering power

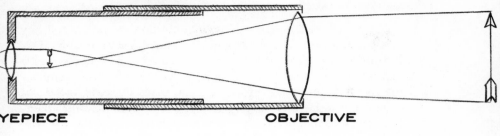

**"TELESCOPING" TUBES**

**EYEPIECE**          **OBJECTIVE**

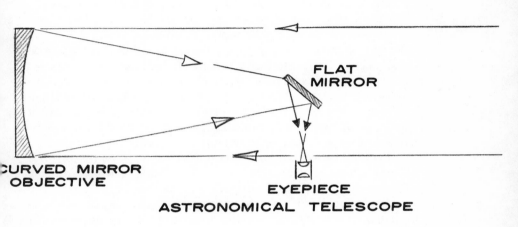

**FLAT MIRROR**

**CURVED MIRROR OBJECTIVE**          **EYEPIECE**

**ASTRONOMICAL TELESCOPE**

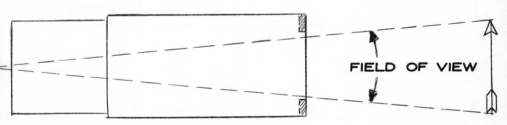

**FIELD OF VIEW**

is a direct measure of how far the telescope "sees," cost is the limiting factor rather than weight. At Mount Palomar they have a telescope with a 200-inch mirror objective—that's almost 17 feet in diameter.

The first number in the description of the lens system refers to the magnifying power. The image will be eight times the size of the object (to your eye) in the 8 x 20 telescope and six times the size of the object in the 6 x 35 binocular. You might think that the larger the magnification the better the instrument, but this is not true. The larger the magnification the harder it is to hold the image steady when looking through the lenses. In very strong magnifiers the image hops around at the slightest movement. This can make you dizzy and tire your eyes. Further, the larger the magnification the smaller the field of view—that is, the smaller the area seen through the glass. So, you generally settle for a compromise of a six- or seven-power glass—strong enough to enlarge the object appreciably, weak enough to be held comfortably and to give a reasonably wide field of view.

One important problem we haven't discussed so far is the erectness of the image. Does the lens system turn the image upside down or does it leave it right side up? The systems described so far turn the image upside down. This makes little difference in the astronomical telescope since the stars will be photographed and it is no problem to turn a picture around. But for normal use, the upside-down image would be very annoying. There are two ways to correct this. Most telescopes use a third lens system about halfway down the tube. It decreases the brightness and clarity of the original lens system, but it is generally worth the small sacrifice to have the image right-side-up.

Binoculars use a different method based on *prisms*. A prism is a solid chunk of crystal-clear glass. The shape is important, particularly the outer surface, so let's see how it is cut.

Imagine a cube of glass that has been cut along a diagonal. The top and bottom surfaces are in the shape of right triangles. This is a standard 90° prism. A ray of light that enters through the diagonal face is bounced between the slanting surfaces and back out the bottom face (see sketch).

Each side of a binocular has two such prisms which take the image made by the objective and turn it upside down for viewing through the eyepiece. The prisms have the additional advantage of permitting the two objective lenses to be separated by a distance greater than the distance between eyepieces, which is determined by the distance between your eyes. The reason this is an advantage is that it increases the stereoscopic effect (see STEREO) and permits the viewer to estimate depth much more accurately than he could otherwise.

In other respects the binocular is just two telescopes mounted together side by side, often with a single focusing control that "telescopes" both tubes simultaneously. Ordinarily there is a pivot at the center between the tubes, permitting them to be swung toward or away from each other to accommodate the different distances between people's eyes. You should adjust this distance so that you see only one circle through the binocular—not the hourglass shape shown in the movies. There is no advantage to the binocular if the images don't overlap completely just as the images from your eyes do.

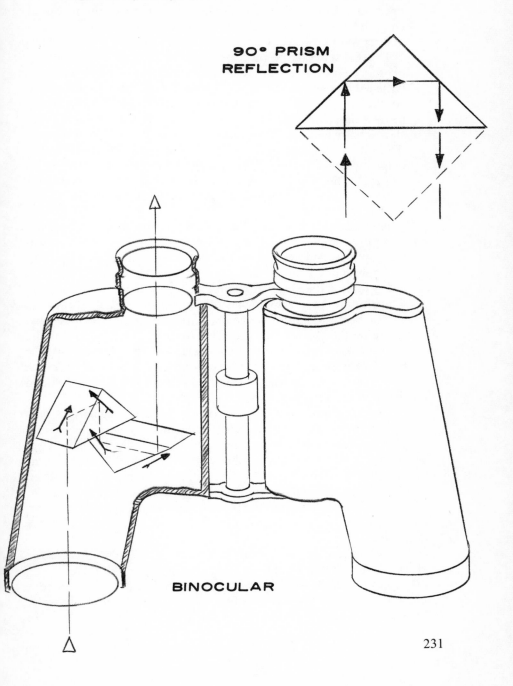

**90° PRISM REFLECTION**

**BINOCULAR**

# TELEVISION

There are people who wonder if the perfection of television was such a good idea. We won't argue the virtues of the newest member of the communications medium, but simply examine the fascinating and ingenious way that an image is sent through the air and reproduced in your home.

The TV set is based on the picture tube, or more technically, on the *cathode-ray tube*. This is an evacuated glass container flattened on one end and tapering to an elongated pipe at the back. At the end of the pipe an electron gun is placed which spews forth a cloud of electrons (see VACUUM TUBES). Since moving electrons—whether in a vacuum or in a wire—constitute electricity, the moving cloud of electrons can be focussed and controlled by magnetic fields because of electromagnetic interaction (see ELECTRICITY). The cloud of electrons is shaped into a very thin beam arrowing down the length of the pipe and striking at the center of the flat face of the tube.

This tube face has been prepared by coating it with a chemical that glows brightly when hit by electrons, and the glow persists for a split second even when the electron beam has moved along to a new spot on the tube.

Up to now the electron beam has been aimed at the center of the picture tube but, by means of a magnetic field, the beam can also be bent away from the center to put a spot of brightness anywhere on the face of the tube. This magnetic field is created and controlled by coils of wire which surround the glass pipe at the back of the tube. They are called *horizontal* or *vertical deflection coils*—depending on whether they bend the electron beam left and right, or up and down, over the face of the tube.

The horizontal and vertical deflection coils regularly sweep the electron beam across the entire tube face in a very special way. They operate rather like a typewriter—that is, the beam is swept across the top edge of the tube from left to right; it then returns rapidly to the left edge of the tube and moves down one row. Then it sweeps across again, then back and down one more row, and so on, until the spot reaches the bottom right-hand corner of the tube. Finally, the beam returns to the upper left corner and starts over again.

The entire scan takes about ⅓₀ of a second. Too quickly for the eye to realize that a single moving spot of light is all there is.

As described so far, however, all you would see would be a brightly lighted TV screen, white from corner to corner. In order to create a picture there must be dark areas as well, and these are made by turning off the electron gun when the beam comes to a place in the picture that is to be dark. Similarly, grays and medium bright whites can be created in certain areas by reducing the number of electrons coming from the gun instead of shutting it off completely.

So we have a means of creating a series of "stills" exactly as a movie does. The signals are a continuing stream of electric signals to the deflection coils and to the electron gun.

The television camera scans the scene to be televised and transforms the image into the series of signals. The signals describe the degree of brightness at each point of each horizontal slice of picture. They also indicate when the upper left-hand corner has been reached so that your TV set knows when the picture is about to start over again. This last is called a synchronizing signal because it "locks" the sweeping electron beam in your TV set to the same position as the scanner in the TV camera.

Vastly exaggerated, the transmitted signal might look as shown (see sketch). When changed into brightness and darkness areas and assembled in correct position, a very realistic scene is produced on the screen.

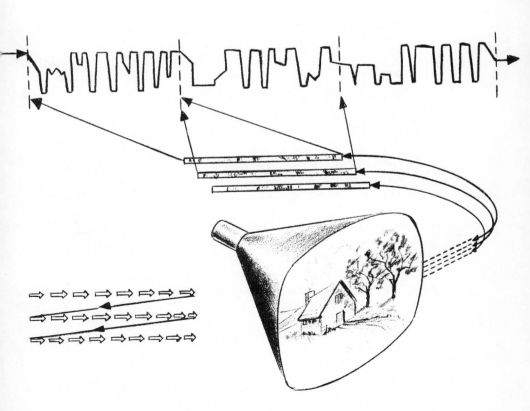

Note that the persistence of the image on the screen fools the eye into thinking it sees a whole picture when in reality the picture is "drawn" by a flying spot of light-producing electrons. Further, each scene is replaced about 30 times a second—the fewest number of stills that look to the eye as a moving image rather than a series of separate pictures.

With this much of the theory understood, it is easy to interpret what the usual television controls actually do. The tuning knob acts exactly as the radio tuning knob does—it centers reception on the station transmitting the chosen frequencies (see RADIO). The horizontal and vertical controls determine the timing of the start of each horizontal or vertical sweep as well as the amount of deflection as the beam progresses from row to row. When the beam moves down too little for each row the image will appear to climb up the screen. When it is too much, the image moves downward. Note that when this happens the bottom of the image is repeated just above the top edge. Thus each complete scan of the scene follows the previous one just like the pictures on a strip of movie film.

The brightness control determines the average level of electron gun activity. Higher level means more electrons, on average, hitting the screen. The contrast control determines how much change in electron gun activity for a given change in signal. The greater the change in electron gun activity, the greater the variation between brightness and darkness on the screen.

# THERMOELECTRICITY

This is a combination word meaning heat (thermo) and electricity. It refers to the direct conversion of heat energy to electrical energy. Heat is normally transformed into electricity by an old but roundabout route. Your power station is a perfect example. Here coal or oil is burned to heat water and make steam—the heat energy is now stored in the hot steam. The hot steam expands in a steam engine or turbine which, in turn, drives electric generators (see ELECTRICITY). The generators make the electricity used in your home to power light bulbs, refrigerator, and sewing machine.

The trouble with this system is that it is such a long way around. All the inefficiencies add up until only about 10 per cent of the heat energy of the coal is actually transformed into usable electricity.

Engineers have been searching for some more direct conversion

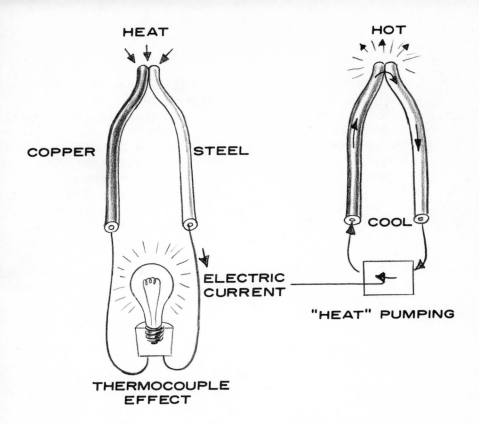

**HEAT**

**COPPER**    **STEEL**

**ELECTRIC CURRENT**

**THERMOCOUPLE EFFECT**

**HOT**

**COOL**

**"HEAT" PUMPING**

of heat to electricity for years—and now they are beginning to see possibilities. The original thermoelectric effect was noticed in the *thermocouple*. A thermocouple is made of two wires of different metals (one copper the other steel, for example) joined in a deep V. If the joined ends are heated and the unjoined ends left cool an electric voltage appears between the unjoined ends.

The system works—has been known to work for over a hundred years—but as originally designed it is even less efficient than the fire-to-steam-to-turbine-to-generator-to-electricity route described above. It is so much less efficient that until recently thermocouples have only been used as temperature-sensing elements (thermometers).

Countries without the network of electric power distribution that we have are content with much lower efficiencies so long as they can get electric power. We have heard reports of Russian thermoelectric generators that hug the glass chimney of an oil lamp and generate enough electricity from the heat of the lamp to power a small radio. It works, too.

In the United States these generators can't compete with the electricity that pours out of every plug. But some of the newer semiconductor materials promise higher efficiencies. Motorless "electronic" refrigerators are being perfected (you squirt the electricity into the gadget and heat is moved from inside the refrigerator to outside). The *solar battery* (see BATTERIES) that powers our pocket-sized radios and some of our satellite equipment is essentially a thermoelectric semiconductor development. There is a thermoelectric power generator in the laboratories that uses burning bottled gas as the heat source and you get portable power for radio, light, or whatever, in the arctic cold or the tropic heat just by turning the gas on and lighting it—there are no moving parts to wear, no friction, and very little chance of freezing or corrosion to interfere with reliable operation.

The heat of the sun can be focussed on these devices to provide a reasonably reliable, and certainly generous, source of energy. This, combined with nuclear energy sources are the two main hopes of mankind as we deplete our oil, coal, and natural gas reserves.

The important problem still to be solved is that of electric energy storage. You can store electrical energy in a rechargeable electric battery, but too small a percentage of what goes in ever comes out. Too much is lost in the charging and discharging process and too much just leaks away on the shelf during the storage life.

Better batteries are sure to come, however. Hundreds of top brains in the commercial and government laboratories are working overtime to give us a home that would be completely self-powered. With a roof of solar cells and an efficient battery storage system, the entire home power needs—electric range, lights, refrigerator, air conditioner—could be satisfied by sun energy.

# THERMOMETERS AND THERMOSTATS

Heat is a form of energy. Picture it as a kind of fluid that flows into and out of spongelike objects. If the amount of heat-fluid in an object is low, the object is cold; if the level is high, the object is hot. Just as fluid can't flow uphill, neither can heat flow from a lower to a higher temperature—and so temperature is the measure of heat level.

It is well established now that heat makes molecules more active. They bounce around in a more or less random way at lower temperatures and move around frantically at high temperatures. If you're asked "How cold is cold?" you can reply, "460 Fahrenheit degrees below zero." That is as cold as anything can become because then molecular activity stops completely and the molecules just sit quietly. Some very peculiar things happen at these ultralow temperatures and a whole science of *cryogenics* has grown around such studies.

But back to warmer climates. The temperature scale was devised in 1714 by a German physicist, named Gabriel Daniel Fahrenheit, who thought the temperature of the human body was a convenient reference point so he called that 100. He also thought that the temperature range between ice and boiling water should be divided in some useful way so he chose 180 degrees (180 being divisible by 2, 3, 4, 5, 6, 9, 10, 12, for a start). This put the freezing point of water at 32° and the boiling point at 212° on Herr Fahrenheit's scale. It wasn't until later that they realized that the human body is about 1½ degrees cooler than originally thought, but by that time it was too late to be troubled by the error.

The centigrade or Celsius scale was invented in 1742 by a much neater mind—Anders Celsius, a Swedish astronomer. Celsius set the freezing point of water at 0 and the boiling point at 100 for a difference of 100° C. Thus 100° C is equivalent to 180° F or 1° C equals 1.8° F. To transform degrees centigrade to degrees Fahrenheit simply multiply by 1.8 (which is ⅘) and add 32.

The reason the boiling and freezing points of water were chosen is that these were the most constant and repeatable temperatures known to man at the time. Once an open pot of water reaches a temperature of 212° F it can't be made any hotter. Every additional bit of heat justs turns some more water into steam. The only way to get it hotter is to raise the air pressure acting on the surface of the water (for example, by closing the top with an airtight cover and letting the steam pressure build up, as in PRESSURE COOKERS). Otherwise the molecules of a water are so active that they can't be held close together any more (as in a liquid). They are forced to separate and turn to steam.

Every material known vaporizes in this way at some temperature. Metals and glass melt and eventually boil (at 5430° F for iron). That is part of the problem in producing thermonuclear energy. Nuclear reactions requiring fusion take such high temperatures (in the millions of degrees) that no material will hold them.

But let's get back to thermometers. Most thermometers are based on the principle that liquids expand when heated. A glass rod with a tiny hole down its length is attached to a small pocket (*bulb*) of mercury or colored alcohol. As its temperature rises the mercury expands and runs up the tube where it can be read against an engraved scale. By changing the markings you can make the same thermometer read in centigrade or Fahrenheit degrees—after all, the mercury doesn't care what you call the marking so long as it is allowed to expand.

*Thermostats* are a form of thermometer too. Most thermostats are based on the bimetallic strip, which is a strip of metal with copper on one side bonded to steel on the other. Since the two metals expand at different rates as the temperature rises, the strip curls over in one direction with rising temperature and straightens out as the temperature falls.

This curling bit of metal can be used to throw a switch, to control an air conditioner, a refrigerator, a house heating unit, or, with modifications, a toaster. For example, suppose your furnace control has been set to 70° F. The furnace warms the house until the desired temperature has been reached. At that point the bimetallic strip has curled away from a contact and opens the cir-

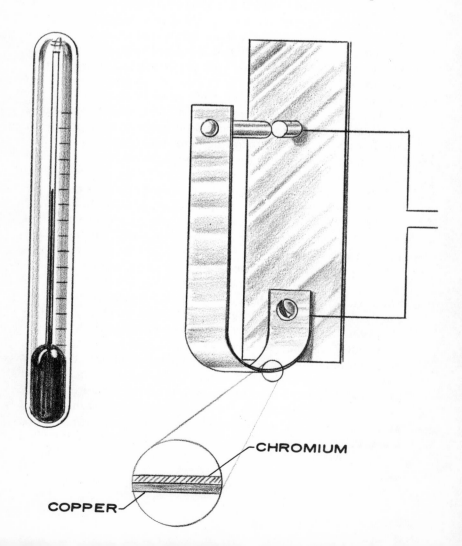

**CHROMIUM**

**COPPER**

cuit to your furnace blower and oil feed pump. No more heat comes up and so the house slowly cools, and slowly the bimetallic strip straightens out until it touches the contact again. It then re-establishes the power to the furnace which starts up again.

A hundred home and industrial controllers use thermostats in one form or another to sense temperature and switch things on and off as a result. They were among the first to take over the nuisance tasks and really automatize the home.

## "THERMOS" VACUUM BOTTLES

Heat has an irresistible tendency to flow from high to low temperature areas (see THERMOMETERS AND THERMOSTATS, and HEATERS), and this makes it very difficult to keep coffee hot or iced lemonade cold for very long. All that lovely heat so carefully stored in the coffee or sucked out of the lemonade will dribble back just as fast as it can by three paths: *convection, conduction,* and *radiation*. With convection the heat flows from the coffee container to the air nearest the container. The warmed air rises and is replaced by cooler air which also receives some heat from the container, and so on, until the coffee is the same temperature as the surrounding air. Conduction is more direct. Contact between hot container and table is bound to make the table warm. Some of the heat flows out of the container and to the table. In radiation, the infrared rays emitted by all warm bodies (even you and me) carry some heat to the surroundings.

The only solution is *insulation*. Insulation stops convection currents by breaking up the air near the container into many small compartments. Or it may take the form of a layer of vacuum surrounding the container (as in the space between two containers, one inside the other) so as to make convection impossible. The walls between the small compartments of air should be as thin as possible and made of a poor heat conductor—wood, rubber, or felt, for instance—to reduce conduction losses. Also it is best if the surfaces surrounding the air or vacuum compartments are silvered so that they act like mirrors to reduce radiation by reflecting the infrared rays.

If you could do all of this to the walls of your house, the heating bill in winter and the air-conditioning bill in summer would probably be reduced by 75 per cent, maybe more. Once warmed to the desired temperature the normal cooking and body heat would probably be enough to keep the house comfortable for hours, or even days, in the coldest weather.

The reason homes aren't insulated in this way is the cost—the cost of the materials and of the labor needed to make and install such walls. But bottles of coffee or lemonade are a different thing entirely which is why "Thermos" insulated jugs, vacuum bottles, and ice buckets have become so popular.

The "Thermos" vacuum bottle is actually two bottles, one inside the other. The bottles are joined at their necks, silvered on the facing surfaces and the space between them is evacuated of air. Thus there is no convection, little conduction, and little radiation between the two glass bottles. Since heat has to flow from one bottle to the other to reach or leave the contained fluid, you have an extremely effective insulator for your drink.

The surrounding metal container, the supports for the two bottles, the cork, and the drinking cup cap are accessories to protect the fragile bottles and to make the container as useful as possible.

Refrigerator insulation could be made in this way but the cost, again, would be too high for what it would save in electricity. Manufacturers used to put insulating wools and packings in refrigerator walls but this meant that the walls had to be pretty thick if

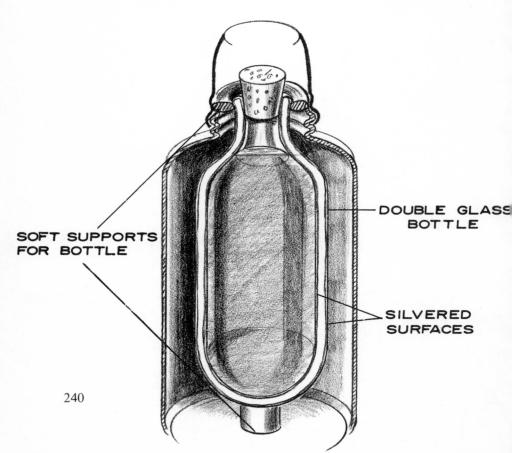

SOFT SUPPORTS
FOR BOTTLE

DOUBLE GLASS
BOTTLE

SILVERED
SURFACES

240

the refrigerator was to retain its cold for long. Today foamed rubbers and plastics are used as insulators in the walls of refrigerators and even in ice buckets and beverage flasks. The foamed plastic creates millions of tiny pockets of air between the outer and inner walls. It is a very efficient heat insulator; note how much thinner the door and walls of the new refrigerators are as a result of this foam insulation.

## TOASTERS

Probably toasters were the first electric kitchen appliances following electric lights. Perhaps you remember the old flap-sided affairs; you browned one side, then flipped the bread over and browned the other side. It took awhile, but the electricity seemed to add something to the toast the old gas stove never could. Today pop-up toasters are the rule. You dial for desired brownness and every slice comes out just like its brother. Science has taken the challenge out of toasting.

Toasters have flat ribbonlike heating wires wound around thin sheets of heat resistant mica or strung like cobwebs on either side

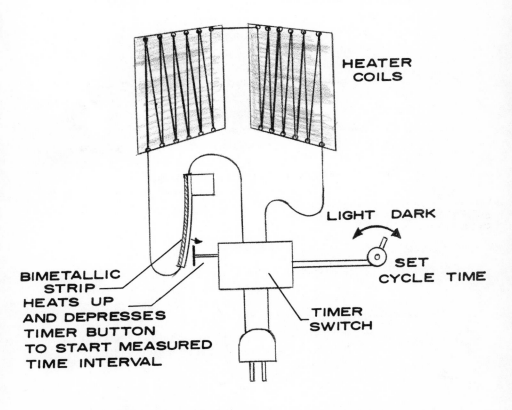

HEATER
COILS

LIGHT  DARK

SET
CYCLE TIME

BIMETALLIC
STRIP
HEATS UP
AND DEPRESSES
TIMER BUTTON
TO START MEASURED
TIME INTERVAL

TIMER
SWITCH

AUTOMATIC  TOASTER  WITH  PREHEAT

of the toast compartment. When the lever is pressed down it latches on a special switch and connects the house current to the heating wire. This wire is made of an alloy called Nichrome (nickel-chromium) specially designed to withstand the heat generated by the current. As the wire heats up it glows red and toasts the facing side of the slice of bread.

After a measured period of time a switch breaks the circuit and simultaneously unlatches the snap-up spring. The toast pops out brown and hot.

The ingenuity in toaster design lies in the linkage and springing used to make the slices pop up when they're done, and in the circuit control which decides when the toast is ready. Sometimes the control is a clock timer set by the brownness dial to measure off a set time—a minute or two—before popping. The problem here is that the second set of toast will be too brown. It starts with the toaster already well warmed up and the slice of bread actually would need less time to finish browning than its predecessor.

Sometimes a thermostatic switch is used instead of the clock timer. In this case the current to the heating coils goes first through a bimetallic strip (see THERMOMETERS AND THERMOSTATS). When the strip is hot enough it curls away from the contact, opens the electric circuit, and at the same time trips the pop-up mechanism. However, the second set of toast is likely to be too light since the bimetallic element is already warmed up from the first cycle—it will take less time to trip the switch.

A combination of clock timer and bimetallic strip for control solves the problem. In this case the clock timer is not permitted to start its timing cycle until the bimetallic strip (and the toaster heating coils) have reached a preset temperature. This warm-up time might be a minute when the first slices are started in a cold toaster but only a few seconds for the second or third sets.

Once the preset temperature has been reached the clock timer ticks off the toasting time and then switches off heating elements and pops the toast. Thus all the slices come out nearly the same.

# TOOLS

This is a big category which includes everything from screw drivers and hammers to automatic turret lathes and boring mills weighing many tons. We will stick to the basic principles and leave the larger machines to the engineers.

Tools divide themselves into several groups. There are those that cut or remove material (planes, chisels, lathes), those that operate by impact (hammer punch), and those that adjust or assemble (screw driver, wrench). Let's consider them in this order and study the operation of the more familiar tools in each group.

The cutting tools started with the *chisel*. This is a strip of hardened steel, beveled and sharpened at one end and provided with a wooden handle at the other. It can be used by hand alone,

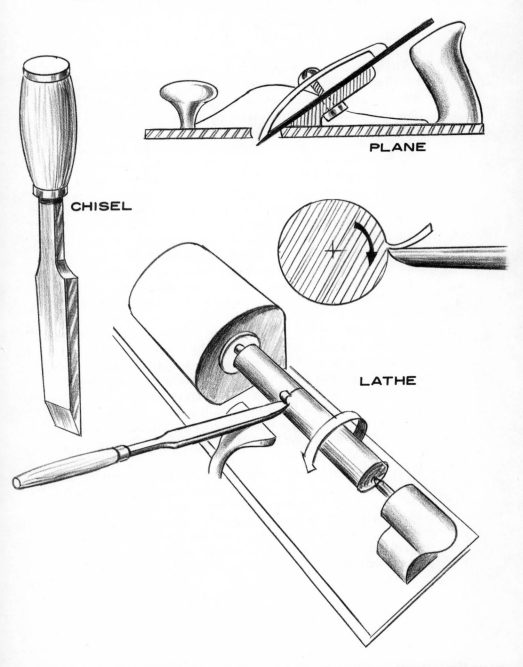

CHISEL

PLANE

LATHE

or sometimes extra cutting force is applied by hammer blows. The chisel cuts right into the material being worked, whether metal or wood. If placed at an angle to the work, it will gouge a chip right out of the surface.

The *plane* is one of the oldest wood smoothing tools. It is really a chisel mounted in a wooden or steel frame so that only a thin sliver of material can be removed at a time. The front and rear flat surfaces help guide the plane into a relatively straight and smooth line of action which, with care, can produce amazingly flat surfaces on large pieces of wood.

The *lathe,* a power tool, turns a rod of wood or steel and forces a cutting tool into close contact with the surface of the rod as it turns. In this way a chiseling or shear action takes place and a thin slice (called a *chip*) of wood or steel is removed. Lathes are still among the most versatile of all power tools. They are used to manufacture just about any round, shaped machine element.

*Drills* for wood or metal differ slightly in shape but their mode of action is almost identical, whether operated by hand or electrically powered. The wood drill (or bit) has a screwlike part at its center which drives into the wood and pulls the cutting edges after it. The cutting section approaches the wood with two sharply pointed knife edges that spear straight down into the wood and cut through the fibers in the cross grains so that they won't splinter. The cutting edges proper, two knives which turn and slant down into the wood, clean out all the wood between the spearing blades and carry it up along the twisted path on the body of the drill.

Metal drills don't need the spearlike parts since metal has no grain and it will be cut smoothly just by the sharpened drill end. Usually the metal drill scrapes away the material at the very center of the hole and cuts it away out toward the periphery. It is driven into the metal by very high pressures and speeds in the drill press or even by hand-held electric drills familiar to do-it-yourselfers. A hole larger than about ¼ inch is usually made by first drilling a smaller hole and then finishing with a drill of the desired hole size.

*Saws* are really a series of chisels placed one after another on a single blade. Normally the saw teeth are cut into the edge of a flat, thin piece of hardenable steel. Hand saws come in various sizes from the keyhole variety through hack-saw blades and carpenter's saws on up to the two-man tree-felling kind. For wood, the teeth may be specially shaped depending on whether the saw is intended for cutting along the grain or across it. When cutting along the grain

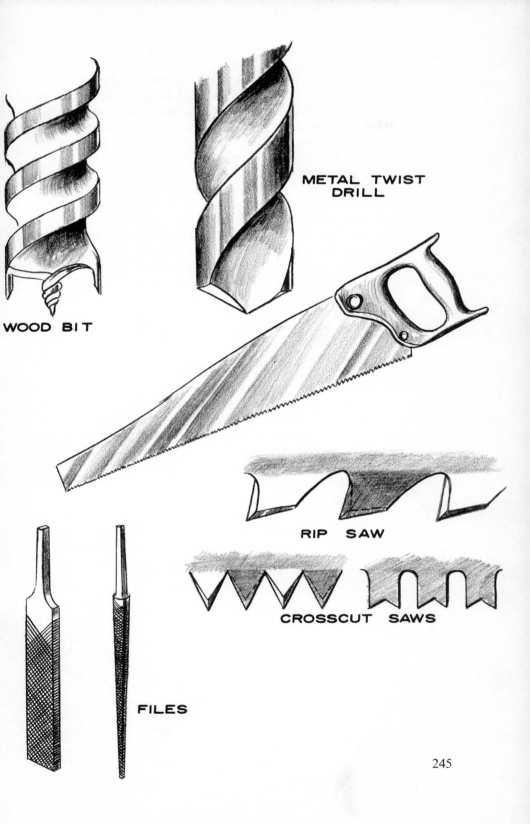

WOOD BIT

METAL TWIST
DRILL

RIP SAW

CROSSCUT SAWS

FILES

245

the teeth are sharply pointed to give good cutting and biting action into the wood. For crosscut the saw scrapes rather than cuts and so the teeth are either M shaped or triangular (see sketches). In either case a certain amount of sideways bend is given to alternate teeth. This sets them out of the plane of the saw blade so that the slot that is cut in the wood is slightly larger than the width of the blade.

*Files* are similar to saws—they are made of a series of cutting edges following one another across the work. But files usually have much smaller teeth, and they are scrapers rather than true cutters of material. Files come in hundreds of sizes from the jeweler's tiny round *rattails* to large wood *rasps.* They come in all shapes too—round, square, triangular, curved on one or more surfaces and even shaped along their lengths.

The most familiar impact tool is the *hammer* and here, too, there are hundreds of shapes depending on the exact purpose. The most familiar, the claw hammer, is intended for general-purpose nailing—the claw at the back removes the errors. The jeweler uses a tiny hammer to strike at the pointed punch that marks a watch as sterling silver, or 14-karat gold. The railroad track layer uses a sledge hammer to drive spikes holding the rails in place.

The important thing to remember when wielding a hammer is that the speed of the hammer head, not your muscle, is what gives maximum impact. It is more important to get a good stroke well placed than it is to get a roundhouse blow. Try to strike the nail with

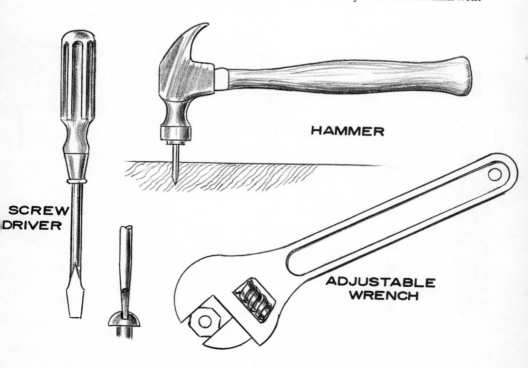

HAMMER

SCREW
DRIVER

ADJUSTABLE
WRENCH

the hammer handle parallel to the work at impact. This means that your hand will be just a little farther away from the surface of the wall or cabinet than you normally think is right. But by keeping the hammer face flat on the nail head on impact, the nail will drive true and straight rather than off to one side—and there's no wasted power. Also try to keep in mind that it is the head of the hammer doing the work, not your arm. Give it a good rotating swing from the elbow, not necessarily from the shoulder.

The assembly tools like *screw driver* and *wrench* are essentials in every home for tightening all the nuts and screws that hold us together nowadays. The *screw driver* is designed to fit the slotted heads of screws (see SCREWS) and to turn them into the walls or threaded parts on appliances. The blade of the screw driver comes in different lengths and widths to suit the various-sized screws. You should not use a thin blade in a wide slot since it will be likely to slip out or shear off the edges of the slot. Note that the larger the diameter of the screw-driver handle the easier it will be to turn.

*Wrenches* are holding or tightening devices for hexagonal or square nuts or for screws with square heads. Some wrenches are adjustable, that is, you can change the distance between faces by tightening a knurled screw. These will work well with nuts of just about any size. Others are designed to operate on only one nut size or shape.

# TRAINS

The distinguishing characteristic of trains—as different from automobiles or other forms of transportation—is the rails. A train must ride on tracks, which means that the engineer doesn't have to steer—he only regulates his speed so as to avoid jumping the track or hitting another train. Obviously, once off the track a train is helpless.

Rails are spaced apart in *gauges.* The standard gauge of 4 ft. 8½ in. between tracks is used throughout the United States and a good part of Europe's main lines. There are other gauges, both wider and narrower, around the world. The model railroader takes his gauge as a fixed fraction of the standard gauge—on HO scale a little over ⅛ inch on the model refers to one foot full scale. This scale is applied on all other dimensions of the railroad—the car sizes, locomotive dimensions, people, houses, roads, etc.

The train of cars is pulled by a locomotive and here's where the engineer talks about *traction, grade, curves, angles,* and such. These are important because the locomotive can't apply any more pull

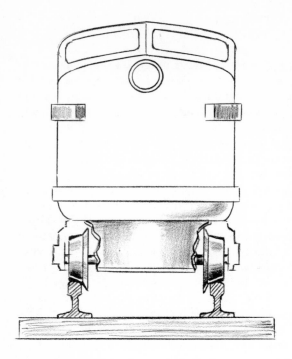

to the rest of the train than the friction there is at its wheels. If the engineer applies more power, the wheels just spin and skid on the tracks. To get as much power as possible the locomotive is made heavy in order to provide the traction necessary to pull trains of 100 cars or more.

Model railroaders have the same problem. They may have plenty of electric power to drive the locomotive, but the engine just isn't heavy enough to give the necessary traction to pull an unusually long train of cars. One of the manufacturers has tried to solve the problem by magnetizing the wheels. Magnetic attraction between wheels and rails increases the traction without increasing the weight of the locomotive.

Most important to the train is the power source. What actually supplies the energy used to power the locomotive? Well, there are many good methods, and most are still in use in one place or another. The oldest source is steam—high-pressure steam created in a boiler burning coal or oil as the fuel. The steam is fed to cylinders (not unlike those in an automotive engine) and the pistons in the cylinders drive the wheels. This creates the familiar puff-puff of steam out of the engine exhaust and the slow powerful driving force.

Steam from burning coal is hardly the cleanest source of power. In cities and crowded suburbs the smoke and noise soon make some other method of powering trains very desirable. Electricity is the answer, though it was some time before a good method of getting the electric power to the locomotive was discovered. Today we automatically think of the "third rail" and perhaps we should examine what that really means.

Electric motors (see ELECTRICITY) can be used to drive the wheels of the locomotive, but you need some means of getting enormous amounts of electricity to the motors. One method would be to pipe the electricity through one of the rails and back through the other. The wheels would have to be insulated from one another, but this isn't a serious problem. The most important drawback is the danger of short circuits across rails open to wind, weather, falling trees, passing cars, and people.

So what they do is supply what amounts to an extra rail, usually higher off the ground and off to one side, which can be protected by a covering of wood or some other insulator, and to which the train reaches with a contacting *shoe*. The current goes out from the generating station over the third rail. It comes back, completing the circuit, through the main wheel rails. There is no danger to people who touch the main rails, because the voltage level is very close to ground level.

Of course there is no rule that says the third rail has to be mounted in this way. Many city trolley tracks have their third rails buried in the ground between the two tracks and reached by an arm that goes down from the undercarriage of the trolley, through a crevice in the city street, and contacts the buried rail safely underground. Overhead wires have also been used, with a springy arm reaching up from the trolley to contact the current-carrying wires.

Model railroads operate at such low voltages that there is no danger in sending current through the two track rails. The serious model railroader uses direct current. He reverses direction by reversing the flow of current to the rails (by switch). The electric train intended as a toy for youngsters is usually powered with alternating current and the reversal of direction is automatic. After each full stop the train starts off in the reverse direction.

Real electric locomotives, to be used on long hauls, can't expect to find third-rail power wherever they go. Instead they make their own electricity. For example, the diesel electric locomotive has a diesel engine which burns low-grade gasoline or kerosene and drives an electric generator which makes the electric power used by the motors to drive the wheels. This probably seems like a roundabout way—why not let the diesel engine drive the wheels directly? The reason is control. The diesel can be driven at its most efficient speed all the time. Station stops and the like don't need slowdowns or stops of the engine. Also the diesel can be run at full speed, making maximum electric power at all times, especially when the train is just starting up and *needs* maximum power. If the diesel engine were connected directly to the wheels it would have to start the train at its lowest power level—when the speed is near zero.

Anyway, it turns out that diesel electric engines are fully competitive with steam engines and they're considerably cleaner running and easier to maintain.

The diesel has its closest competitor in the newer gas turbine locomotives. Here fuel is burned and the hot gases blow against a series of buckets mounted on a turbine wheel (see AUTOMOBILE ENGINES). The turbine drives the electric generator and you have the same electric motors and power control that the diesel electric locomotive has.

No matter what the basic method of power drive, the locomotive is a fearfully complicated machine. Think of the brakes for example—you can't just apply brakes on the wheels of the locomotive because if you did all the rest of the train would plow into the locomotive. So each car in the train has its own brakes and all are controlled from the locomotive. Since all the brakes have to be applied at once, the extra long trains present quite a problem—how do you get the signal to travel back over a mile of train almost instantly? Electricity, and "fail-safe" provisions (when the line snaps the brakes are applied automatically) have helped to solve these problems.

Subway trains are similar. They are powered by individual motors in each car and each takes its own power from the third rail. The cars are hooked together and controlled by the engineer up front so that they all act at once. Again, electric signaling and control apparatus solved the timing problem.

## TRANSMISSION AND REAR END

When we talked about AUTOMOBILE ENGINES, we traced the power to the CLUTCH (just behind the engine) which connects or disconnects the engine shaft power from the transmission. Now let us look into this area immediately after the clutch, the transmission and read-end drive to the wheels.

The whole purpose of the transmission is to vary the gear ratio between the wheel axle and the crank shaft coming out of the engine. This is necessary because the engine has its highest power output at speeds of about 4000 revolutions per minute—these are the speeds at which the advertised horsepower is rated. Thus to get enough power for acceleration when the car is at standstill, you have to run the engine relatively fast while the wheel axle must turn much more slowly. To do this you use a pair, or several pairs, of meshing gears. If the wheels are to turn slowly you put a small gear on the engine drive shaft and a big gear on the wheel drive shaft. The engine shaft then has to make several revolutions for the wheel drive shaft to turn once. This is first gear.

Conversely, at seventy miles per hour, the engine drive shaft should turn over much more quickly relative to the wheel drive shaft. In this case you put a larger gear on the engine shaft and a smaller one on the wheel drive shaft. This makes the third gear on most American automobiles and fourth, fifth, or even sixth on some foreign sports models.

The older style manual gear shift was controlled by a stick that stood up from the floorboard to the right of the driver. Later designs put the shift lever in convenient fingertip position behind and just to the right of the steering wheel. In either case the shift lever actually moves sets of gears into and out of mesh. A much simplified version is shown in the sketch. In this design only two speed ratios are possible. The first is as shown, the second would come about if the lever were moved up, slipping the gears (right-hand pair) down along their shaft. The speed ratio would change from slow speed forward to high speed forward. A somewhat more complicated arrangement is used in the standard manual gear shift arrangement where you have three forward speeds and one reverse speed, but the principles of design are the same.

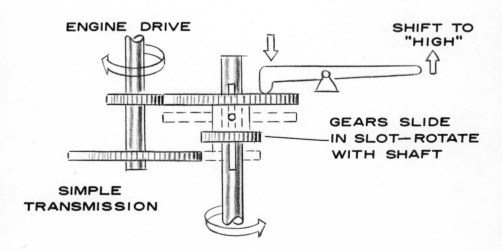

ENGINE DRIVE

SHIFT TO "HIGH"

GEARS SLIDE
IN SLOT—ROTATE
WITH SHAFT

SIMPLE
TRANSMISSION

Now you have a better idea of the purpose of the clutch. We said (see BRAKES AND CLUTCHES) that the disengagement of the clutch was necessary during starting and stopping maneuvers, otherwise the slowing or stopped wheels would stall the engine. The clutch is also necessary during gear shifting. If there were no clutch, every time you wanted to shift from first to second gear you would pull the gears out of mesh (which wouldn't be so troublesome) but then try to remesh them at the next speed level. At this point the engine would be running slowly if you took your foot off the throttle, fast if you absent-mindedly stepped down hard. Certainly the engine would be running at some speed other than the perfect one to provide a smooth mesh into second gear. You would hear a horrible gnashing of gear teeth—and the gears would be stripped if you persisted. Stripping simply means that teeth are torn right off the gears. This is an expensive repair job.

The clutch, then, frees the engine drive shaft from the transmission drive shaft so that gears can be shifted without damage. A special device is installed in the transmission which tends to bring meshing gears to mating speeds. Thus shifting gears is quick and quiet with the clutch depressed. Just release the clutch pedal which joins the engine shaft to the transmission drive shaft slowly.

Automatic transmissions take over most of this shifting and co-ordination. Clutching and gear shifting are done automatically at a signal from the wheels—that is, when the wheels reach the set shifting speed a signal goes to the transmission which automatically shifts the gear sets to the next higher speed. Most automatic transmissions have four forward speeds and one reverse.

Automatic transmissions have a gear-shift lever similar to that on the manual gear shift, but its purpose is slightly different. You have five different lever positions from which to choose. The first is *park* and this locks the wheels and disconnects the ignition so the engine cannot be started (it will continue to run, however, if already started). The next position is *neutral* and this is the position in which you start the engine. It disconnects the engine from the wheels just as if the clutch had been disengaged. The next position is *low* and this limits the maximum gear to which the automatic shift changes to the equivalent of second speed. If you drive on slippery roads and want to restrict speed, or down a steep hill and wish to use the braking action of the engine to assist your foot brake, you use this setting. Then there is *drive* for all normal forward driving, and *reverse* for backing and parking.

The transmission, whether automatic or manual, is located just behind the clutch in most American automobiles. Behind the transmission, and running down the length of the car to the rear wheels is the drive shaft, also called the *propeller shaft,* which moves in a drive shaft tunnel—intimately known by many owners of the newer, lower models. The drive shaft is geared to the rear wheels with a *differential.*

At either end of the drive shaft there is an interesting pair of shaft couplings called *universal joints.* These are always used in pairs and they permit the rear axle to move up and down on springs relative to the transmission without breaking the drive shaft. The universal joint consists of two mating Y-shaped yokes, one attached to the end of the drive shaft and the other to the transmission output shaft. The two yokes point their "antlers" at each other. They are connected by a crossed member carrying pivots at each of its four ends. The universal joint permits the two shafts to take practically any reasonable angle to each other. By putting

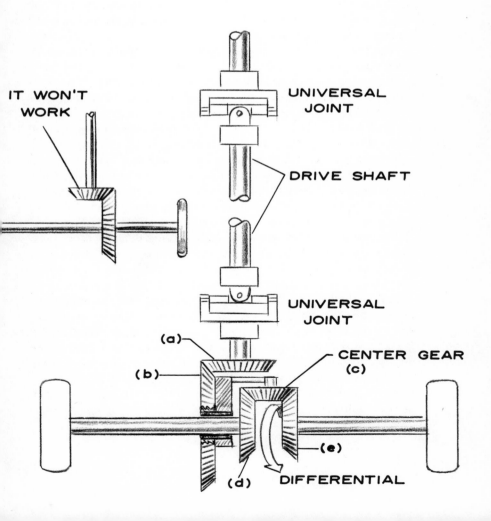

IT WON'T WORK

UNIVERSAL JOINT

DRIVE SHAFT

UNIVERSAL JOINT

(a)

CENTER GEAR (c)

(b)

(e)

(d)   DIFFERENTIAL

universal joints at either end of the drive shaft, the automotive designer frees the rear axle to move up and down without putting any strain on the drive shaft and without interfering in any way with the main purpose of the drive shaft—to transmit rotation of the transmission to the differential.

If you were designing a car your first inclination would be to set both rear wheels on a single shaft, or axle, running across the back of the car. You could drive the axle from the drive shaft with a simple set of bevel gears (see sketch). But what would happen when you wanted to turn a corner? Note that the outer wheel of the pair must then travel farther than the inner wheel and so either the shaft must twist and wind up (an unlikely solution) or the inner wheel will skid around a little (rather hard on the tires). This skidding is what causes the wheels to shriek on railroad trains and subway cars.

Some unsung genius invented the *differential*—a set of gears that permits the inner wheel to turn more slowly on turns than the outer one, yet drives both wheels at the same speed when the automobile is going straight.

The trick is to separate the two wheel shafts, put bevel gears on their facing ends (d) and (e) and drive them through a third bevel gear (c) which moves *around* the other two (see sketch). The third bevel gear (c) is itself driven by the drive shaft through a pair of larger bevel gears (a) and (b).

Let's see how this works. The drive shaft picks up speed and turns the center bevel gear (c) through the large pair (a) and (b). This gear (c) is free to spin on its own axis, but it has two opposing bevel gears (d) and (e) on either side to contend with. When the car is going straight the center bevel gear (c) does not need to turn on its own axis, it simply swings like a planet around the two axle gears (d) and (e) and drives them and their attached wheels. If one tire presents more resistance to turning than the other (as it would if it were the inner wheel on a turn) the center bevel gear reacts by turning on its own axis, thus permitting the inner wheel to turn more slowly than the outer one.

This is really a brilliant design, but it has one very serious drawback. The differential can't tell the difference between a turn and an icy road. If one of your wheels is on ice and the other on dry pavement the iced wheel will be permitted to spin freely—at so great a speed that the outer wheel will not need to move at all. All the accelerating and throttling you like will not bring one ounce of power to the outer wheel until the inner wheel is somehow restrained.

# TYPEWRITERS

The typewriter was made possible by two important ideas. The first was that of the round *platen* to carry the paper and hold it firmly in position. The platen has two important motions. It rotates on its own axis and thus brings fresh paper into position; it slides horizontally to take each letter impression in its turn and to return to the start of a line.

The second important idea is that of the *type bars*. These are a series of links carrying raised letter shapes on their ends and pivoted so as to strike the platen at exactly the same point (relative to the typewriter frame) every time. As the platen moves sideways past this point it presents new paper surface to each succeeding letter or numeral.

The cage of type bars now used in most typewriters is not the only possible solution. All of the characters can be put on the circumference of a drum which is turned to the proper position and then swung into contact with the platen. As a matter of fact this method is actually used in certain specialized typewriters where the ease of switching from one type face to another (by changing drums) is an important advantage.

In all other respects the typewriter is really only an ingenious combination of familiar components. For example, the carriage return lever operates a ratchet encircling one end of the platen so that the platen rotates one or two or three line spaces at each swing. The ink ribbon rises between the moving type bar and the platen at each stroke, and then lowers so that the typed letter will be immediately visible to the typist. If the ribbon stayed in its operating position, you would not be able to see what you had

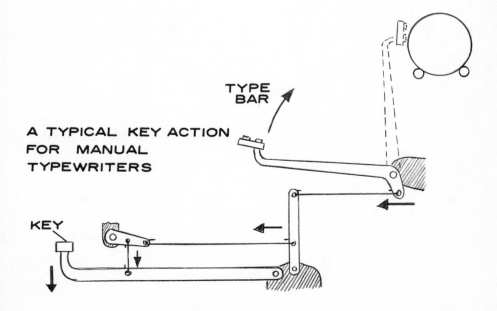

TYPE BAR

A TYPICAL KEY ACTION FOR MANUAL TYPEWRITERS

KEY

just typed. The ribbon advances automatically after each typed character and automatically reverses when the end of the spool has been reached.

The shift key raises the platen (or drops the type bars). The purpose for this is to make a second set of characters available. These additional characters are set above the group already mentioned on the type bars, and they include the capital letters as well as many signs and symbols. The addition of a second character on each type bar doubles the number of characters available to the typist.

Let's look at the normal typing of a line to see how many operations are involved. You start by wrapping the paper around the platen, push the carriage to the extreme right (where it strikes a margin control) and start to type by pressing the carriage shift to give you a capital letter. You follow by typing a sequence of letters. After each type bar strikes the platen it leaves a trace of black ink on the paper. The ribbon moves into position just in time and then drops out of the way. As the type bar retracts it kicks a release which moves the entire carriage over one space. You continue in this fashion until you reach the right-hand end of the paper or a preset margin. At this point a bell rings and a few spaces later the carriage stops and will accept no further typing unless you deliberately press the margin release. A simple sweep of the carriage return sets the carriage back to the extreme left and simultaneously turns the platen to reveal a new line of paper ready to receive words.

A very recent development, and one that is sweeping the business offices of the country, is the electric typewriter. Here most of the effort of depressing the typewriter key to swing the type bar sharply against the paper has been supplied by electric power. In addition, the carriage is returned by electric power, and so the typist's efforts are considerably reduced and the typing speed and regularity of letter weight are greatly improved. The operation is essentially the same as that of the manual typewriter. The difference is the inclusion of a motor-driven rotating bar that runs across the typewriter back under the keys. As each key is touched it only has to move a fraction of an inch when a linkage is caught by the rotating cylinder. This throws the chosen type bar against the platen.

Typists trained on manual typewriters, who later switch to electric machines, have the strange feeling that the new typewriter has a mind of its own and it seems to type by itself. This feeling comes from the extreme sensitivity of the keys—the slightest touch will

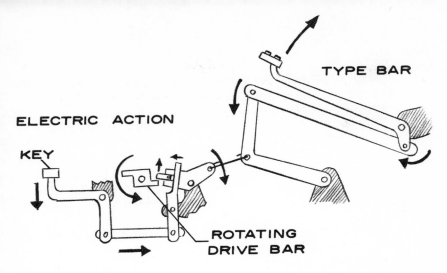

ELECTRIC ACTION

KEY

TYPE BAR

ROTATING
DRIVE BAR

set them off, and so the typist cannot rest the weight of her hands on the keyboard as she has been accustomed to do on the manual typewriter. But the feeling passes, and most are convinced that they type faster and produce much better looking pages than they ever could on the manuals.

We should not leave typewriters without saying something about some new developments in typing and about the future of stenography and typing in general. The manufacture and acceptance of the electric typewriter brought with it many principles which were quickly adapted to computers. You can now store an entire letter on a perforated paper roll rather like the old player-piano rolls. The paper passes over a line of holes in a metal bar. Air pressure senses the holes in the paper and transmits signals to an electric typewriter so that the typewriter types the proper letters and spaces automatically. Fantastic? Many of the letters you receive from insurance companies and banks are actually composed by a young executive who picks out the sequence of paragraphs he needs. The secretary starts the letter in the electric typewriter, types your name and address, and then turns the typewriter over to the automatic typer which produces the paragraph at high speed, and without a mistake, from the paper roll. At the end the typist comes over, types in the writer's name and title—and you receive a charming, tactful but precisely expressed letter announcing the company's position in your case.

Where will it all end? Ultimately we will have machines which eliminate the stenographer-typist job completely. You will dictate a letter into a microphone which will automatically translate the sound into words and type them out on a piece of your stationery. Researchers are admittedly having a hard time. Why should *tough* be spelled that way rather than *tuff*? What would a "voicewriter" do with *weigh* and *way?* But it is entirely possible that we will change our language (or at least its spelling) or even forgive these homonyms for the convenience of automatic operation.

# V

## VACUUM CLEANERS

Just what is air and air pressure, and what makes a vacuum something "nature abhors"? Well air is a gas—a mixture of oxygen, nitrogen, and a few other minor gases—that surrounds the earth in a blanket several miles deep.

Air has weight; each cubic foot of sea-level air weighs a little more than one ounce. We specify "sea-level air" because as you go up in altitude the air becomes less dense. Air is compressible and the great weight of air above squeezes sea-level air into a relatively small volume. At an altitude of 25,000 feet, with much less air squeezing down from above, a cubic foot of air weighs less than half an ounce. A column of air one inch by one inch square and as high as the sky weighs just under 15 pounds—which is why engineers speak of sea-level atmospheric pressure as approximately 15 pounds per square inch.

This pressure acts on us just as water pressure acts on the deep-sea diver. When you enlarge your chest cavity, air rushes in to fill the space. To expel the air you contract your chest, creating an internal pressure a little higher than the outside air pressure, and so the trapped air is pushed out. Any pressure lower than atmospheric air pressure (as in your chest when inhaling) is called vacuum. *Soft vacuums* refer to pressures only slightly under atmospheric air pressure. *Hard vacuums* refer to pressures near absolute zero.

Incidentally, what we sometimes forget is that pressure is not the normal or average state of the universe; vacuum is. There is far more vacuum in interplanetary and interstellar space than there is pressure on earth or on all the atmosphere-covered planets there are or could be. Thus, vacuum, or nearly complete emptiness is far more *natural* than a space filled with earth, brick, air, or even people.

However, vacuum is unusual on earth and it can therefore be used in many interesting ways. One of these, the vacuum cleaner, gets atmospheric air to rush into a tube, carrying the dust and dirt along with it. The air is pushed into and through a porous cloth or disposable paper bag. The dust and dirt particles are too big to pass through the pores in the bag. They're trapped, collected, and disposed of in this simple and convenient way.

A vacuum cleaner consists of a motor-driven fan to create the vacuum, a removable bag immediately in front of the fan to collect the dust, tubing or ducts to direct the dust and air to the bag, and a foot or shoe at the end of the tube designed to pass over rug or furniture or wall. Atmospheric air adjacent to the shoe is pushed into the tube by outside air pressure.

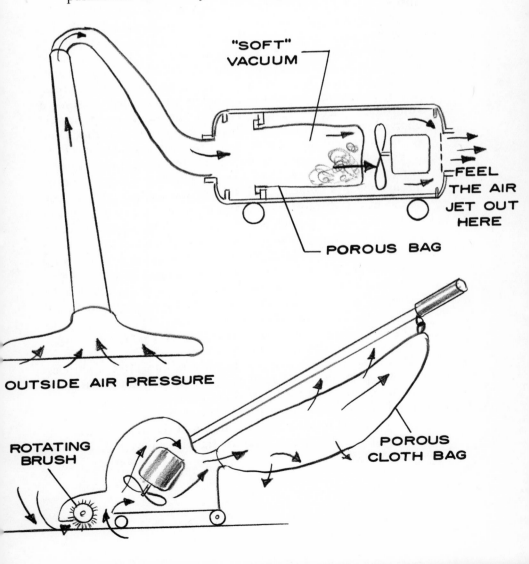

"SOFT" VACUUM

FEEL THE AIR JET OUT HERE

POROUS BAG

OUTSIDE AIR PRESSURE

ROTATING BRUSH

POROUS CLOTH BAG

In this way the vacuum cleaner does a lot more than just brush off the surface of the rug. The air sucked into the pipe comes from below the rug and from inside the overstuffed pillows.

Standing type vacuum cleaners usually have a rotating brush to help loosen the dust. Tank type cleaners have combs built into the cleaner shoe.

# VACUUM TUBES

This is called a *valve* by the English because its operation is so much like that of a standard water valve installed in a pipe line. Here's how the most useful kind of vacuum tube works.

A filament—much like the one in your lamp bulb—is coiled inside a tube of metal called the *cathode*. The cathode is heated by the filament and throws off a cloud of negatively charged electrons because of the high molecular activity (see THERMOMETERS AND THERMOSTATS). The electrons are attracted to a *plate* on the other side of the evacuated tube which has a strong positive charge. But in order to get to the plate the electrons must pass through a *grid* much like a tiny window screen which itself has a controllable electric charge. Now if the screen is negatively charged it repels all the electrons coming from the cathode and so they surround the cathode and permit no additional electrons to boil off. If the grid has no charge, or is slightly positive, it attracts some electrons and a good number will continue on through the grid to the plate. If the grid has a relatively high positive charge, it attracts a lot of electrons and a large number of them continue on through to the plate. The flow of electrons from hot cathode, through the grid, across the evacuated tube, and to the plate (or *anode*) is as much current flow as the flow in a wire.

So the level of charge on the grid is like a wheel on a valve. Open it up and a lot of current flows. Close it down and you can stop the current entirely. The current flow is closely proportional to the charge and the small amount of electric power necessary to change the charge on the grid will result in a very much larger change of current between hot cathode and plate.

This tube is called a *triode* because of the three electrodes (cathode, plate or anode, and grid). There are tubes that have only two electrodes (called *diodes*) and those that have as many as ten and twelve electrodes, depending on the complexity of the job to be done. It is sufficient if we realize that the triode, because it permits the amplification of electric signals, makes radio and TV and radar possible.

260

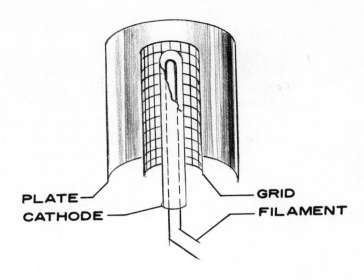

PLATE

CATHODE

GRID

FILAMENT

All such electronic devices require amplification—the very weak signals your antenna picks up must be made powerful enough to activate the phosphorescence of your TV screen and move the speaker cone back and forth. Fantastic as it may seem, the amplification is on the order of millions of times. The signals in the air can produce perhaps a few millionths of a volt at the antenna terminals of your set. The voltage at the speaker terminals often goes

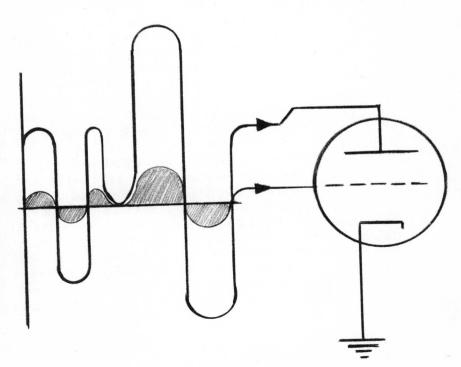

as high as 20 volts. Furthermore, the amplification must bring in no unwanted signals nor modify the shape of the incoming signal. What goes out in the form of relatively powerful signals must be true duplicates of what came in.

This is where the art of electronic engineering comes in. Thousands of patents have been issued, each with a different idea of how to hook up the vacuum tubes and resistors, capacitors, and other components of the electronic shelf into new and more powerful tools of an advanced technological age. Vacuum tubes make it possible for your voice to travel around the world through telephone lines. They calculate your paycheck and signal railroad trains. They guide the mass production machines in Detroit and the flow of chemicals in a plastics manufacturing plant.

The soft glow of vacuum tubes, barely half a century old, has already had its first serious rival in the *transistor* and now dozens of other gadgets of this kind are on the way. But no one will argue the fact that Lee de Forest, the American inventor who is often called "the father of radio," made the current technological revolution possible.

## VENETIAN BLINDS

They used to be made out of thin wooden slats, but now they're practically all of metal—thin, shaped, and painted to match your walls. There are two controls: the pair of braided cords on the right are hooked together so when pulled they lift the blind from the bottom. On the left two cords control the tilt of the blinds so that the amount of light may be adjusted from unimpeded sunlight to almost complete darkness.

The slats rest on individual crosspieces sewn between pairs of tapes at the right and left ends of the blinds. They're spaced apart just enough so that when the slats are adjusted for darkness they overlap slightly.

The two sets of control cords work independently of each other. The right-hand set is really one long cord that starts at the lowest blind between the left pair of tapes, rises up through a set of matching holes in all the blinds, runs across the top section and down at the right. It then goes back up, across the few inches to the right-hand tape pair and down through the blinds to attach to the lowest slat. By pulling the double cord on the right you lift both sides of the lowest slat at the same time and it moves up slowly collecting slats as it goes. When you release the control cord it is locked in place by a locking lever (see sketch) and the blind is set at the desired level. By pulling down on the pair of cords a little you release the locking lever and can keep the blinds moving freely as long as you hold the cords to your right, away from the locking lever teeth.

The two tape pairs are attached to circular sections up at the top that are pivoted on a shaft extending the full length of the blind. The shaft is geared to a wheel turned by pulling one or the other of the tilt control cords. The wheel turns, the gear turns, and the shaft slowly lifts one side of the tape and lowers the other. As the tapes go, so go the blinds.

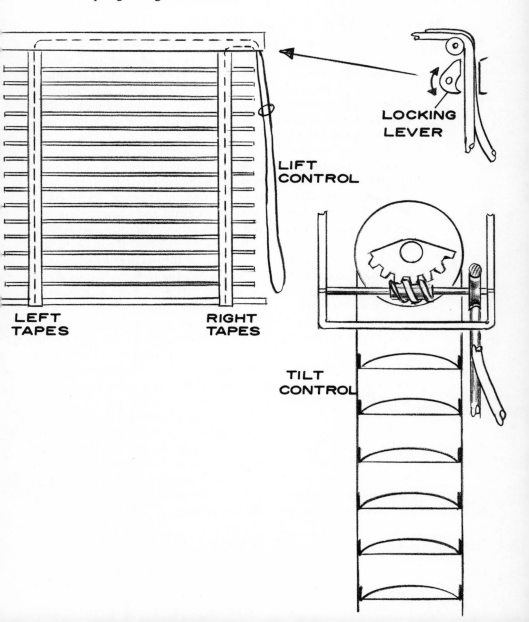

LOCKING LEVER

LIFT CONTROL

LEFT TAPES

RIGHT TAPES

TILT CONTROL

# W

## WAFFLE AND STEAM IRONS

Their purposes are very different but the methods are much alike. In both an electric heating element of Nichrome (nickel-chromium) wire is wrapped in a heat-resistant, electrically insulating sheath and buried in the heavy iron base. Electric current goes to the heating element through a thermostat (see THERMOMETERS AND THERMOSTATS) which stops the current flow when the iron is hot enough, turns it on again when the iron gets too cold.

In a waffle iron the two dimpled sections are heated to cooking temperature and then a light or indicator turns on, telling you that the iron is ready. Your pour in the cold batter and this cools the iron so the indicator drops or the light goes out. The thermostat starts current flowing to the iron again and when the iron has been reheated to the original temperature, the indicator signals, and your waffles are done. It is interesting that the cooking just consists of heating the cold batter to the set temperature—you don't have to peek or watch the steam, the temperature indicator does that for you. Note how similar this is to the experience with meat and meat thermometers (see MEAT THERMOMETERS).

A similar thermostatically controlled circuit heats the steam iron. However, here the set temperature may be varied by a dial which adjusts the location of a contact relative to the bimetallic strip in the thermostat (see sketch). The farther the contact is from the strip the more the strip must curl to make contact and so the hotter the iron will get before current is shut off.

Steam irons do not have solid metal sole plates—the plates are honeycombed with passages leading from an open section in the center of the iron to holes or slots in the bottom face. Water drips from a tank in the upper section of the iron into the open section in the sole plate. It instantly bursts into steam, which jets through the passages and out the bottom of the iron. To stop the steaming you simply close off the flow of water.

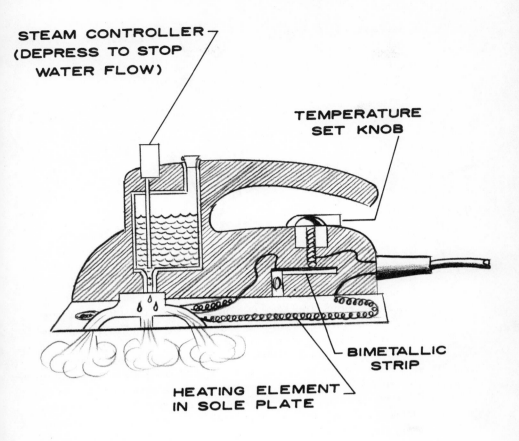

STEAM CONTROLLER
(DEPRESS TO STOP
WATER FLOW)

TEMPERATURE
SET KNOB

BIMETALLIC
STRIP

HEATING ELEMENT
IN SOLE PLATE

## WASHING MACHINES

Atomic power, airplanes, telephones, movies, and tape recorders would be impossible if man had to turn on and off the many complex switches or make the continuous small adjustments necessary to their operation. Machines now regulate themselves faster, more accurately and more reliably than man ever could.

Of course man has always been looking for ways to make life easier for himself. The first primitive animal traps were automatically sprung by the animal so that the trapper could stay home near the warm fire. To control things by time took more ingenuity, plus a means for measuring time. Your alarm clock is the simplest example. It turns the alarm on at a present time and (if the clock is electric) the alarm continues to ring for an hour or two before it shuts off in preparation for the next wake-up signal. Similarly, a radio clock turns the radio on when the preset time has been reached.

265

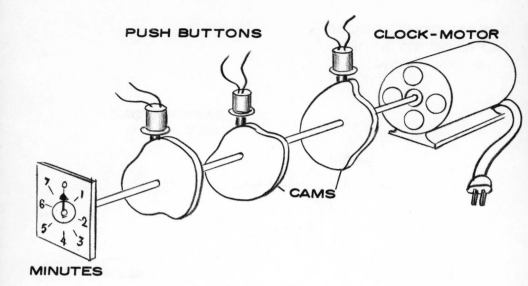

PUSH BUTTONS CLOCK-MOTOR

CAMS

MINUTES

In exactly the same way you could design a clock that would control the time for toasting bread, percolating coffee, or starting up a furnace at six in the morning.

The heart of such controllers is a small electric motor which runs at a constant speed. It is called a *synchronous motor* because it regulates its speed by the alternating house current that powers it. Since house current is very closely controlled to exactly 60 cycles each second (at the generating station there is a machine which counts the cycles and makes sure you get exactly 5,184,000 cycles in each 24 hour period), the little motor runs at a speed synchronized with the power supply—hence the name (see Clocks and Watches).

This little motor turns a series of *cams*. The cams are flat disks of metal with odd-shaped cut-outs spaced around their circumferences. A series of push-button switches are lined up facing and just touching this row of cams. As the motor turns the shaft, the notches and bumps on the cams push the buttons in and out at odd intervals. Thus a series of buzzers or lights could be made to turn on and off depending on how you cut the cams.

This may seem like a long way around to come to washing machines, but the brain of the machine is its control—a synchronous motor-driven cam shaft similar in principle to the one just described.

Suppose you were asked to design a washing machine, what would it need to do? You'd need a basket or tub to hold clothes or dishes, hot and cold water, soap, some means of agitating the mixture, a way to drain the soapy water, a way to pour in and drain

266

rinsing water, and perhaps a high-speed spinning operation to get most of the water out of the clean, but wet, clothes. Most of all you would need a controller to tell the machine when to pour in water, when to agitate, when to rinse and drain, and when to spin dry. This we have in motor-driven cams, so the toughest part is really already figured out.

There are two kinds of clothes washing machines. One tumbles the clothes in and out of the soapy water. You fill a rotatable basket with clothes and then run soapy water into the surrounding tub so

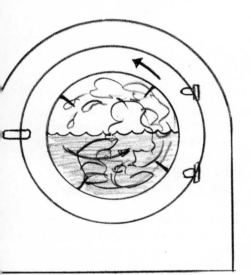

**TUMBLER**

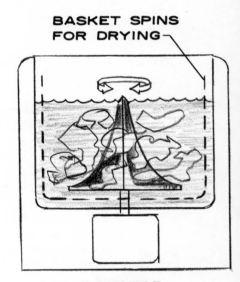

**BASKET SPINS FOR DRYING**

**AGITATOR**

the suds come about halfway up the sides. The basket turns slowly on its axis like a water wheel and the soggy clothes are lifted and flop over into and out of the water.

The second type has an agitator standing in the bottom center of the tub. The agitator looks something like a model of the Eiffel Tower and it turns back and forth or up and down forcing the soapy water around and through the clothes.

So we have a controller and a means of agitating the clothes. Let's run a pair of pipes from the hot and cold water lines into the tub, each to and through an electrically controlled valve. What kind of valve is this? Under FAUCETS you'll find a picture of a valve turned on and off by a hand wheel. Instead of the wheel you could substitute a coil of wire called a solenoid (see ELECTRICITY) sur-

267

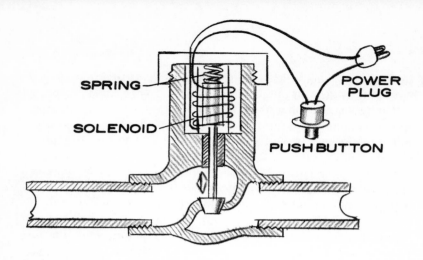

**SOLENOID – CONTROLLED VALVE**

rounding a straight valve *stem*. (The stem is the rod coming up out of the valve from the tapered cone that seals off the flow channel.) When current flows in the coil the valve stem is pulled open, when current is cut off the valve springs shut.

We also need a way to drain the tub. Here we can use another solenoid-controlled valve and a pump to suck the dirty water out and send it to the house drain line.

That just about completes the list. The controller will have five cams, one for the agitator motor, one for each inlet valve, one for the drain valve and one to turn the drain pump on and off. Here's how it might go:

| Time | Cam 1 Agitator | Cam 2 Hot water valve | Cam 3 Cold water valve | Cam 4 Drain valve | Cam 5 Drain Pump |
|------|------|------|------|------|------|
| Start | ON | ON | ON | CLOSED | OFF |
| 2 min. | ON | OFF | OFF | CLOSED | OFF |
| 10 min. | ON | OFF | OFF | OPEN | ON |
| 12 min. | ON | ON | ON | CLOSED | OFF |
| 14 min. | ON | OFF | OFF | CLOSED | OFF |
| 20 min. | ON | OFF | OFF | OPEN | ON |
| 22 min. | FAST SPIN | OFF | OFF | OPEN | ON |
| 30 min. | OFF | OFF | OFF | OPEN | OFF |

In this washing cycle the soap is put in with the clothes at the start. Water pours in for two minutes then shuts off by time control. Washers sometimes have a *float control* instead (see WATER CLOSETS) to shut off the inlet valves when the water has reached the desired level. The wash cycle continues for eight minutes, then the drain line opens and the pump sucks most of the soapy water out. After two minutes of draining the washer fills with fresh water and then rinses for six minutes at which time the water is drained again. The spin dry cycle lasts eight minutes and then everything shuts off. The drain valve stays open to allow the last few drops of water to drain out leaving the washer dry inside.

There is no limit to the variations possible in this control cycle. You can rinse as often as you like, spin dry for as long as you have patience, or vary the water temperature for different kinds of clothes. It only takes a correctly cut and timed cam.

Dishwashers are slightly different. Obviously fragile dishes can't be tumbled, so a rack is provided to hold the dishes. The agitator is replaced by an attachment to the water inlet which distributes the water in a strong jet on the dishes. Very hot water is used. It spouts up from the bottom and bounces around the sides and off the top of the washer, striking forcefully on the dishes and silverware. Ordinarily soap isn't added until after the first spraying and so an automatic soap dispenser is added—solenoid-operated and cam-controlled to release its contents at exactly the right time. The machine goes through several rinse cycles and then sometimes a heating coil is switched on at the end of the wash to speed drying of the dishes.

*Ultrasonic* washing and cleaning are still in the future but they are being talked about. Ultrasonics refers to sound frequencies above the ability of the human ear to hear (see SOUND). Ultrasonic energy is transmittetd to water by a special crystal which changes shape when an electric voltage is applied. Since we have equipment to generate just about any frequency of electric voltage, we can make a crystal change shape 20 or 30 thousand times each second.

If you dip a vibrating crystal into a bucket of water the sound waves travel through the water in pressure waves just as they do in air. The pressure can get as high as it likes in water—the water just squeezes a very little bit smaller and then sits there, undisturbed—but during the low pressure part of the cycle (the *rarefaction*) the water molecules are actually pulled apart into water vapor. This produces vapor bubbles for a tiny fraction of a second. The bubbles don't last long because right behind the low-pressure wave is another high-pressure wave that slams the water together again.

This whole process is called *cavitation,* because cavities are

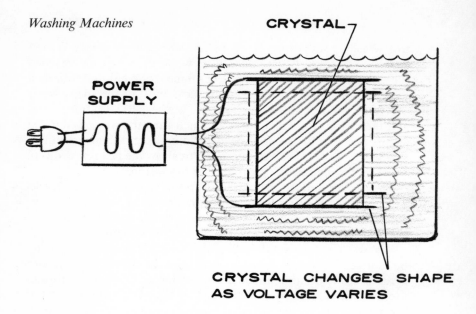

CRYSTAL

POWER
SUPPLY

CRYSTAL CHANGES SHAPE
AS VOLTAGE VARIES

formed and almost immediately closed up in the water. The little
bubbles of vapor are about as agitated as water can be and so it
was natural to think that they might substitute for the agitator in
washing machines. They might, they can, and they have. Ultrasonic
cleaning is now used in certain industrial cleaning operations where
the expense of special high-frequency electric power equipment can
be justified by the large amounts of cleaning that has to be done.
For example, automobile manufacturers degrease auto parts by
dipping them in special ultrasonic baths. But it may be a while before home units are economical enough to justify substituting them
for the agitators described above. Note that the rinsing and drying cycles are not eliminated by the addition of ultrasonics.

## WATER CLOSETS

You can thank the inventor of the *toilet trap* for moving out-
houses indoors. It's such a simple idea, you wonder why nobody
thought of it sooner.

The trap consists of a U-shaped tube partly filled with water.
The back end of the tube drains into the sewer pipe. The front end
opens into the bowl. The water forms an airtight seal between sewer
and bowl and so none of the unpleasant odors can get in. Exactly
the same tube trap is used for your kitchen or bathroom sink drain.

When the bowl needs flushing, a quantity of water is dumped
rapidly into it. This raises its level above the water level at the rear

of the U-tube and so the water rushes down and around the tube carrying the waste to the sewer pipe. Just enough clear water remains to seal the pipe as it was before flushing.

The name, water closet, probably refers to the tank, or closet, of water standing back of the bowl or attached, sometimes, up

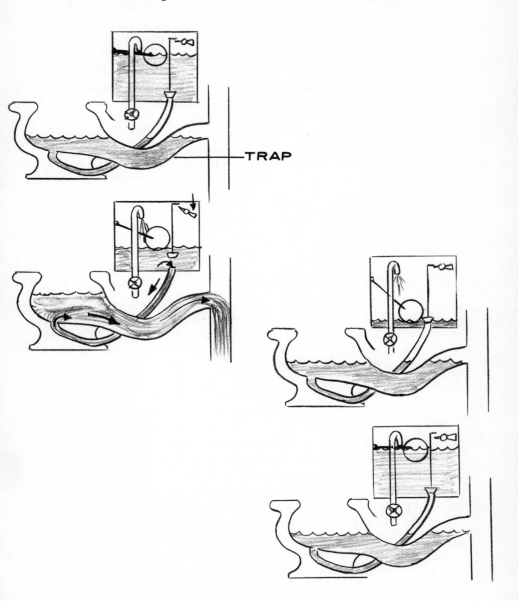

TRAP

near the ceiling. The tank is the source of flushing water and it is emptied and filled by a very ingenious pair of valves.

When you pull the chain or flip the toggle you lift a wooden or hollow metal plug that normally keeps the water from flowing down into the bowl. This permits the flushing cycle to start. Most of the water flows out of the tank and down to the bowl. When the tank water drops to the level of the plug the weight of the plug (no longer surrounded and buoyed up by the water) causes it to drop and close off the opening.

The tank is refilled from a pipe connected to the regular cold water supply, and the newly collected tank water bears down on plug and keeps it snug against the pipe opening, holding the tank in readiness for the next flushing cycle.

The cold water refill supply runs through a *float-operated valve* up near the top of the tank. The float is a large wooden or hollow metal ball that rides on the surface of the water. When the water level drops during flushing a rod connected to the float pulls the inlet valve open permitting tap water to flow into the tank until it refills to the desired level. At this level the float has risen to the point at which its attached rod closes off the inlet valve.

And all is quiet once again.

# WEATHER REPORTS

We've said something about temperature and how it's measured (see THERMOMETERS AND THERMOSTATS) and about HUMIDITY. We've talked about air pressure (under PRESSURE COOKERS and VACUUM CLEANERS)—but perhaps we should see what all these effects mean to the weatherman.

The weatherman tells you what the temperature and humidity are and what they are likely to be for the next 24 hours. He tells you if rain is probable or cloudiness, and if the barometric pressure is rising or falling. He also includes wind direction and speed.

What do all these mean and how do they influence what tonight or tomorrow's weather is going to be? Well, weather predicting is a complicated business. So complex, as a matter of fact, that meteorologists have just recently set high-powered computers to analyzing weather data in the hope that their predictions will be made more accurate. They have had only limited success so far.

The problem is that we simply don't know what causes changes in the weather except in a very general way—weather-eye satellites and computers will help, but not in the near future, to make tomorrow's weather as certain as yesterday's.

So with all these qualifications in mind, here's what weather reports mean:

*Barometric pressure* refers to the atmospheric air pressure measured by a *barometer*. The barometer is a glass tube, closed at one end, filled with mercury, and upended in a dish of mercury. The tube is about 36 inches long and so the column of mercury starts out 36 inches high. It drops to about 30 inches above the level in the dish at which level it holds relatively constant. Above the mercury in the closed end of the tube is a near-perfect vacuum. Air pressure acts on the exposed mercury surface in the dish and this holds the column of mercury up to about 30 inches.

Mercury is used because it is the heaviest liquid we know—this reduces the necessary height of the tube. A column of mercury one square inch in cross section and 30 inches high weighs exactly 14.7 pounds—just the necessary weight to balance the normal atmospheric air pressure of 14.7 pounds per square inch. A column of water one square inch in cross section would have to be 34 *feet* high to weigh 14.7 pounds.

Now air pressure varies from place to place on the earth's surface. This is caused by the variations in altitude and temperature around the world and by the moving air currents (winds). High temperature makes air expand and so it is lighter (less dense) than an equivalent volume of colder air.

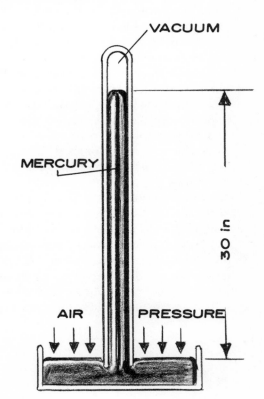

Variations in barometric pressure tend to be localized and high-pressure areas are called *highs* and low-pressure areas are called *lows* on the weatherman's map. These highs and lows move across the earth's surface and help guide the weatherman in his predictions.

Temperature and humidity have been covered adequately elsewhere in this book, but we might spend a moment on the *degree-days* concept used by the oil or coal suppliers for their calculations. The company figures that in winter you will burn an amount of oil or coal more or less proportionate to how cold it is outside. When the temperature dips below 50 degrees, say, they know most people will call for furnace heat.

So the company keeps track of temperatures day by day. They take the average temperature for the day, subtract it from 50 degrees and call the result so many degree-days. If the temperature averages 45 degrees on Tuesday then Tuesday contributes 5 degree-days to the summation. As the days pass the degree-day accumulation rises to a set limit for your oil tank—maybe 1000 degree-days. The company knows that you will burn up all your fuel in 1000 degree-days and so they come around to refill after 800 degree-days or so, just to be safe.

*Wind speed* is of most importance to airplane pilots and ship captains. It is measured by an *anemometer*—a set of metal teacups mounted on the ends of the spokes of a free-turning wheel. The faster the wind blows the faster the wheel spins and so a correlation can be made between wind speed and wheel speed which the weatherman reads and reports.

*Wind direction* is measured by a weather *vane*. The weather vane is a freely pivoted arrow with the tail of the arrow presenting a large area to the wind and the point a very small area. The broad tail area is pushed by the wind until it aligns itself with the wind direction and therefore the arrow points to the direction (see COMPASSES) from which the wind comes. That is why the weatherman often is heard to say that the wind direction is "out of" the north, or south or whatever.

The weatherman has as his raw material all of the detailed data of this kind reported by weather stations all over the world. These stations send in temperature, humidity ratio, barometric pressure, wind direction and velocity, and a description of cloud cover and precipitation (rain, snow, sleet, etc.) if any. Such reports are entered on a weather map covering many thousands of miles—the whole North American continent for example.

To this raw material is added the reports from weather planes

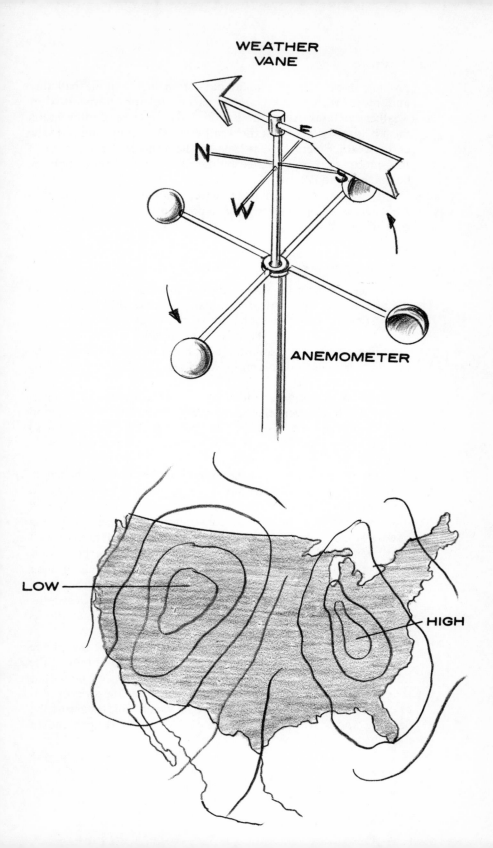

probing storm centers, similar data from high-altitude balloons, and, more recently, the cloud cover photographs transmitted by weather satellites. All of these thousands of pieces of information must be processed so that the weatherman has at his fingertips the entire weather picture of, at least, his hemisphere. On the basis of this information, and assisted by the computers mentioned above, he makes a prediction.

His average is just a little better than even—the Farmer's Almanac based on daily weather reports of the last hundred years is nearly as good.

## WIND INSTRUMENTS

The second most important class of musical instruments—and the first, by far, in the history of man—are the wind instruments. Their sound is very different from strings or percussion members of the orchestral family because the amplifier is not a wooden sounding board or a resonating box, but a metal or wooden tube in which the enclosed column of air is set vibrating by a pulsating pressure at one end.

*Horns* are generally sounded by the vibrating lips of the performer. He half covers the opening with his tensed lower lip and blows with a sharp puff of air. The lip opens and closes rapidly so that air puffs into the horn and produces a series of pressure waves running down the length of the tube.

The frequency or pitch of the sound is determined by the length of the column of air. A trumpet, if completely uncoiled, would measure about six feet from the mouthpiece to end bell. A tuba (the deep-throated brass boa constrictor you see in marching bands) would measure 18 feet from end to end. The length of such instruments can be changed by the performer in several ways. Trumpet and tuba have extra passages connected along their lengths and valves are opened or closed to add or subtract loops of tube to the air passage. The slide trombone has a telescoping section that similarly changes the length of the air column and its pitch.

*Reed instruments* are usually uncurled (except for the saxophone which has only two bends—one at the top and the other at the bottom) and the opening through which the performer blows has a reed to make the puffs of air. The reed is a flexible strip of reed or cane, thinned down to a feather edge, which vibrates across the opening and starts pressure waves of air in the upper end of the tube.

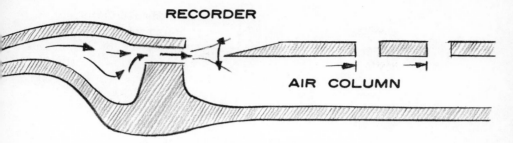

**RECORDER**

**AIR COLUMN**

**AIR REED: WHISTLE,
RECORDER, OCARINA, FLUTE,
PICCOLO, FIFE**

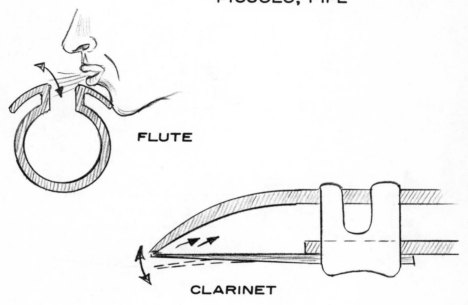

**FLUTE**

**CLARINET**

**SINGLE REED: CLARINET,
SAXOPHONE, BAGPIPE,
ACCORDION, HARMONICA**

The pitch of sound coming from a reed instrument is determined by the unbroken length of the resonant tube. The shorter the tube, the higher the pitch. The performer changes the pitch of

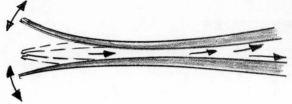
DOUBLE REED: OBOE,
ENGLISH HORN,
BASSOON

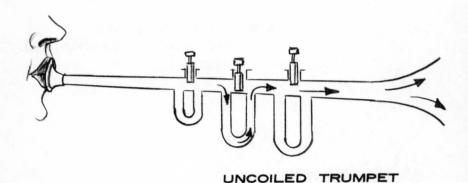
UNCOILED TRUMPET

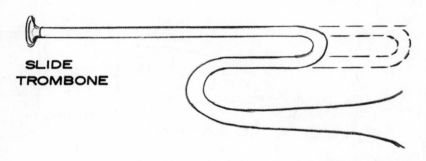
SLIDE
TROMBONE

LIP REED: BUGLE, TRUMPET, CORNET,
FRENCH HORN, TROMBONE,
TUBA

sound by opening or closing holes along the length of the tube. This effectively changes the unbroken length.

There are several other ways to get tones from a tube. You can blow across the opening as the piccolo player does or mechanically pump air to individually tuned (and reeded) tubes as in the organ.

# WINDOWS

There's nothing really complicated or troublesome about the familiar double-hung window except that it occasionally sticks or rattles, or won't stay at the desired height.

Perhaps you didn't realize that each movable window is counter-balanced to permit it to hold still wherever it is set. Two metal weights hang from cords or chains in hollow spaces in the sides of the window frame. They are called *sash weights,* and the movable window itself is often called the *sash* (upper and lower), though strictly speaking the sash refers to the wooden or metal frame surrounding the panes of glass.

The sash slides in grooves or slots between thin wooden strips nailed to the side surface of the window frame. To remove a sash you simply remove the strip holding it in place. If it has been painted over this looks a lot harder than it is. Actually the strips are held in place by thin molding nails and a wide chisel or a putty knife can easily be forced between the strip and the window frame to lift it and free the sash.

The sash cord or chain runs up to the top of the window and over a pair of pulleys recessed into the window frame. The cord goes over the pulley and down into the hollow frame where it is tied to the heavy lead or iron counterweight. You can hear the counterweights fall or strike against the sides of the window frame if you move the sash up quickly.

An access door gives entry to the counterweight compartment. This may also have been painted over so that the screws have been covered completely, but the door is always there and it may be found by tapping and listening for the hollow sound.

When a cord or chain breaks, the counterweight will drop to the bottom of the counterweight channel and the only way you can get at it is to remove one of the strips holding the front sash, slide the lower sash out, and open the access door. Then, with a new cord or a new chain over the pulley and running into the counter-weight chamber, you can reattach one end to the weight and the other end to the slot provided in the top edge of the sash.

If the sash sticks because of wet paint or swollen wood, you can sometimes free it by pulling both sash cords away from the sides of the window frame and releasing them so that the falling counter-weights snap sharply at the sash.

Casement windows are just what they seem: glass doors with hinges and a latch to hold them closed. However, crank-driven casement windows, and the new louvred glass windows, are a

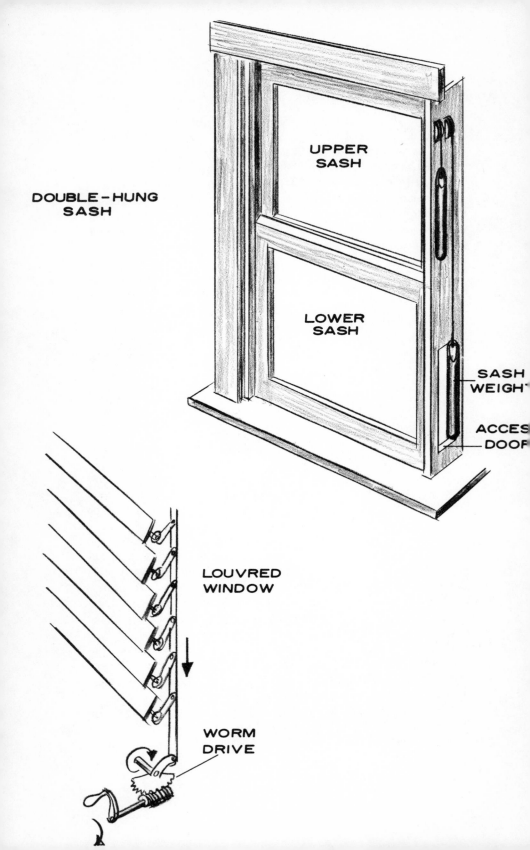

DOUBLE - HUNG
SASH

UPPER
SASH

LOWER
SASH

SASH
WEIGH'

ACCES
DOO

LOUVRED
WINDOW

WORM
DRIVE

little more complicated. Both of these have a hand crank sticking out at the bottom. The crank turns a threaded *worm* which drives a gear. The gear pushes a link connected to the glass louvres, turning them all at the same time to open or shut the window.

# X

## X RAYS

X rays are the tools of the physicist just as the needle is the tool of the seamstress. Without the discovery of X rays there could never have been an atomic age.

But what are X rays? We've talked of radio waves and light waves in other sections of this book. X rays are waves too, higher in frequency and shorter in wave length than the others, but they are electromagnetic in character just as light waves and radio waves are. Just as high frequency sound waves tend to "punch" forward in a straight line rather than spreading around, as the lower frequency sound waves do, so the high frequency X rays have a lot of "punch." They are so strong that they can spear through most solids as easily as light waves go through glass.

This can be dangerous of course, but it also can be useful. A second useful property of X rays is this: When X rays strike a photographic plate they produce the same chemical reaction that light does. The areas exposed will turn black on the film when it is developed. The unexposed areas will remain clear. Thus a picture can be taken by the "light" of X rays just as easily as by the light of the sun. The difference is that many things opaque to sunlight, such as heavy black paper, metals, etc., are transparent to X rays. Only thick layers of a heavy metal, like lead, can stop the X rays.

An image is created on the film by the stopping power of the solid bodies placed between the source of the X rays and the film. You can place your hand on the film and expose it to a source of X rays for a few seconds and the developed negative will show a clear outline of your finger and wrist bones and a darker outline where the more transparent (to X rays) flesh and blood are. In this way doctors were for the first time able to examine fractured bones, and lung and heart tissues, without surgery. In many ways modern medicine began with the discovery of the X ray.

281

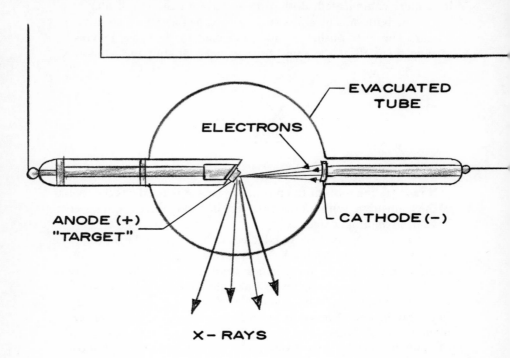

EVACUATED
TUBE

ELECTRONS

ANODE (+)
"TARGET"

CATHODE (−)

X − RAYS

The fluoroscope is a simple modification of photographic film. Here the film is replaced by a thin paper or cardboard screen which has a layer of special chemical on its surface. The chemical glows brightly when struck by X rays. It remains dark or dim otherwise. The doctor can thus get a quick look at what goes on inside by placing you between a source of X rays and the screen. If the results need more study he takes a picture, if examination by fluoroscope reveals no trouble that's all there is to it.

X rays can be very dangerous. When these high-power rays strike flesh for long periods of time they will destroy the tissues, and cause permanent damage if not death. Only trained operators should be permitted to use these machines and you should tell your doctor if you have had several X rays over a short period of time.

X rays are created in a vacuum tube somewhat like the one in your television tube. In the X ray tube an envelope of glass surrounds two electrodes. Most of the air is sucked out of the tube and then it is sealed and a high voltage (thousands of volts) is applied to the two terminals. This voltage creates a flow of electrons from the *cathode* (the negatively charged electrode) which strike out toward the *anode* (the positively charged electrode). The electrons strike a *target,* a piece of metal purposely placed in the path of the electrons. When struck by the high speed electrons the target gives off X rays which spray away from the tube.

# Z

## ZIPPERS

While most of the devices described in this book were the culmination of many men's work, the zipper was the invention of one man and it was made practical by another. The first patents for the zipper principle were granted in the 1890s. However, it wasn't until 1913 that the slide fastener, as we know it today, was perfected and it took ten more years before manufacturers would even consider it for galoshes and even longer for ready-made clothes.

The fastener had to be flexible, relatively accidentproof (at first it had the unfortunate habit of popping open) and, very important, automatic machinery had to be invented to clamp on the individual metal pieces that go to make up the zipper.

Today, of course, most trousers and dresses have at least one zipper. They're made in metal or plastics. They come in many sizes, strengths, and colors, and some are waterproof.

We often forget how strong the zipper is, yet how easily it is opened. An inoperative zipper can be one of the greatest trials a lady has to face. Let's see what actually happens when a zipper is zipped, how it holds, and how it opens.

A zipper is made of three parts: dozens of identical metal or plastic hooks, two strips of fabric with one of the long edges built up into a sort of rib, and a Y-shaped slider to open or close the fastener. The hooks have jaws at one end to grip the rib of the strip or fabric. On the other end the hooks are shaped into a point aiming along the strip and with a matching hollow in the back.

Automatic machines clamp the hooks on the strip in precise spacing for as long a zipper as you want. Two strips are then placed side by side, with their hooks facing, and the slider draws them into mesh. Ordinarily the bottom of the zipper is sewn or stapled so that the two strips can never again be separated completely and the slider can't run off the zipper.

Note that the cloth strip is flexible. It may be bent so as to spread the hooks, separating their shaped ends, and facing hooks can later be interlocked in precise mesh. The slider simply provides an easy way to bring the two strips together; you can do it by hand if you're careful and patient, and this is sometimes necessary when a hook is broken off or the zipper parts.

Zipper troubles can be catastrophic and a lost hook is probably the worst. The slider works only one way in each direction—it meshes up and separates down. If you've meshed it up and the zipper opens below, the separated sections can't be rejoined by the slider—they have to be joined by hand. Further, when the slider hits the open spot it may jam or slip right off one strip entirely.

Less permanent, but equally annoying, is the jammed slider. It won't move up or down, probably because the slider has picked up a loose fold of fabric, usually on the underside where you can't see or get at it. Patience and careful freeing of the slide will cure this.

In general, however, the zipper is strong and reliable. It is made by many different manufacturers, now that the earliest patents have expired, and it will probably remain our most popular fastener until a similarly brilliant invention comes along.

There is one new contender on the market. Velcro is made of two sturdy tapes, one is covered with many small flexible plastic hooks that grow out of the flat side of the tape. The second tape is covered with a matting of many small loops of thread.

When you press the two tapes together the hooks entangle themselves in the loops, making a tight fastening. Velcro is separated by peeling the two tapes apart as you would a piece of adhesive tape. The hooks bend open and release the threads without damaging themselves or the loops.

Velcro is somewhat thicker than a zipper, thus it is less desirable as a clothes fastener. It's adjustability is an advantage sometimes (a belt, for example) but of no value for a trouser fly or the side closure of a dress.

# INDEX

# Index

# Index